Heroes

of the

Hook

John Hollands MC

Quill Publications,
Buckerell,
Devon,
EX14 3GJ

Quill Publications,
2 Orchards Farm,
Buckerell,
Nr. Honiton,
Devon,
EX14 3GJ.

Email: hollands12010@hotmail.com
Website: www.johnhollandsbooks.co.uk

First Published: 2013
Second printing August 2013
Third printing September 2013
Fourth printing November 2013
Copyright:
Douglas John Hollands

Copyright Illustrations:
David Chapman-Andrews.

Heroes of the Hook

Printed and bound in the United Kingdom by:
Imprintdigital
Upton Pyne
Devon.

Memory and Imagination

The fictionalized Memoirs of Sajit Contractor

VOLUME III

HEROES OF THE HOOK

John Hollands MC

Also by John Hollands

The Dead, the Dying and the Damned,

Able Company (US only)

The Gospel According to Uncle Jimmy

Never Marry a Cricketer

Never Marry a Rugger Player

Not Shame the Day

The Exposed

Blundellian Writers

Poetry of the Korean War (Contributions)

Black Rain

The Court-Martial

Gran and Mr. Muckey

What a Fag!

The War Poems of a Young Soldier

Picture and Map

The front cover picture, taken by the author with a Baby Brownie, shows the original 12 Platoon, Dog Company, 1 DWR, on arrival in Korea in 1952.

The map of the Hook trench layout on the back page is not to scale and it should be noted that in the 18 months of battles many bunkers, weapon pits, OPs, and tunnels changed frequently.

Dedicated to the memory of the
late Major Alan Fradgley MBE.
One of the Old Brigade

"There is no greater power than the
power of imagination."
Harper Lee

Acknowledgements

My very sincere thanks are due to Christopher Price, Trevor Hunt, Jonathan Hollands, Mark Hollands, Lesley Pyne, Penni Cotton, Ken Fisher, and especially to my illustrator David Chapman-Andrews.

Author's Note

Heroes of the Hook is Volume III of my fictionalized memoir, ***Memory and Imagination***. It continues the story of my life as seen through the eyes of my alter ego or literary clone, Sajit Contractor. The period in question covers October 1951 to October 1953. During that time I served as a National Serviceman in the British Army and became a platoon commander in Korea and served on the notorious hill known as the Hook. As in Volume I and Volume II, Sajit Contractor recounts my adventures in life. All events have a factual basis but, as the title implies, stories and incidents are frequently embroidered by my imagination. In other words, this book is fiction; not a novel but a fictionalized memoir. It gives a true-to-life picture, but it should not be regarded as factual in the true sense of the word. Among other things, Sajit often changes or modifies real events, historical locations, timings, and personal details, to assist the flow of the narrative. Likewise, military terminology is sometimes simplified for the benefit of those unfamiliar with military matters.

Those seeking an accurate historical account of Korea should consult regimental records. This memoir digs deeper and relates what life as a National Serviceman was like in personal terms, especially in Korea.

Numerous real people have been mentioned in ***Heroes of the Hook***, mainly officers I served with in The Duke of Wellington's Regiment. On occasions I have changed the names of characters to save the possibility of embarrassment.

The main action of the book takes place on the Hook, a hill on which more men were killed than any other hill in Korea. The artillery bombardment the hill received on the night of May 28th/29th 1953 was, and still is, without equal. Around 70,000 shells landed on the hill in the space of a several hours. In size, the Hook is about the same as Haytor on Dartmoor.

At dawn on May 29th Brigadier Joe Kendrew (a veteran of World War II with four DSOs) viewed the hill through his binoculars and said: "My God! Those Dukes were magnificent. Only the Dukes could have withstood that lot."

This is the story of a few of those Dukes, nearly all of them National Servicemen ... 12 Platoon, Dog Company, 1st Battalion DWR.

Memory and Imagination.

The Story So Far....

Sajit Contractor was born in Edgware, North London, in 1933, the third son of an Anglo/Indian untouchable and a Welsh mother from the Rhondda Valley.

Edgware, in those days, bristled with Jewish immigrants from Fascist Europe, and in this racial cauldron Sajit's family sticks out like a sore thumb, especially on account of his Indian Grandmother.

Volume I (*Gran and Mr Muckey*) tells of Sajit's childhood in London at the start of World War II. He and his brothers are evacuated and later on Sajit helps his father to fire-fight in Camberwell Green during the Blitz. When the family moves away from London to Silver Coombe, at Godstone, the interest of the memoir centres on the romance between Sajit's Indian grandmother and their rustic old gardener, Mr. Muckey, all of which ends tragically.

Sajit's eldest brother (Brother Nothing) is a constant thorn in his side, and his mother doesn't help when she decides he has a screw loose and sends him to a special Prep School in the wilds of Exmoor. From there, Sajit cheats his way through Common Entrance to gain a place at Blundell's and his five years at the famous West Country school (Volume II: *What a Fag!*) gives an insight into Public School education during the late 1940s, early1950s.

While at Blundell's, Sajit develops an ambition to become a novelist. However, his English master advises him that before he can pursue this profession he needs to have some experience in life, so he recommends that during his two years' National Service he should volunteer for the Korean War. Not realizing that this advice was given with tongue in cheek, Sajit does just that.

So here is Volume III. It takes Sajit from a schoolboy to a combat veteran.

Main Characters

Sajit (also 'Din') Contactor	Literary clone of the author.
Private Rupert Sandwitch	Batman and friend of Sajit
Private 'Animal' Evans	Boiler man/Bren gunner 12 Platoon
Private Fletcher	Rifleman 12 Platoon (Hard case)
Private Bertie Mee	Rifleman 12 Platoon.
Private Harry Wilmott	Rifleman in 12 Platoon
Private Hurst	12 Platoon. Bren gunner
Corporal Holroyd	Section Commander, 12 Platoon.
Sergeant Gough	Drill sergeant, Catterick
Major 'Earl' Gray	Dog Company Commander
Gilbert Gilbert	2nd Lt. Old school friend of Sajit's
Katsumi Matoba	Japanese house-girl

Minor Characters

Dad	Father of Sajit
Brother Nothing	Sajit's elder brother
Sgt Verity	Instructor at Leaders' Wing.
Sgt Evans	Instructor at Leaders' Wing
RSM Copp	RSM at Eaton Hall OCS
CSM Clogg	CSM at Eaton Hall
Captain Rushmoor	Instructor at Eaton Hall
Lt Col Robins	Fanatical cricket organiser
Captain Hawthorn	Dukes adjutant
Sergeant Brummell	12 Platoon sergeant.
Lt Col Bunbury	Commanding officer, Dukes.
Kim	Young Korean refugee/house boy
Captain 'Copper' Bowden	Second in command, Dog Company
Cpl Bridges	Dog Company Clerk
Cpl Turnbull	Second Dog Company clerk
Gunner Clancy	New Zealand patient at MASH Unit
Eddie	Clerk at HQ, Japan.
Akiko	Japanese house-girl
Lt Col Gibson	CO at HQ, Japan.
Private Bainbridge	Australian murderer, Seoul.
Lt Col McIlroy	CO Legal Department, Kure.
Sergeant Cuthbertson	Military Police 'screw', Seoul
Corporal Underwood	Engineer on the Hook

PART ONE

STAND BY

YOUR BEDS

"I joined the army perfectly willing to do my bit;
Even assume duties for which I was quite unfit,
But the ranting sergeant forever after my hide
Wouldn't even concede that I was on his side."

Rupert Sandwitch

1

Intake 541

The shouting and cursing and the effing and blinding started from the moment we arrived at Catterick Camp Railway Station, the bleakest spot in Britain. As the train jerked and clanged to a halt, I stuck my head out of the carriage window and gained an inkling of what lay in store for us. Drill sergeants from 7th Training Regiment Royal Signals were lined up in perfect dressing at regular intervals along the platform. There were dozens of them, all standing to attention as straight as billiard cues, their turn-out immaculate, and their lips curled back, ready to unleash well-rehearsed and blasphemous fury.

We had been warned what to expect, but nothing could have prepared us for what spewed forth from these brutalized individuals. Because they'd been put through the mincer in their youth, they were now determined to mete out the same treatment to us. To them we were the Post War Generation: sloppy, ill-disciplined and pampered; little darlings who were ripe for a touch of the old what-for if we were ever to become proper soldiers.

The train stopped. Carriage doors crashed open. We alighted. As our feet touched the ground we were greeted by a cacophony of unintelligible and foul insults. Hysteria rent the air. It flashed across the platform like forked lightning. The air turned blue and we cringed en masse. One of our braver souls, a Cockney named Fletcher, jumped back into the train and shouted: "Don't think I'll join after all, thanks!"

Over 2,000 of us alighted from that train. We were known to the army as 'Intake 541, 7th Training Regiment, The Royal Corps of Signals'. The shock and confusion caused by the orders coming at us from all angles meant that although we got the general drift, the precise details of what was expected of us remained obscure. This made the NCOs shout all the louder, swear all the harder, and generally work themselves into such a fury that spittle flew far and wide. Eventually, as we cringed before their onslaught, they manhandled us into compliance. I was grabbed by the sleeve and shoved across the platform with the cry: "Get the fuck over there, Sambo!" Another recruit from our carriage (wearing a bowler hat and carrying a tennis racket) was seized by his astrakhan collar and deposited beside me with the yell: "Right, Fred Perry ... You're the right fucking marker!"

Elsewhere along the platform, others were being treated in a similar manner and eventually we were formed into three enormously long ranks. Then, after we'd been counted off into tens, making squads of thirty men each, we were marched off into the heart of Catterick Camp, a vast, sprawling, conglomeration of soulless huts, barrack blocks, and parade grounds, organised and run by the greatest collection of neurotics, paranoids, and general nut cases the UK has ever known.

Our squad sergeant was named Gough. He was a short, square, Yorkshireman, so ugly, morose and soured, that his natural aggression was easy to understand. As we shambled along, trying to get in step, he introduced himself. With genuine pride he declared: "I am the nastiest fucker the fucking British Army has ever fucking known." Even on such a short acquaintanceship we believed him, but we soon discovered that at Catterick--- where all politeness, manners, refinement, and consideration for others, had long since been discarded--- Sergeant Gough was nothing out of the ordinary. Indeed, he was pretty average.

The aims and traditions of Catterick demanded that all NCOs should be absolute shits. They gloried in being shits. It was more than their jobs were worth not to be a shit. Being shitty got results. Quite a few of them had been such complete and utter shits for so long that they had become militaristically deranged, petty tyrants and psychopathic bullies; men who loved to hate and gloried in being hated; men who had been sent so far round the bend by army bullshit that they now existed in a twilight world of Blanco, Brasso, stamping feet, quivering salutes, falsetto screams, and violent threats.

Also, we were now in the land of the F-word. I was of course well acquainted with the F-word and it would be pointless and dishonest of me to ignore its regular usage throughout the army. In my sheltered upbringing, with a strict mother and a private education, I only came across it occasionally, but now I was due to become very familiar with it. For many at Catterick it was a very versatile linguistic tool which enabled them to convey a wealth of different meanings by the mere inflection of their voices. When Harry Wilmott (who you will meet shortly) declared something to be "fooking perr---fect!" you knew straight away that it was an accolade quite beyond dispute.

Some claimed that the entire structure of communications at Catterick was based on the F-word, but this was an exaggeration, a fallacy that came about due to the word having so many variations (nouns, verbs and exclamations etc.). In fact, the F-word was a panacea for the less articulate. It enabled them to convey their meanings with perfect clarity. Sentences that consisted entirely of F-words (give or take the odd definite article), such as 'The fucking fucker's fucking fucked the fucker!' left even the dimmest of recruits in no doubt that some fucker had really fucked up. At other times many of the less gifted managed to lay greater emphasis on things by splitting syllables and inserting the F-word between them, as in 'abso-fucking-lutely'. This was granted respectability in 1998 when *Foyle's English Usage* referred to it as 'the inserted fuck'. However, they did advise that in formal writing it was best left to writers with appropriate expertise, such as Martin Amis and D. H. Lawrence.

We spent most of our first day being issued with kit, filling in forms, and undergoing medicals. Our first visit was to the Quartermaster's Stores. Here, kit was issued so quickly that had it not been for the unorthodox behaviour of the fellow in the bowler-hat, astrakhan overcoat, and tennis racket (Rupert Sandwitch), we would have been through the stores in two minutes flat. We passed down a long counter behind which storemen were posted at regular intervals. As we drew level with them they gave us a cursory glance, selected a bundle of clothing, pushed it across to us, and then justified their selection by shouting out, 'small', 'medium', or 'large'. We were required to accept these bundles without comment, and only Rupert Sandwitch had the gumption to object. Putting his tennis racket aside for a moment, he had the temerity to point out that his physique was such that it could not be categorized by 'small', 'medium', or 'large'. He explained that he had the misfortune to be out of proportion. Some of his parts were small, some medium-sized, and his extremities (especially his head and feet) were definitely XXL. He also pointed out that his size eleven-and-a-half feet needed a broad fitting to permit them to breathe properly, otherwise there would be unfortunate repercussions (which there certainly were!).

The storeman dealing with him had no idea how to respond. It was as though Oliver Twist had asked for more. As the point was being debated, the Quartermaster Sergeant burst forth from his inner sanctum. Silence descended. Here was someone the like of whom we had never seen: Catterick's own version of Frankenstein. Without warning, he let out a high-pitched scream that could have meant anything. We shrank under the withering blast of his beery halitosis. Throughout Catterick he was known as 'Deep Purple' on account of the mass of broken veins that pulsed on the end of his bulbous nose. Still screaming like a soprano diva straining for top C, he paced up and down behind the counter, eyeing us with disgust. Then his voice dropped several decibels and he informed us that in this man's army there were no such things as half sizes in boots, or broad fittings, or high heels, or short legs, or long legs; and no allowances for in-growing toe nails, knock-knees, pigeon chests, pigeon toes, elongated pricks, or balls the size of light bulbs.

"What you fucking get is what you fucking wear!"

Undaunted, Sandwitch spoke up again. He pleaded on behalf of his abnormalities, explaining quietly and reasonably that off-the-peg trousers that fitted his waist only ever reached halfway down his calves, and the ones he had just been given certainly wouldn't reach his anklets, let alone have sufficient material to overlap. He held them against himself and concluded: "These will never fit."

"Fit!" exploded Deep Purple. "Fit! Of course they won't fucking fit! What do you think this is? Montague-fucking-Burton's? Just swap things around among yourselves."

From the stores we went to the Squadron Orderly Room for form-filling. Here, the atmosphere was calmer. Indeed, the half-a-dozen or so clerks scattered about the room were so moribund that it was positively peaceful. When it came to filling in the forms, it was soon became clear that several of us were illiterate. Those thus handicapped appealed to Sergeant Gough for help, only to find that his expertise in this field was so limited that it precluded any advice. So they turned to Sandwitch on the strength of his bowler hat and his initiative in querying his kit. He helped readily enough but his advice, and the manner in which he gave it, indicated that he was not what the army would term a natural acquisition. Every time he filled in a form for someone he proceeded to talk in rhyming couplets. After the first form he completed, he said:

> *"Now you've signed upon that dotted line*
> *There's no going back. You can't resign!"*

To another he helped, he commented:

> *"Regardless of any allowances you request,*
> *The army won't be in the least impressed."*

When someone thanked him, he replied:

> *"Don't mention it, my dear old chap!*
> *No problem at all with army crap..."*

Most of us found this amusing, but not Sergeant Gough. He watched in silence and his body language (he kept twitching) made it easy to read his mind: things were getting out of hand. Fucking Fred Perry was too cocky by half. He seemed to think the whole thing was some kind of pub outing. That wasn't in line with Sergeant Gough's training. He had been brought up on the army's simplified version of Pavlov's theory whereby mute creatures (squaddies), on receiving repetitive stimuli (being shouted and sworn at), responded in a predictable manner (jumped to attention and yelled: "Sergeant!") and then did exactly as they were told.

Gough strode over to Sandwitch to sort things out: an eyeball-to-eyeball confrontation, the British NCOs answer to all acts of defiance.

However, Sandwitch wasn't intimidated. He listened attentively to Gough's tirade and nodded every now and then as though acknowledging the wisdom of his drift. Finally, when Gough ran out of obscenities and spittle, and drew back to rearm, Sandwitch stretched forth a hand and placed it on Gough's shoulder like a Clerk in Holy Orders dispensing a blessing. Speaking softly, but imitating Gough's Yorkshire accent to perfection, he said:

> *"Nay, lad! No need t' rant and rave t' be 'eard,*
> *Still less t' keep using that four-letter word."*

Sergeant Gough was left speechless. His mouth opened and shut several times but nothing came out. It was our first indication that for all his aggression and bluster he had definite limitations when confronted by the unorthodox.

After the form filling, came medical examinations. They should have been straightforward but the first man to come out of the MO's surgery turned to the rest of us and said: "Nothing to it, lads! A pint of blood out of each arm", whereupon the next three men in the queue fainted. Then, after their recumbent bodies had been dragged away, there was a delay whilst Private Fletcher (the Cockney who had got back into the carriage) was examined. Fletcher was from a deprived area of Bow and suffered from bowed legs (mild rickets) due to a poor war-time diet. From what was heard by those at the front of the queue, the doctor refused Fletcher's demand for a second opinion as to his suitability for military service and told him that if he found his condition embarrassing he should tell people that he was an apprentice jockey.

"Charming," responded Fletcher. "That'll only make them ask: 'Where's your fucking horse.'"

I also had difficulty with the doctor. As I stood before him, stark naked, he ordered me to bend over and touch the ground between my parted legs. Then, peering into my backside, he queried: "Do you ever have headaches?" I replied in the negative and enquired anxiously if he had found something up there to indicate that meant I might be liable to. He regarded this as rank insubordination and threatened to put me on CO's Orders.

In fact, the main purpose of the medicals was to give us injections which gave us sore arms and lumps under our armpits.

I was the first to finish these formalities. Then, following instructions, I went to barrack room J2 in Barrack Block N to claim a bed. I had only just finished storing my kit away in a metal bedside locker when

Sandwitch entered. I watched him wander around. First he tested the beds for comfort and then he tried each light switch. When satisfied that the beds were all the same, and that the lights all worked, he selected a corner bed. After he had sorted out his kit he removed his bowler hat. He polished it lovingly on his sleeve before placing it in the top compartment of his locker together with his tennis racket.

It was only then that I realized what an odd-looking bloke he was. His most arresting feature was his head. It was too big and wobbled about as though it was not properly tethered, his neck being far too thin to support its weight. His hair was the texture of wire-wool and rose in a great plume in the style of a Sudanese Fuzzy Wuzzy, suitable for a bowler hat but certainly not for a close-fitting army beret. His face looked as though it had been constructed from spare parts. His eyes were different colours (one green, one brown) and his right ear was larger than his left and protruded, whereas his left ear sat normally. His skin was smooth and rarely needed the attention of a razor and although he had good teeth, his nose was so thin and pinched that it wasn't surprising that his mouth was permanently open.

He smiled broadly as he saw me watching him. He seemed to think he was at the start of a marvelous adventure. His brush with Gough and Deep-Purple clearly didn't worry him. I doubt if it even occurred to him that he was now a marked man. Then I realized that he was studying me with as much interest as I was him, no doubt wondering how someone of Indian descent had ended up in the British army. Eventually, a bugle call sounded in a distant part of the camp. When it finished Sandwitch struck a dramatic pose and cried out:

> *"A million squaddies manned the garrison.*
> *Not one of them fit to answer the warison."*

I ignored him. The last thing to do was encourage him. However, he wasn't deterred by my indifference. He strolled over, sat on the bottom of my bed, and asked: "Where were you educated?"

"Blundell's."

"Really? I went to Buckpass."

"Oh dear …"

He laughed. "I know what you mean. It was certainly pretty spartan, but nothing compared to this place." Without warning he leapt to his feet and with a theatrical wave of his arms cried out:

> *"Catterick! Hell camp where all will freeze.*
> *Scant hope here of browning your knees."*

"Do you do this all the time?" I asked.

"Yes. I love poetry. Do you?"

"I don't mind it. But I don't love it."

"It's my whole life."

"Then you'd better remember that these days it isn't supposed to rhyme. Not serious poetry."

"That'll change. I'm going to make rhyme and rhythm fashionable again."

"Well if you take my advice, you'll lay off antagonizing Sergeant Gough. Many more of your rhymes and we'll all end up suffering."

"Can't help it, old boy. I think in rhymes. They just slip out."

I left it at that, pretty sure that by the time Gough had finished with him he would be able to help it. When he showed no signs of moving from the bottom of my bed, I asked: "What's a warison?"

"It's a bugle note. Ordering attack." He was thoughtful for a moment and then added: "That's a pity. If you don't understand it, I'll have to think of something else."

"Don't worry on my account..."

"No, no! Poetry must be understood. There's no point in it otherwise. Only literary snobs and idiots read what can't be understood."

My sentiment entirely, so I modified my opinion of him. I guessed--- correctly--- that at Buckpass (a Devon school I knew quite well) he had been considered a budding genius and that he had a place at Oxford or Cambridge awaiting for him on completion of his National Service.

When other recruits entered the barrack room, Sandwitch returned to his bed. As everyone settled in there was hardly any conversation. We were still reeling from the shock of our reception. Eventually, after several individuals had got off their beds and tried the light switches, conversations picked up and it became evident from the accents that we hailed from all over the UK. I remained on my bed, content to observe. I knew it would be best to let others grow accustomed to my colour gradually. The last thing people want from those who are different is pushiness. In contrast, Sandwitch was an eccentric who considered himself perfectly normal and he wandered around the barrack room introducing himself to everyone in turn. Soon, they were all chatting away. They took a closer look at their uniforms and started on the laborious business of swapping.

Rupert Sandwitch only tried one swap. He got a pair of trousers which were ideal in length, but which ballooned out in front of his waist like clowns' trousers. After that he gave up, deciding that if that was what the army had issued him with, that's what he would wear. If they didn't like it, bad luck on them. However, this did not stop him being generous with his advice to others. At one point he watched Fletcher try on a different battle dress tunic and he couldn't resist exclaiming: "Oh, la la! Tres Francais…"

"What yer mean?" demanded Fletcher.

"C'est Toulon et Toulouse."

Fletcher grabbed him by the tie and demanded: "Look 'ere, mate! What's your fucking game then?"

It was a good question to which Sandwitch offered no answer.

"Any more of your lip and I'll mash you up."

I had heard so many derogatory reports about National Service, and read so much in the national press about bullying, scrubbings, boot blackings, and pointless 'bull' in basic training, that I was curious to discover if Catterick really was that bad. Our initial reception certainly indicated that it was and when I spoke to several old hands they assured me that things like cutting lawns with scissors, being thrown out of bed, whitewashing heaps of coal, digging holes and then filling them in again, and men being drilled until they dropped, happened all the time.

Yet in our squad things never got that bad, and in retrospect I put it down to our resilience and determination to stand up for ourselves. Squads which accepted everything dished out to them came off far worse than those with enough spirit to fight back. Not that our fighting back amounted to much, but we did have two natural leaders in our midst: Sandwitch and Fletcher. We also had several others, including myself, who gave them support.

Sandwitch and Fletcher could hardly have been in greater contrast. Rupert was open and polite, yet gently sarcastic with his rhyming couplets; whereas Fletcher--- as became a friend of the Kray twins--- was snide, cunning, and sinister, everything based on threats of violence which he was quite capable of putting into practice despite being a physical wimp. At first, when he used the expression 'mash-up', we were doubtful as to what he meant, but it soon became clear when he was seen digging dirt out of his toe nails with a long-bladed flick-knife which was obviously designed for more sinister purposes. He also spent most of his waking hours boasting about his friendship with the Krays and how he and his brother were regarded as their right-hand men when it came to mashing-up dissenters in the underworld.*

Fletcher's pet hate was officers, especially newly commissioned 2nd

---

Fletcher's elder brother joined up with the Krays. The twins were soon imprisoned for the duration of their National Service for the attempted murder of their drill sergeant. Fletcher senior tried the same thing with the RSM but came off second best and after three weeks in hospital, and 28 days inside, spent the rest of his service in Hong Kong.

Lieutenants--- who he referred to as "pimply twits". He held them in such contempt that it was no surprise that our first clash with authority came when he sorted out the orderly officer during our initial visit to the mess hall. This was a great barn of a building, hardly conducive to creating a hearty appetite. Even if one could muster enough courage to swallow the revolting mixture of fat and gristle that masqueraded as Irish Stew, one then had to contend with the crude surroundings: the breeze-block walls; bare tables; benches with enormous splinter potential (that tipped up when too many bums congregated at one end); unswept floors which attracted mice; and a multitude of sparrows flying around the rafters crapping indiscriminately.

It was one of these sparrows which gave Fletcher his chance to demonstrate his contempt for young officers. On entering the mess hall we joined a long queue stretching along a side wall, shuffling forward towards the serving counter with our mess tins held out in front of us. Unobserved by anyone, a sparrow tried to fly through an air extractor fan near the ceiling and got decapitated. The head fluttered down gently and landed in Fletcher's mess tin. It was so light, and Fletcher was so busy threatening to mash-up a queue-barger, that he would never have known of its existence had not his neighbour nudged him and said: "By 'eck, Fletch! That's bloody good service! But not much of a helping."

Fletcher took one look at the head and said: "Bloody hell, I'm not standing for that!" He then marched off to find the orderly officer, who was wandering around adjacent tables tapping his leg with his swagger stick and making the occasional obligatory enquiry: "Any complaints?"

For a time, Fletcher stalked him, waiting for him to repeat: "Any complaints?" When he did, Fletcher tapped him on the shoulder. "You bet I bloody have! This is what I've been bloody served up with!" He then thrust his mess tin beneath the officer's nose. The officer took one look at the decapitated head and fainted.

"Well I soon mashed him up!" said Fletcher, and his reputation was made.

Catterick was full of little Hitlers. Everyone with a chevron on his arm loved to shout and scream at any recruit he laid eyes on. Perfect strangers we passed in corridors whilst going quite innocently from A to B would demand: "And where the fuck do you think you're going?" Others would shout at us to swing our arms or stand up straight. Some were so far away that they were nothing but blurred images. One lance-corporal, on approaching the corner of any building, would shout out: "Stand up straight, you horrible little fucker!" purely in the hope that someone was approaching around the other side. When they were, they marvelled at his ability to see round corners, but eventually he came unstuck. He turned one corner too many and came face-to-face with the RSM.

Even in our barrack room we weren't safe. Any Adolf who happened to be passing by would stick his head around the doorway and shout: "Stand by your beds!" He would then walk up and down the length of the room (swearing and threatening all the time) before disappearing as suddenly as he had appeared, leaving us standing rigidly to attention like so many idiots. It didn't take us long to realize that this was known in Catterick as 'a grip' (try-on) and whenever a little Hitler appeared and shouted, "Stand by your beds!" we responded as one with a mighty shout of "Piss off!", which they always did.

When alone and undisturbed, we grew accustomed to endless hours of bulling our equipment. We had to Blanco our webbing equipment green, polish our brasses, eradicate 'pimples' from our boots by rubbing them with an iron or the reverse side of a hot spoon, and then polish the toe caps by going round and round in tiny circles with Cherry Blossom until a thick film of polish built up and they shone like plate glass.

It was during these long hours that we got to know each other. As we went about our spit and polish the barrack room was full of banter. What surprised me was that so many of us had a definite agenda or ambition during our service. Rupert Sandwitch saw it as a means of getting to know how the other half lived, thus giving his poetry a new dimension. My aim (although I never mentioned it) was to gather material for a novel by volunteering for Korea. None of the others had ever considered that they might end up at the sharp-end in either Malaya or Korea, probably because the army was always telling them that they had a great opportunity to learn a trade, cipher clerk being by far the most popular. A handsome lad named Beatty was desperate to be posted to Cyprus where his girlfriend had just got a job in a Famagusta strip club.

"You're wasting your fucking time, mate," Fletcher advised him. "Every bugger wants a posting in Cyprus. And anyhow, by the time you get there she will have been fucked bandy."

"Is that how you got bandy, Fletch? Too much of the other?"

Fletcher wasn't amused. He cast aside his best boots and pointed a finger at the man. "Watch it, mate. Or I'll mash you up!"

No more was said. There was something about Fletcher which was unnerving. None of us knew what to make of him. Was he just a loud-mouthed Cockney weed, or really a minor member of the Kray gang? All we knew for sure (because he kept on about it all the time) was that he also had an objective during in his National Service. He was desperate to be posted to Hong Kong. According to his elder brother the sex on offer in Hong Kong was out of this world. This was not just because of the abundance of lovely and willing young girls, but because their vaginas were horizontal rather than vertical. Fletcher's brother said it elevated sex to new heights of splendour and gave intercourse, if not a new sense of purpose, certainly a new sense of direction.

A feature of National Service was the number of men who became determined to work their ticket. I had been warned about this by Brother Nothing.* He had yarns galore about his comrades at Lark Hill who had succeeded. One man, when told to Blanco all his kit, had done just that, including his uniform. Another, desperately keen to take up a place at RADA, utilized his acting skill by faking St Vitus Dance, culminating in jerking a mess tin of tea over the catering officer. Another had heard that consistent bed-wetters were discharged. The only trouble was that he found the act of urinating in bed so repugnant that he just couldn't do it, so he reverted to tipping half a bottle of Friary's Brown Ale over his sheets every morning. It worked like a charm.

Brother Nothing also tried to work his ticket but he made the fatal error of leaving it too late. He explained that one had to get in early, before the unit's MO and his team of psychiatrists suspected what was going on. Once their suspicions were aroused, no one succeeded. Thus when he claimed he was allergic to his uniform and couldn't stop sneezing, they didn't believe a word of it. They told him straight that he'd have to think up something far more convincing than that.

In our Intake at Catterick, the nearest we got to someone trying a similar stunt was Fletcher, with his relatively mild remarks to the MO about his bandy legs; yet two of our members were discharged without even trying. The first came about through our inability to march in step on the square (or parade ground). Sergeant Gough's efforts to rectify this proved futile. He tried all manner of things but none of them worked. Within seconds of marching off we would be reduced to shuffling about, none of us knowing who was in step and who wasn't. Gough kept yelling: "Left! Left!.... Left, right left!" but that had no effect. Fletcher, like several others, couldn't tell his left from his right, and shouted back: "Sarge, for Christ's sake stop yelling that... You're just confusing us..."

Fletcher spent the rest of the morning doubling around the square.

At one point, Gough blamed me for our inability to keep in step, but when he pulled me out of the squad it made no difference. However, he persevered with pulling different men out. On about his tenth try, he pulled out a man named Adams. With him standing to one side, we marched perfectly. When we did an about-turn and marched back

---

*For details of Brother Nothing, read Volumes I and II.

towards Adams the trouble was staring us in the face. Adams was listing very heavily to one side.

Sergeant Gough circled him several times--- a normal prerequisite before indulging in the beloved eyeball-to-eyeball confrontation. "What do you think you are then? The fucking Leaning Tower of Pisa?"

"It's my right leg, Sarge. It's three inches shorter than my left leg."

Gough circled him again. "Can't you stand up straight?"

"Only with a great deal of effort, Sarge."

"Well fucking strain yourself!"

Adams straightened up, transferring all his weight on to his left leg, which left his right leg dangling. "Fuck me!" exclaimed Gough. "We'd better enter you for a three-legged race."

Gough decided that a man with legs of different lengths was beyond his remit. He stood us at ease and went to fetch the Squadron Sergeant-Major. When he arrived, he took one look and said: "Fuck me! Hop-along Cassidy!"

Next, the adjutant was summoned. His inspection of Adams was more sophisticated and circumspect. On seeing Adam's right leg dangling, he said: "Oh deary, deary, me! And what do we have here?" He gave the dangling leg several prods with his swagger stick and when it swung to and fro like a pendulum, well clear of the ground, he ordered Adams to be escorted off the square. He was never seen again.

The second of our squad to be discharged came the following day. We had progressed to the elusive art of 'Dressing, by the right!' This required that on the command: "Right Dress!" each man raised his right arm so that it touched the shoulder of the man next to him and at the same time all heads were jerked to the right in order to shuffle into a straight line (dressing). Sergeant Gough then went to the end of each rank and adjusted men backwards or forwards, as necessary. When he got to the rear rank he discovered that a man named Yorath had his head jutting forward and was looking the wrong way. All Gough could see were dozens of scars on the back of his head, the result of his army haircut the previous day.

This caused much vain shouting on the part of Gough. He couldn't remember Yorath's name and since Yorath was still looking the other way he had no idea that he was the one being shouted at. Consequently nothing happened. With mounting fury, Gough marched to the other end of the rank and confronted Yorath. "So there you are!"

"Oh, hello, Sergeant ..."

"Don't you fucking 'hello Sergeant' me!"

Eventually, Yorath explained that several months before he had broken his neck in a motor cycle accident and his head now jutted forward permanently, inclined to his left. The Sergeant-Major was summoned once more and was sympathetic. The adjutant took a different attitude. Two malingerers on the trot was more than he was prepared to tolerate. He seized Yorath's jaw in his right hand, the back of his head in his left, and twisted with all his might. This produced loud crunching noises and screams of agony from Yorath. It also made his head loose on its mountings. It began to loll about like the head of one of the toy dogs which (years later) people loved to put in the rear windows of their cars. When the wobbling became more pronounced, and Yorath suddenly went cross-eyed, the adjutant decided against any further manipulations and sent for the MO. Like Adams, he was never seen again.

As Gough prepared to restart our drilling, Sandwitch's voice came from the rear rank:

> *"Thirty scruffy nig-nogs, all marching in a row,*
> *Two worked their tickets. Twenty-eight to go!"*

I have no doubt that Gough would have loved to have scored a hat-trick and got rid of Sandwitch as well, but establishing that a man was crackers was far more difficult than establishing a broken neck or a short leg. So Gough had to be content with making Sandwitch double around the square for the rest of the morning. Whereas this punishment put the fear of God into others, Sandwitch lapped it up. He was the thin, stringy type with enormously long legs who enjoyed running. His one claim to athletic fame was having been captain of cross-country at Buckpass. Each time he completed a lap and came level with us he waved cheerily and made rude gestures behind Gough's back; and on about his thirtieth lap he marked-time behind Gough, waited for a pause in his shouting, then called out, "The prayer of the long distance runner:

> *'Oh Lord of great renown!*
> *You pick them up*
> *Then I'll put them down'."*

Sergeant Gough wheeled round, but Sandwitch was off and away.

2

Trouble with the General

We soon settled into a daily routine. In the mornings it was up with the lark, ablutions, a foul breakfast, then barrack room chores consisting of sweeping our bed-spaces and the centre of the floor. Then a barrack room inspection by Gough and our officer, Mr. Collier, before drilling on the square. Finally, we had a lecture from the MO on personal hygiene, which took us up to a foul lunch. The highlight of our afternoon training was a visit to the gym. This made a welcome change but was spoilt by our PTI expecting us to shower and change back into our uniforms within two minutes, a physical impossibility.

In the evenings, after a supper of baked beans-on-toast or sardines-on-toast (sometimes with Tomato Ketchup, sometimes with Daddy's Sauce, but always with the danger of bird shit), we returned to our barrack room and concentrated on cleaning our equipment. This took up more of our time than anything, and in a way it was restful and relaxing. We sat on the edges of our beds and got to know each other better as we chatted away.

What really got us down was drilling on the square. This was not only exhausting but incredibly boring. We went through the same moves time after time until eventually we mastered 'Halt!' 'About turn!' 'Right turn!' 'Left turn!' and 'To the front, salute!' Then we went on to arms drill, for which Sergeant Gough appointed a 'Two-Three' man. He gave this task to Fletcher. He was sick of the sight of his bandy legs and by making him the 'Two-Three' man it meant he disappeared into the middle of the squad. Once there, Fletcher's task was to call out softly "Two-Three" when more than one movement was required, thus enhancing our timing. This smartened us up, but with Sandwitch in our midst we still had no chance of winning the inter-squad drilling competition.

Not that we were worried by that. Our main concern was passing muster on the Saturday morning barrack room inspections. These were normally carried out by our Squadron Commander, Major Pearce. Unlike the daily inspections by Gough and Mr. Collier, these weekly inspection included all our kit, right down to spare boot laces, a second razor, and a reserve tube of toothpaste. Everything had to be laid out on our beds in a strictly prescribed manner, with our blankets squared off to perfection at the bed-head. Also, our metal lockers had to shine brightly, with not a speck of dust anywhere.

These inspections were not only vital to us, but also to Sergeant Gough and Mr. Collier. When a barrack room failed to pass a Saturday morning inspection the sergeant and officer in charge were likewise punished with extra orderly officer and orderly sergeant duties. Consequently, Gough made sure we had everything in perfect order by lights-out every Friday. He then made us sleep on ground sheets in our bed spaces.

Our third Saturday in barracks was a special occasion. Intake 541 was to be inspected by Lieutenant-General Sir Charles Huxley, DSO MC, Commanding Officer, Northern Command. It was General Huxley's way of keeping in touch with the basics. If we failed the inspection we would be confined to barracks for another month, but if we passed we were to be rewarded with our first week-end pass out of camp. This was such a coveted prize that we went about the task of scrubbing and cleaning with rare zest, determined to seize the opportunity to enjoy a pub crawl in Richmond and/or partake of the pleasures of the girls who were bussed into the Garrison Naafi Centre every Saturday evening from Leeds.*

Our ablutions were the most vital part of our inspections and for three days we spent every moment of our 'free' time on our hands and knees, scrubbing and scraping with Brillo Pads, Vim, razor blades and dousing the toilets and hand basins with Domestos. By the time we'd finished our ablutions appeared never to have been used, and Gough was so determined to preserve this image that in the meantime he made us wash beneath a solitary outside cold tap and urinate on a piece of waste ground well to the rear.

General Huxley entered our barrack room with his ADC. Sergeant Gough and Mr. Collier followed in their wake. We were all standing by our beds, rigidly to attention. The General was an old hand at barrack room inspections, having been commissioned through the ranks. He left nothing to chance. He ran a finger along every flat surface, searching for dust. He looked under each bed, and as he progressed down the barrack room he moved every locker and poked around behind it. When he reached Rupert Sandwitch we all held our breath. His bed space was our weak link.

Overnight, several of us had helped him, trying to make his layout presentable, but it still lacked the perfection of the others. For example, he had somehow contrived to break his spare boot laces and although they were coiled up as specified, they also boasted granny knots. Even

---

*Bussing in girls from Leeds was standard procedure. Competition in Leeds on Saturdays was so fierce, with so many part-timers and amateurs thronging the streets, that the professional ladies preferred the easy pickings at Catterick: anything better than propping up lamp posts, kicking the backsides of sniffing dogs.

more condemning was his spare string vest. This was supposed to be the centre piece of the displays, laid out like a piece of chain-mail armour, but Rupert (in need of something to hold up his drawers cellular), had unravelled it, cut a length off it, and what was left of his vest was now sitting in the middle of his layout masquerading as a ball of string.

The general missed all this and was more interested in what might be behind Rupert's locker. As he pulled it to one side, he said: "Do you know what I'm looking for, soldier?"

"Well, to be honest," answered Rupert in his usual conversational style, not even throwing in the odd 'sir', "I haven't the faintest idea. But if you press me, I'd venture the suggestion that ...."

"Fag ends, soldier. That's what I'm after. Fag ends!"

"I say!" exclaimed Sandwitch "No need for that. Have one of mine."

We did our utmost to contain our laughter. In most cases we succeeded, but Fletcher let out a mighty guffaw and said: "Fucking hell, I like that!"

"Silence in the ranks," yelled Gough.

The General glared backwards and forward between Sandwitch and Fletcher and it was obvious there would be repercussions. He stomped off to inspect our ablutions and sure enough his ADC soon reappeared and told us that our ablutions were a disgrace and that we were confined to barracks for another month. We knew it was a trumped-up excuse, a sneaky way of punishing us, and it meant of course that Sergeant Gough and Mr. Collier would also be punished.

What Mr. Collier thought about this was hard to tell, but Gough's reaction was predictable. He put Sandwitch and Fletcher on 'orders'. They were hauled up before our OC, Major Pearce, and were awarded 'jankers', a punishment that required them to report to the Guard Commander twice a day immaculately kitted out in full battle order.

Fletcher did not take this lying down. He retaliated by deliberately fouling up things as our 'Two-Three' man. He either varied his timings so outrageously that it put us all off, or else he reverted to muttering 'four-five' or 'six-seven' and this caused so much amusement among us that chaos ensued. Eventually, Gough realized what was going and gave the job to someone else. He then got even with Fletcher by making him double around the square. This exhausted Fletcher so much that by the end of the each day's training he just flopped on to his bed and slept right through until reveille.

Gough's tactics with Sandwitch were different. With him, he relied on verbal abuse. He would go up to him and shout the most appalling insults straight into his face. He told him he was the biggest scruff in Catterick, making point after valid point, jabbing each disaster area of Sandwitch's turn-out with his right index finger. He likened his beret to a cow pat; pointed out that his cap badge was over his left ear instead of his left eye;

that where everything should have come together tidily around his waist, it all fell apart in chaos; that his trousers had tram lines instead of creases; and that the bottoms of his trousers were once again hanging over his anklets, instead of being tucked in.

Gough soon stopped calling him Fred Perry. Instead he became 'Bloody Sand Witch!', his name split into two syllables since that was how Gough read it off his roll call. Not that Gough's bullying worried Rupert one bit. Whilst the rest of us jumped to attention and yelled "Sergeant!" every time he shouted at us, Rupert just smiled softly, looked Gough straight in the eyes, and spoke back to him as though they were passing the time of day in a bus queue, more often than not working in one of his rhyming couplets.

On one occasion Gough criticized him mercilessly, finally yelling: "You're nothing but a fucking moving shit house ... What are you?"

This time Sandwitch forsook a rhyming couplet. Instead, he replied: "If I interpret you correctly, Sergeant, I suppose I will have to plead guilty to the rare distinction of being a copulating mobile latrine."

Then came a calamity!

Our barrack room iron (an early electric model we'd inherited from previous Intakes) packed up. Ironing was the most important of all our chores and proved to be beyond our competence, mainly because in those days it was deemed beneath the dignity of males to get involved in such a feminine activity. We hadn't the faintest idea how to handle such a lethal weapon, especially when trying to match up heat with different fabrics. Nasty accidents were frequent, most of them caused by laying the iron flat, instead of standing it on its end. Several of us burnt holes in our shirts, vests, and drawers cellular, and Sandwitch--- by far the worst ironer among us--- first of all scorched an imprint of the iron on the seat of his battledress trousers, making it look as though he had been branded, and then, when trying to eradicate 'pimples' off his best boots, ended up with Cherry Blossom on the face of it which proved impossible to remove and spread over everything else. Next, he set fire to one of his socks. This happened when involved in a long argument with Fletcher (next in turn on the iron) as to whether it was necessary to iron socks in the first place. His final act of incompetence was to leave the iron on all night. Since it had no thermostat it became red hot around 0200 hours and eventually self-destructed with a loud report around 0400 hours, fusing all the lights in the process. This happened at a particularly vital stage, especially for Sandwitch and Fletcher with their twice-daily inspection at the Guard Room.

Our salvation came in the form of Lance-corporal David Evans.

Evans was a maverick, not so much due to his personality but to the circumstances and the environment in which he existed. He personified the old adage: the exception proves the rule. The rule in question was that although the army was administratively an incredibly efficient organization, which kept tabs on hundreds of thousands of men, it did occasionally suffer a monumental cock-up. Lance-corporal Evans (known as Animal Evans) was just such a case, probably the army's biggest post-war cock-up on a purely personal level.

We were sitting on our beds, polishing boots and brasses, when Evans appeared in our doorway, cutting a sinister and dusky figure. He was a very big and powerfully built man and had about him a wild, aggressive look which at first suggested that with the least provocation he would take great delight in putting a bunch of fives down anyone's throat. Such a demeanour demanded immediate respect, and we dreaded that he--- like all other Little Hitlers--- would shout: "Stand by your beds!", thus testing our collective courage to respond with our usual, "Piss off!"

As it turned out we were not put to the test. Evans showed no aggression towards us. On the contrary, he stood in the doorway and started to hiss "Pst! Pst!" as though he was an Arab trying to sell us a female relative. In fact, he was hoping to sell us something quite different. He was forever in need of additional income and he generated this by soliciting trade from new Intakes, offering to bull their Best Boots, Blanco their webbing, polish their brasses, and--- above all--- press their uniforms. He even had a fairly modern iron and he offered all these services for the very reasonable fee of 5/- an hour.

In our Intake only Rupert and I could afford such a luxury. I jumped at the chance through sheer laziness and Rupert because of his inability to do these things properly himself, knowing he would be on jankers for the rest of his basic training unless he did something to improve his appearance. It was very much to his credit that he offered to finance Fletcher's requirements as well, this despite his dislike for the Cockney. Consequently a deal was soon struck. The three of us put everything we could Animal's way, making us men of relative leisure and enabling Sandwitch and Fletcher to pass their inspections with flying colours.

(A word of explanation. Animal Evans was destined to play such a vital role in my army service that a few words about his background are appropriate. Technically, he was lance-corporal in charge (i/c) of hot water and central heating in Barrack Block N. I say 'technically' because neither hot water nor central heating had been available in N Block for years. He lived as a recluse in the boiler room, a well-concealed dungeon measuring 8' X 8' in the basement. His dusky appearance was due to a coal chute which went from the roadway straight down into his boiler room. Although there hadn't been a coal

delivery for a decade or more, there was still a large deposit of nutty slack in the corner of his accommodation and whenever eastern winds swept across Yorkshire they whipped straight down the chute and coal dust billowed about like sand in the Sahara.

Evans joined the Royal Signals in 1938 and at the start of World War II he was a qualified linesman, seconded to the Green Howards. He became involved in Dunkirk, with the Green Howards forming the backbone of the British rear-guard action around Torhout. When they ordered Evans to lay a new line back to the Dunkirk beaches, he set off with numerous reels of wire. That was the last the Green Howards ever saw of him. When he reached Brigade HQ, adjacent to the beaches, he found that it had been demolished by Stuka dive bombers, so he sought guidance from the Beach Master who told him to forget everything else and join the queue of men wading out to the boats heading for England. Meanwhile, as the Green Howards joined the exodus to the beaches, they came across a pair of soiled army trousers flapping in the wind on a snag halfway up a telegraph pole on the outer reaches of Dunkirk. They assumed that these must be all that was left of Evans and reported him 'Missing in action: presumed dead'.

Once back at Catterick, Animal learnt of his demise with amazement and he took immediate steps to re-establish himself. He found this easier said than done. It involved reams of red-tape and even when the army acknowledged that he was still alive and started paying him again, the lack of weapons after Dunkirk made it necessary for them to slot Animal into a spurious job that didn't require firearms. Thus, Animal was promoted to lance-corporal i/c hot water and central heating in N Block. He had been there ever since, a forgotten man. Even the few people who were aware of his presence in the coal-hole (such as Sergeant Gough) found it expedient to leave him well alone, allowing Animal to lead a tolerable existence based on nightly visits to the garrison cinema and satisfying his basic instincts every Saturday night with a girlfriend named Blossom who was bussed in with all the other girls from Leeds. Here endeth the explanation.)

Sandwitch, Fletcher, and I often went down to Animal's dungeon to collect our kit and we soon got to know him well. Indeed, I soon formed a close affinity with him and realized he was very lonely. Once he started talking he found it difficult to stop and it was only a matter of time before he took us into his confidence and explained his curious situation. He was also a mine of information about Catterick's various quirks and foibles. His explanation of why Catterick was the most barbaric boot camp outside the French Foreign Legion was most enlightening. He explained that towards the end of WWII most of the NCOs at Catterick knew they were unfit for civilian employment and therefore did their utmost to avoid demobilization by currying favour in high places. This was achieved by ever-increasing discipline and nastiness towards recruits.

Then, in 1947, everything changed. Peace-time National Service was introduced and the employment of drill sergeants became guaranteed. However, by this time they were so inured with aggression and bullying that rather than change their ways they simply adapted them. A professional necessity became a sadistic pleasure. They were like actors competing for Oscars. In the sergeants' mess they did nothing but boast about their most recent performances, even though they had to concede that no one could ever match the exploits of the current RSM. He was the Laurence Olivier of Catterick. During a memorable week in 1948 he drove two men to suicide and reduced a third to such a gibbering wreck that he was dragged off the square screaming: "Mummy! Mummy! Help me, Mummy!"

Every morning, as the adjutant and the RSM toured the parade ground, drill sergeants braced themselves. It was their chance to make a special effort, to so impress that it would enhance their prospects of promotion. The volume of their cursing increased. Out came fresh insults with their ridicule aimed at hand-picked targets. In our squad there were three of us. Fletcher because of his bandy legs ('Where's your fucking horse?'); Sandwitch because of his general incompetence and scruffiness ('God give me strength!'); and myself on account of my colour ('Wake up, Sambo!').

A month after General Huxley's inspection, we got a pass out of camp. Apart from Rupert and myself, everyone donned their Teddy Boy suits, saturated their hair with Brylcreem and then, under Fletcher's leadership, roared off on the razzle. Rupert and I went to the garrison cinema to see a Humphrey Bogart film: Casablanca. As we soon discovered--- especially as the weather turned colder--- the garrison cinema was the only warm place at Catterick, and thanks to Animal Evans doing all our bulling for us, we were able to go there every night to enjoy double feature programmes which changed daily, a tremendous bargain at 6d a time.

Animal also went there every night, bar Saturdays, when he was otherwise engaged with Blossom. To Animal, going into the cinema was like entering another world, a make-believe existence in which he completely immersed himself. He became so absorbed by the film that he forgot the presence of others and indulged in pithy and constant barracking, sometimes critical, at other times so approvingly that he clapped. Not infrequently he called out advice to individual characters rather like a child at a pantomime, yelling out, "Watch out... He's behind you!" or "Let him have it, you mug!" While this would never have been tolerated in a civilian cinema, the squaddies loved it. Forgetting the warmth factor, many of them went there more to hear Animal's asides than to see the films.

The first aside Rupert and I heard was typical. It was during a B movie and there was a scene in which a Chicago gangster (Broderick Crawford) felled his gorgeous girlfriend (Virginia Mayo) with a vicious right hook. He then looked down at her luscious figure, with her glorious tits on the verge of popping out, and moaned: "Oh, gee! Oh, my God! What have I done? She's dying... What shall I do?", to which Animal Evans, sitting in the front row of the stalls, yelled out: "Shag her quick while she's still warm."

There was a roar of approval from the audience and, to a man, they craned forward in their seats as though it might really happen; but when Broderick Crawford looked up, stared straight into the camera, and said "I know... I'll call a doctor!" there was a chorus of groans and cat-calls.

When Casablanca ended Rupert and I went across the road to Miss Daniel's Soldiers' Home, a dilapidated caravan in which an old dear served tea, coffee, and hamburgers. To Rupert and me it was a godsend. It was convenient and guaranteed us peace and quiet since very few people ever went there. Oddly, one of those who did occasionally call in was Animal Evans. The first time he came in it was obvious that it was his first visit and he had followed us in; but he behaved very strangely. He'd lost his loquaciousness and sat in silence some distance from us. It wasn't until we took the social initiative and bought him a second hamburger and a cup of tea that he spoke to us.

"I hope I don't spoil the films for you. With my interruptions?"

We assured him that we enjoyed them as much as everyone else, that it was all part of the fun. "Splendid audience participation," said Rupert. "Just like the Globe in the Bard's time."

Eventually, Animal came over and joined us, but he still didn't say much and seemed happy to listen to our conversation. Then, for no particular reason, he said, "Oh, well. Best get back," and off he went, even though we realized there was nothing for him to go back for.

This puzzled us, but we never dwelt on it. It was only months later, in Korea, after sharing all manner of experiences, that Rupert claimed to know the reason why he joined us at Miss Daniels, but he would never divulge his theory. He just tapped his nose and smiled secretively.

My friendship with Rupert was far more conventional, and one I came to treasure, and always will. Miss Daniels Soldiers' Home was the cradle of it and those evenings were the most memorable of our times together at

Catterick. On our first visit, no sooner had we settled down to giant hamburgers oozing tomato sauce than Rupert produced a school exercise book from his map pocket. He wrote in it until he had completed two pages. Eventually, he paused, giving me the chance to enquire what he was doing.

"Writing a critique, old boy. Every time I see a film or a play, I write one. Then I compare it with what the professionals say ... Harold Hobson mainly. When I think mine is better, I send him a copy."

"And what does he think?"

"God knows. He never writes back ... Far too jealous ..."

He read out his critique of Casablanca and I was very impressed. He had picked out several touches which had escaped me, notably Claude Rains's comment, 'My heart is my least vulnerable spot' , and Bogart's line to Ingrid Bergman, 'I remember the fall of Paris. The Germans were in grey and you wore blue'.

Not to be outdone, I argued that the ending was wrong, nothing but sentimental tosh; that Bogart should have shot Claude Rains, gone off with Bergman, and to hell with the pompous and sexless do-gooder, Laszlo. I was being deliberately contentious, knowing that Rupert was itching for a heated discussion. What followed was certainly animated. I enjoyed playing the devil's advocate but point by point I was forced to concede his argument that the film was an accidental masterpiece.

This discussion set the pattern for our visits to Miss Daniel's Home. Each night we saw a fresh film and then spent two or three hours dissecting it, scene by scene. We rarely agreed, but that didn't matter; the more we argued the more we enjoyed it. It took us out of ourselves, away from the army, with our grey matter revitalized. We consumed tea and hamburgers galore and whenever we dismissed a film as a dud, we reverted to various other aspects of culture we were familiar with: plays we'd seen, music we liked, set-books we had studied at school, West End shows we'd seen, and novels we'd read. Most of all, Rupert talked about his real passion, poetry.

He was clearly my intellectual superior and whilst I could argue a point and sustain a good defence, Rupert had originality. He was an opinion-former. His thoughts and theories broke new ground. He revealed an amazing depth of reading for someone of his age, but I couldn't help noticing that however much he drew on this, our conversations invariably reverted to his poetry and how he was going to set the literary world alight once he'd settled down at Oxford University.

What he actually wrote remained a secret. He claimed his poems were hibernating prior to being revised, and he assured me that his constant use of rhyming couplets was no more than a trivial amusement to him. He said he was practising, just keeping his hand in like a novice musician playing scales.

He had a theory about literature which he called, 'The Eclipse of the Middle Ground'. He was convinced that literature would polarize and that the middle ground (its real strength) would disappear and leave nothing but incomprehensible intellectualism or semi-illiterate trash. He was convinced that superb novels such as **The Good Companions, Of Human Bondage,** and **A Town Like Alice**, would never be seen again. Lurid and sadistic whodunnits and endless spy stories would be the best we could hope for.

He was adamant that good poetry should be easily understood and that writers who produced obscure works should be shunned, not admired. To him, such writers were arrogant, so in love with their own cleverness that they saw far more in their flowery phrases and obscure symbolism than actually existed. Rupert admired rich and original prose, but he maintained that those capable of it invariably got so carried away by it that they lost lucidity, with their prose becoming an end in itself. Rupert likened it to sitting through a perfectly dreadful film with no story or point and then proclaiming it brilliant on account of it being in Technicolor.

Most of all, Rupert despised schools of 'realism', 'post modernism', 'pre-modernism', 'revivalism', and any other 'ism' one cared to mention. Likewise, he swore he would never demean himself by writing poetry that didn't rhyme, scan, and have rhythm. Kipling, he claimed, would live on, but the only thing future generations would remember of T.S. Elliot would be his cats.

They were good evenings. We no doubt talked a load of rubbish but that didn't matter. It kept us sane.

Every morning we woke again to the world of Gough. Our conflict with him never slackened, but thanks to what we had learnt from Animal Evans about the mentality of Catterick NCOs we were able to take his punishments much more in our stride; we even began to take the mickey out of him, especially on the square. Whenever the adjutant and the RSM hove into sight we embarrassed him by making elementary mistakes; none more so than Fletcher.

Fletcher--- or Fletch as he was soon generally known--- was the dominant personality in our squad. No subject ever cropped up without him holding forth on it and if any one dared to question or doubt him he cut them down with biting sarcasm. His parrot cries of aggression continued as ever. If he wasn't threatening to mash people up, he was singling out junior NCOs who crossed him by declaring: "I'll get that bastard if it's the last thing I do!" What I found most off-putting was his habit of going up behind others, grabbing them around the waist, then simulating sex, calling out, "'Ello, darling! How about a length?"

None of the others minded and I was amazed by the admiration he garnered amongst them. It was based on his stories of the London underworld, populated by villains with nick-names like 'Mad Frankie', 'Flick-blade Freddy', and 'Raper McNulty'. Eventually, I for one was highly relieved when his dominance was first of all tested and then reduced by the arrival of a new recruit, Bertie Mee.

Bertie Mee turned up out of the blue on a Sunday afternoon. He'd come from Oswestry where he'd been in the Royal Artillery. He'd joined the army on the same day as us, but for some reason he was suddenly transferred to the Royal Signals. In the absence of any official guidance, he occupied the bed vacated by Adams. Physically, there was nothing notable about Bertie Mee. He was short and slight and had such large, odd-shaped ears that he resemble a mouse. Yet there was nothing mousey about his personality. He was irrepressibly lively, a young Welshman with a broad accent and the gift of the gab. He burst into song far more than Rupert ever spouted verses and within a few hours of his arrival we knew all about him, especially his ambition to become a Rock and Roll star. He produced a mouth-organ which was so elaborate that he insisted it was a harmonica; and he was soon treating us to his rendering of 'Rock Around the Clock', complete with wild cavorting around the barrack room.

Rupert and I viewed this exuberance with reservations but the others welcomed him as a lively addition to our numbers. At first it looked as though he and Fletcher were going to be great buddies, but that didn't last long. Fletcher's attitude towards him soon soured. He realized he was losing the limelight in the squad, and what he wanted were side-kicks, not a rival. They had several sharp verbal exchanges, the first of which came one night at 'lights out'. Once we were in our beds, Bertie Mee decided to give us a version of 'Goodnight Sweet-heart', followed by 'Kiss me Goodnight, Sergeant-Major'. The latter came to an abrupt halt when a well-aimed boot from Fletcher knocked Bertie's harmonica out of his mouth and broke one of his front teeth.

The most memorable thing about Bertie Mee was his first appearance on the drill square. He took up a position in the middle of the back rank, where he went unnoticed by Gough. Nothing untoward happened until Gough saw the RSM and the adjutant approaching. As was his custom, he braced himself and ordered: "Right! Smarten up! No more mistakes."

Mee responded by calling out: "Roll on demob!"

"Who said that?" demanded Gough.

"Me, Sarge."

"Who the fuck are you?"

"Mee, Sarge."

Gough went forward to investigate and when he saw a stranger confronting him he demanded: "Where've you come from? And who the fuck are you?"

"Mee, Sarge."

There was general laughter.

"Are you a fucking idiot? I'm me, too ... We're all fucking me ... So what's your name?"

"Mee, Sarge..."

"Now look here you little ..."

Sandwitch stepped forward. "Excuse me for interrupting, Sergeant. Perchance I could be of some assistance ..."

"Christ, I doubt that ..."

"He is indeed Mee, Sergeant," continued Sandwitch, unabashed. "He spells his name with two e's ... The second of which is silent ..."

"Like when you have a 'p' in your bath, Sarge," chipped in Fletcher, desperate to get in on the act.

The laughter that followed was too much for Gough. Like General Huxley he couldn't stand being laughed at. Anyhow, he'd already had enough of Fletcher and Bloody Sandwitch and he certainly wasn't going to put up with another fucking comedian. In his fury he forgot that the RSM and the adjutant were closing in on us. He was so incensed that he even forgot the NCOs Golden Rule and yelled: "Don't take the piss out of me, you *BASTARDS!*"

That did it! The Golden Rule was shattered. Calling a recruit a bastard was strictly taboo. Anything else was acceptable, but never *'BASTARD!'*

Gough's yell of *"BASTARDS!"* echoed around the parade ground. It brought deathly silence. The scene froze. It was like a Bateman cartoon. The adjutant and RSM stopped dead in their tracks. The RSM swelled up like a bull-frog. Then, having recovered from the shock, he took out his indelible pencil, licked it copiously, and entered Gough's name in his note book. In a trice, Gough's hopes and dreams of promotion vanished.

We thought this incident would curtail Gough's extreme behaviour, that henceforth he would take things a little easier, but not a bit of it. He knew he was up to his neck in trouble so he took the attitude that nothing else now mattered, and he came back fighting, more belligerent than ever, hoping that a brazen dose of sadism might mitigate his faux pas. He had tricks up his sleeve we had never dreamed of.

His basic tactic was to pick on one man at a time and predictably enough his first choice was Fletcher. He knew that petty crooks were gutless at heart, so he made Fletcher's life such hell that he cracked him within three days. Being well aware of Fletcher's aversion to running,

Gough excluded him from drill parades and instead made him double around the square in full battle order with four house bricks in his pack and his rifle at the high port. Every night Fletcher assured us, "I'll get that bastard if it's the last thing I do!" but in practice there was nothing he could do and each day, as he plodded around the square, his legs became more and more bandy until his backside was practically dragging along the ground. Eventually, he could take no more and he made a gesture of defiance of which the Kray twins would have been proud. He waited until the adjutant and RSM were present and then staggered to the middle of the square, removed all his equipment, dumped it in a pile, and yelled out at the top of his voice: "Get fucked, Gough! I've had enough."

Then he limped off from square, giving the adjutant and the RSM a two-finger salute as he went.

"Oh well! That's Fletcher well and truly mashed up," said Rupert with unconcealed amusement.

As a first offender Fletcher got off lightly. When he appeared on CO's Orders he was given 28 days in the Colchester Detention Barracks. What none of us realized was that his time in Colchester would not count as part of his National Service. As things turned out, that proved disastrous for him.

3

Bloody Sandwitch Disappears

The Gough saga then moved into a final climax, but I missed it. To everyone's surprise (especially my own) I was transferred to the Potential Leaders Wing, with a view to attending the War Office Selection Board (WOSB) to try for a commission. My transfer came after an interview with three personnel officers and two psychiatrists whose task it was to direct us to a trade for which we were most suited. In our squad, only Rupert and I were regarded as Potential Leaders. At first, Rupert made a brilliant impression. His ten distinctions in Higher School Certificate impressed mightily and his Exhibition to Balliol College, Oxford, even more. Typically, however, he was his own worst enemy. When asked the routine question, "And why do you want to be an officer?", instead of giving the routine answer, "I want to make the best of things and shoulder responsibilities," he replied:

"Behold! There comes a time in the affairs of a man
When it behoves him to grab the cushiest job he can."

Humour was not among the attributes of the selection panel and when Rupert saw their expressions, and explained that he was only joking, it was already too late. When he rejoined the others in the barrack room, Sergeant Gough was waiting for him, determined to crack him, just as he had cracked Fletcher.

Because of my promotion to the Potential Leaders Wing I am unable to give a firsthand account of how things panned out, but the 'narrative reconstruction' I now present gives, I believe, give a true and reliable picture of what happened.

When it became obvious that Sandwitch was going to get the full treatment from Gough, the others gave him no chance and therefore saw no point in rallying to his cause. They shared Gough's view that he had a bloody nerve to consider himself officer material and on top of that they considered he'd already pushed his luck far enough with all his damn silly rhymes. Whenever he got into trouble it invariably involved the others as well and they were fed up with it. Now, they reckoned that if Gough got shot of him, life would calm down and Gough would revert to being semi-human.

However, Rupert was made of sterner stuff. Despite being gawky and a bit of a toff, he had enormous mental resilience and physical stamina.

Gough played a crafty game. When he punished Rupert he included the others. When he doubled him around the square with four house bricks in his pack the others went too, only minus the bricks. When Rupert got more jankers, so did some of the others, and for good measure Gough introduced route marches into their training and whilst Rupert enjoyed these, the rest of the squad loathed them.

One of Gough's routine ploys was to make Rupert permanently responsible for sweeping the centre of the floor in the barrack room. To anyone unfamiliar with basic training, sweeping the centre of the floor might sound a dilly of a job, but in the dust-ridden barrack rooms of Catterick, sweeping the centre of the floor was a nightmare, a highly skilled job with considerable responsibilities. What made it so difficult was the broom. Good, soft, brooms absorb dust, and let nothing escape through their dense bristles, but Rupert's broom was old and balding, with bristles so stunted that no matter how carefully he swept, the brush dispersed dust rather than absorbed and directed it. After each forward sweep, dozens of thin dust trails were left in its wake. The technique for overcoming this, developed by previous Intakes, was to complete two forward sweeps, twist the broom-head into a vertical position, tap it gently on the floor to rid it of dust, and then re-sweep. Gough described this technique as "Sweep! Sweep! Tap! Sweep! Sweep! Tap!"

As with so many other military tasks, Rupert proved incapable of doing it. He lacked the delicate touch and whilst Gough stood over him, repeating: "Sweep! Sweep! Tap!" Rupert could only "Sweep! Sweep! Whack!", sending up a cloud of dust which meant that those in adjacent beds had to sweep their bed spaces once more.

Gough didn't have the sense to stop shouting, "Sweep! Sweep! Tap!" and thereby allow Rupert to master the technique in his own time; and for his part, Rupert found the repetition of the order totally humiliating and a slur on his manhood. He could take practically anything the army dished up, apart from being treated as an apprentice chambermaid. It emasculated him and shattered his equanimity. It drove him to do two things he had been thought incapable of: he lost his temper and swore.

"For Christ's sake, Sergeant!" he yelled, throwing the broom down. "What the hell is this? A bloody domestic science class at Roedean?"

On another occasion, Rupert went even more berserk and shouted: "Why not put it to music, you silly bugger? Make it into a bloody dance routine for chorus girls ... All together now, girls ...

"Sweep! Sweep! Tap!
Waggle your boobs and gyrate your hips,
Stick out your bums and pucker your lips,
Sweep! Sweep! Tap!

"That should keep all you military poofters happy!" Rupert threw the broom down and stalked off, adding: "Now, if you don't mind, Sergeant Gough, I'll get on with my knitting ..."

Gough smirked. He had Bloody Sandwitch on the roll. The fucker was cracking up. Gough was so sure of success that he brought his final ploy into action. He produced a screw-driver and made Rupert gouge out decades of gunge from the joints in the floorboards, a process that had Rupert on his hands and knees for hours on end and entailed moving everyone's beds and lockers, which didn't endear him to anyone.

When Rupert completed this task, Gough thought up a new trick, this time centred on the antiquated wood-burning stove in the centre of the barrack room. As the night-time temperatures sank below zero it was essential to have the stove going throughout the night. Gough drew up a roster and had Rupert on the worst shift, starting at 0400 hours. It was his job to keep the fire going until reveille. However, due to Rupert's usual incompetence and his insatiable craving for warmth, he stuffed too much wood into the stove and opened the flu far too wide, so that instead of it burning steadily it roared like a furnace and then, on declining, issued forth noxious fumes which woke everyone up in fits of coughing and deposited soot over everything, adding to their cleaning chores.

Eventually, the situation was brought to a head by two disastrous Saturday morning kit inspections. On the first, Major Pearce at last spotted that Rupert's spare string vest had become a ball of string. On the second he saw that his spare tube of toothpaste was SR and not Macleans. Rupert gave a very reasonable explanation, pointing out that SR was kinder to his gums, cost less, contained an exclusive anti-bacterial ingredient, and had a special offer of 33% extra paste; but this spiel failed to pacify the major. He grabbed the blanket beneath Rupert's kit lay-out and ripped it away, sending everything crashing to the floor. He then stamped on the tube of SR so that it squirted out in all directions. As a final act of vindictiveness he confined everyone to barracks.

This reflected directly on Gough and Mr. Collier. Each got two weeks extra orderly duties and they made it perfectly clear that it was never going to happen again, although when challenged as to how they would prevent it, they had no idea.

Then providence smiled on them. Fate changed everything. Whilst playing rugby for the Garrison XV Major Pearce broke a leg. (More accurately, he had it broken for him.) Because the re-setting of his femur was botched, he was confined to the Garrison Hospital for over two months and his weekly kit inspections were taken over by the adjutant, who was not familiar with individuals in the various squads.

The night before the adjutant's first inspection, Gough and Mr. Collier inspected the kit displays. They were so appalled by Sandwitch's that they went into an emergency conference. Bertie Mee, with his mousey ears twitching, picked up everything in his nearby bed space.

"It's no good, sir. We'll just have to get rid of the fucker. "

"A contract ..."

"A contract, sir! That's a fucking good idea. You know someone ..."

"Of course not ...   I thought that was what you were suggesting."

Gough laughed bitterly. "No, sir. We don't have to swing for him. There is another way out ..."

"But surely you've tried everything?"

"Not quite. Now the adjutant's doing the inspections, we can hide him. The adjutant will never know the difference...."

"Hide him? Where?"

"The broom cupboard, sir. No one ever inspects that."

"What about his bed?"

"We'll strip that. And dump it down in the boiler room with Animal Evans.   Then we'll spread the other beds out a bit. And once the inspection's over he can come out again until next week."

So every Saturday morning, Rupert was made to disappear. It worked perfectly for three weeks. Unfortunately, the broom cupboard was situated in the passage just off the barrack room, and on the adjutant's fourth inspection he was on his way out when the dusty atmosphere in the cupboard made Rupert sneeze.

"What's that?"

"Rats probably, sir ..."

"Rats? You've got rats?"

"Well, no, sir ... Not as such ..."

"Not as such? What are you talking about? What was it?"

"Central heating knocking, probably, sir ..."

"There isn't any central heating."

Rupert sneezed again. The adjutant strode over to the cupboard and yanked the door open. Rupert was revealed. He was grinning inanely, squatting on his haunches amid a collection of broken brooms, dustpans, mops, scrubbing brushes, dusters, filthy rags, buckets, and--- somewhat incongruously--- a bedpan.

"What are you doing in there?"

"Writing an Ode, sir ..."

" An Ode?"

"Yes, sir. I thought an Ode would be appropriate ..."

"Ode to what?"

"Ode to a Broom Cupboard, sir."

The adjutant glanced at Gough in amazement. Gough tried to bluff it out. He shrugged his shoulders as though someone in a broom cupboard writing Odes was typical of all National Servicemen; an occupational hazard which required no explanation. He might even have got away with it, had not Rupert piped up: "Would you care to hear my Ode, sir? To be honest, I'm rather pleased with it ... And I've tried not to be influenced too much by Keats ... See what you think, sir ...

> *"Ode to a Broom Cupboard*
> *Clouds of dancing dust and fragmented flakes,*
> *Close kith and kin to suppurating bent brooms,*
> *Conspiring together to choke and suppress*
> *The rookie who from the barrack room looms...."*

"Get out !" roared the adjutant.

"There are ten more lines yet, sir ..."

"Get out! And stand to attention!"

News of Rupert being hidden in a broom cupboard flashed around the garrison. Within weeks it was army folklore. It has since become one of the army's oldest chestnuts and nowadays hundreds of ex-servicemen seek to impress their grandchildren with false stories of how they too suffered the broom cupboard treatment.

For Intake 541, the outcome was far from happy. Mr. Collier was posted to a Royal Signals unit in Malaya and died of malaria. Sergeant Gough was reduced to the ranks and served under a National Service corporal who took great delight in doing unto Gough what Gough had done unto him. Animal Evans was fully investigated, stripped of his anonymity, reduced to Private, and made to rejoin the real army. Finally, Rupert, Animal Evans, Bertie Mee, and one or two other hard cases (including Fletcher when he returned from Colchester) were transferred to Strensall, the notorious recruitment centre for the Yorkshire Infantry Brigade. There, they were made to go through basic training all over again. Their new sergeant was named Claughton. On their first parade he paced up and down in front of them and eyed them with disgust. Then he informed them: "I am your platoon sergeant. And I am the nastiest fucker the fucking British army has ever fucking known."

4

A Surprising Success

Meanwhile, I was having a very pleasant time in the Potential Leaders' Wing. Here, I discovered just how diverse the army could be, and how one's life-style could be transformed overnight. It turned out that Catterick basic training wasn't typical of the army after all. We had jumped in at the deep end and had assumed it to be the norm, but it wasn't. Basic training was merely the army's way of breaking us in as though we were wild young mustangs; and once our spirit was tamed, the principle of discipline and instant obedience established, then everything changed. Men passed on to units which behaved in a perfectly rational manner.

The Potential Leaders Wing was very civilized. It remained tough and strict but those in command were reasonable and caring, and the standard of education among the ORs was quite exceptional. We had eleven Oxbridge graduates, two from Manchester, and one from Southampton, and of the others I was the only one without a place awaiting me at a university. Bad language was reduced to civilian-type moderation and topics of conversation did occasionally rise above the groin. In fact, what we talked about most were our experiences in basic training. Now it was behind us, it became a unique and hilarious experience, something we would never have missed for the world.

The best thing about the PLW was that it had a clearly defined purpose: to pass the War Office Selection Board. Those who passed qualified for further training as officer cadets at either Mons Barracks in Aldershot (Corps), or at Eaton Hall (Infantry) near Chester.

Before the course got underway, we were given 72-hours leave passes.

It seemed as though I had been away from Silver Coombe for months, but in reality it had only been a few weeks. During that time, very little had changed. Brother Nothing was enjoying himself at Oxford and my other brother, James, was still in Cyprus doing his National Service as a sergeant in the Intelligence Corps. Both had written recently. Brother Nothing was adamant that I wouldn't stand a chance of passing WOSB and James advised me not to waste my time trying, as he had. Dad told me to ignore them. He was well aware of my plans to be commissioned and volunteer for Korea, and however foolhardy he considered this to be he nevertheless admired my ambition and gave me his support. He found my experiences in basic training highly amusing and after every story I related he chuckled gleefully, "Good! Good!", and when I told him what a nasty piece of work Gough was it revived his faith in the army.

Mum wasn't in the least impressed. She dismissed Rupert as a complete nincompoop who deserved everything he got, and she chastised me in her usual way for ever mixing with people like Fletcher. In the end she suggested that Dad and I should don our tin hats, go into the study, and leave her in peace. In other words, she wanted to listen to 'Much Binding in the Marsh' with Kenneth Horne and Stinker Murdoch. With her, nothing was ever allowed to interrupt 'Much Binding' until the advent of Coronation Street.

Dad and I didn't just talk about the army. As he sank deep into his sumptuous leather armchair, with his feet on the coffee table, gradually disappearing behind clouds of cigar smoke, he related how his business was thriving, especially the retail outlets selling tyres, batteries, and exhausts. He was also highly optimistic about the future of his new political party. Membership had leapt to over 100, thanks to the support of his employees who, after receiving an above-union-rate pay increase, had joined en bloc.*

Dad had been doing regular stints at Speakers' Corner and he insisted that I should go to Hyde Park on Sunday morning. He claimed to have a regular following and I didn't doubt it. I'd only seen him perform once at Speakers' Corner and that had been his debut at the end of my final school holiday. Then it had been pouring with rain and his audience consisted of a lone, on-duty policeman. This worthy had been so impressed by Dad's passion and logic that he had signed up as the second member of the Party (Miss Beaumont, his secretary/PA, was the first). Now, I was anxious to see how he performed under pressure, handling the heckling for which Speakers' Corner was famous.

When we got there, Miss Beaumont was waiting for us and I could tell by her smiles that we were in for a good time. No sooner had Dad opened up his step ladder and climbed to the top rung than a crowd gathered. All around us people deserted other speakers. Some came running. Dad was like a magnet drawing-in iron filings. One man who joined us turned to his mate and said: "Just listen to this bloke, Bert ... England's answer to Ghandi ... He's a bloody scream ..."

"What does he talk about?"

"Gawd knows ... He's heckled so much it's impossible to tell."

---

*Dad's new political party--- The Commonwealth Party--- should not be confused with The Common Wealth Party, a socialist creation of JB Priestley and Sir Richard Acland, founded in an effort to destroy the war-time pact of co-operation between Tories and Labour--- a sly move typical of its founders.

Dad was the only right-wing speaker there. Apart from an old lady pleading for compulsory dog licences, the other speakers were either religious or socialist fanatics. They presented a curious contrast. The socialists were forever demanding more money, better working conditions, and shorter hours, claiming that happiness and justice would only come through a bloody revolution; whereas the religious fanatics denounced money as the root of all evil, urged everyone to work hard for the good of their souls, and that it was only by enduring hardships in stoic silence and turning the other cheek, that they could expect to find happiness.

The best-known speakers were Tony Turner--- who spoke for Karl Marx--- and Dr. Donald Soper--- who spoke for God. For years they had monopolized things, but once Dad arrived on the scene their audiences first of all drifted away and then deserted them in droves. Dad's ultimate triumph came when they were reduced to so few listeners that they packed up for the day and went to listen to him instead, fearing that he may have found a third way to happiness which left both religion and socialism redundant.

By virtue of his colour and his comical appearance--- dressed as always in a camel-hair overcoat and a trilby with Tyrolean feathers stuck in the side--- Dad was heckled from the moment he opened his mouth. Cat-calls and ruderies never stopped, but he fed off them avariciously, giving back far better than he got. One of his best exchanges was initiated by a man standing behind Miss Beaumont. He'd been calling out facetious remarks from the start, despite furious glares from Miss Beaumont. Eventually he yelled: "'Ere, mate! Why aren't yer wearing a bleeding loincloff what like yer old mate Ghandi always done?"

"Because it's too bloody cold!" retorted Dad. "And never mind Ghandi. When I was in India I was so poor I dressed like Gunga Din:

> *'And the uniform 'e wore*
> *Was nothin' much before,*
> *An' rather less than 'arf o' that be'ind'."*

That made them roar with laughter and an old crone clinging to the heckler's arm, cried out: "Ooo-er! I say! Whatever next ..."

On another occasion a man put a long, complicated question. Dad listened patiently and then did his best to give a sensible response, but the man was scornful and shouted: "That's a bloody awful answer."

"That's because it was a bloody awful question."

Dad spoke for an hour and despite all the banter, interjections and laughter, he managed to put across a clear message about his new

Commonwealth Party. When he finished he got a generous round of applause and several called out about seeing him again next week.

"Don't worry, I'll be here," responded Dad, climbing down his step ladder. "And I'll explain how this country should run its finances. Like a good housewife running her family budget."

"Blimey! Don't tell us your trouble and strife will be Chancellor when you take power?"

"Why not? She'll be a bloody sight better than old Cripps. And as for Butler! What this country needs is people with experience in everyday life."

Dad got carried away by the exchange and, much to everyone's delight, he remounted his step ladder and went on for another twenty minutes. Eventually, he realized he was using up next week's tirade so he called it a day amid more cries of "Good luck, mate!" and "See you next week!"

I felt proud of Dad. He had enjoyed every minute of it and what he loved most of all was Miss Beaumont's admiration. Eventually, we piled back into the Jag and went for a slap-up lunch at a Spanish restaurant in Fulham. Dad never stopped talking and halfway through the meal he got so excited over some point or other that he accidentally put his hand on my knee instead of Miss Beaumont's. His embarrassment, and the speed with which he withdrew it, left me in no doubt that they were enjoying an affair.

Our barracks at the Potential Leaders Wing was known as a "Spider". It was a complex of wooden sheds which had been nailed together by a local carpenter a decade or two before Lt-Col. Peter Nissan invented his huts. The Spider was in such bad repair that it was impossible to keep clean, but as things turned out that didn't matter. My new unit had a refreshingly relaxed attitude towards the value of domestic science. Even our weekly kit inspections were a doddle. Our OC, Second-Lieutenant Willis, would be greeted at the entrance by the duty sergeant. He would say: "The Spider is looking very smart this morning, sir," to which Mr. Willis always replied: "Good show, Sergeant." He then walked up and down each barrack room without looking at a thing before disappearing back to the officers' mess.

We were given passes out of the camp every week-end and because several of us had returned from our leave with a motor cycle or a car (on my Panther 250cc motor cycle the journey took me nearly all day), we enjoyed considerable freedom. Some went into Harrogate every Saturday afternoon to visit a posh tea shop and then on to a cinema. The rugby players among us went either to Gosforth or Edinburgh to support Gemmell, one of our number who was capped for Scotland later that season. Others went to watch Darlington FC play in the Third Division

North. The first time they went, they rang up before hand to find out the time of the kick-off.

"What time can you get here?" the player/manager responded eagerly.*

Our senior instructor was Sergeant Verity. He was softly spoken, highly intelligent, and expert at his job. He knew the requirements of WOSB backwards and during his introductory lecture he explained that all we had to do was follow his instructions implicitly. "Of course, some of you won't do that because you've got Higher School Certificate or a university degree. Whereas I've only got three stripes. And from what you've seen of army sergeants so far you're convinced that that makes me a complete moron. So you'll assume that you know better. But you don't. And if you go on thinking that, you'll fail. Also, I have to warn you that some of you will be sent back to 7th Training Regiment because you are not officer material. To be an officer, you've got to be young, immature, well-mannered, well-spoken, cool-headed, and malleable. What they are looking for are alert young men to mould into their own image. Young men who will accept responsibility when things go wrong. Who do not panic and are keen, but not overzealous. They will expect you to read either The Times or The Telegraph and you must be a credit to the Officers' Mess. You must be able to charm the Colonel's wife and be relied upon not to roger his daughter. In short, you must be a gentleman. Of course, very few of you are, or ever will be gentlemen, but listen to me and you'll have no trouble in faking it. And once you've faked it, you're home and dry. Some people will then say you're made for life. Others will say you are scarred for life. It depends on the company you keep."

Sergeant Verity smiled. "Quite a catalogue. But the whole thing can be summarized by a Punch cartoon that appeared in the darkest days of the Great War. It showed a colonel and a subaltern standing in a trench, surveying the desolation of a disaster in no man's land. The caption read:

'**Colonel**: *What we need now, Carruthers, is a first-class futile effort.'*
Carruthers: *Right, sir! I'm just the man you're looking for'."*

Sergeant Verity said the key to success was the ability to communicate, and to achieve this he made us deliver a series of talks, using only one

---

* *This answer was a well-known leg-pull among Third Division Clubs. It originated at Aldershot FC when a new season ticket holder (the first since WWII) proposed at the AGM that the kick-off at home games should be delayed until 2.45 pm to coincide with the arrival of his bus from Cove. The motion was carried unanimously.*

word reminders on post cards. Our voices had to be clear, to ring out an octave or two higher than usual, and we had to guard against hurrying our delivery at the end of sentences. We were forbidden ever to say, "Um ..." or "Er ..." or "You know ..." and if any of these slipped out, Sergeant Verity encouraged everyone else to call out: "Um ..." or "Er ..." or "You know ..." as applicable. It was a technique that worked like a charm.

Later on, as we grew more confident, Sergeant Verity threw out a new challenge. Without prior notice he would nominate a subject on which we had to talk for five minutes. My subject was grass. For a moment I was thrown, but in desperation I came out with the remark: "Grass is the staple diet of cows, sheep, and lawn mowers." From then on I was okay.

Sergeant Verity wasn't our only instructor. There was also Sergeant Jones, a stocky Welshman, a typical Taffy, devoted to rugby, male voice choirs, and chapel worship. When I told him that Dad had served with the Royal Welch Fusiliers in the Great War we became firm friends and this was further cemented when I told him that Mum's Uncle Dai was a member of the Treorchy Male Voice Choir.

Sergeant Jones was responsible for some of my best times in the army. He looked after our physical training and although he pushed us hard and made us wonderfully fit, he was adamant that we had to enjoy our training. He drilled us with such expertise that it was better than being accompanied by a military band. Most of all, he loved to take us on 20-mile route marches. We devoted two days a week to these. We marched out into the Yorkshire Dales, tramping up and down the narrow, winding, lanes. We rarely encountered traffic, just the odd tractor or maybe a local bus. The roads were flanked by dry stone walls and the hills were rounded and bleak, usually well scattered with gorse bushes which, when we stopped for the obligatory ten minutes' rest in every hour, we set alight in order to keep warm.

Our route marches ended at one of Sergeant Jones's favourite villages. These were half-hidden in steep valleys and constructed in the local stone, built around a traditional square. We would stay overnight and then march back the next day. In each village, Sergeant Jones had special arrangements with the publican. They had palliasses on which we slept in outbuildings and in the mornings we would wash and shave at horse troughs in the centre of the yard, icy water supplied by means of a wrought-iron hand pump. Part of our training was to set up a field kitchen and cook our own meals, all of which were far superior to anything we got in camp. From eight o'clock in the evening, extending into the small hours, we would be in the public bar, sinking pints of beer. Licensing hours were ignored since the local constable invariably supped beer with us, in one case even serving behind the bar.

In this beer-soaked and smoke-laden atmosphere, we did our best to please Sergeant Evans by imitating a Welsh Male Voice Choir, with him leading us in classics such as 'Sosfan Bach', 'Cym Rhondda', and 'Men of Harlech'. Then we would revert to rugby songs, ballads about Old King Cole and The Good Ship Venus; songs which were raucous and bawdy but which, under Sergeant Jones's direction, at least became harmonious.

The locals loved it. They were predominantly farmers, all of them rugged and dirty, straight from their cow sheds; all of them smelling of dung and drinking mild and bitter which they tossed back with abandon. They were aged around 40 and during the war they had been in a reserve occupation, something which they now regretted. They listened to Sergeant Jones's stories about life in Cairo and Alexandria and felt cheated, as though they had missed out on life. Consequently, they eyed us with envy, knowing that we were on the brink of similar world-wide adventures, whereas they would never venture out of the Dales. They also became convinced that the present-day army was a holiday camp: nothing but one long sing-along. We sang as we marched into the village; we sang all the time we were there; and when we marched off the next morning we were still singing.

I was one of Sergeant Jones's soloists, my speciality being an old army song, the title of which eludes me. The words go:

> *I don't want to join the army,*
> *I don't want to go to war,*
> *I'd rather hang around Piccadilly Underground*
> *Living on the earnings of a high-brow lady.*
> *I don't want a bullet up my arse-hole,*
> *I don't want a bollock shot away.*
> *I'd rather be in England,*
> *Merry, merry, England,*
> *And fornicating my bleeding life away,*
> *Cor blimey!*

The chorus then came in, relating the seduction of a young girl over the course of a week. Everyone in the pub mimed as we sang along.

> *' On Monday I touched her on the ankle,*
> *On Tuesday I touched her on her knee,*
> *On Wednesday success, I undid her dress...*
> *On Thursday night upstairs I took her.*
> *On Friday I touched her on the thigh,*
> *On Saturday she gave my balls a squeeze,*

> *But on Sunday after supper…*
> *I rammed the fucker up 'er!*
> *And now I'm paying seven and six a week …*
>   *Cor blimey!*

Two weeks before we were due at Barton Stacey for our WOSB we were ushered before Mr. Willis, Sergeant Verity, and Sergeant Jones for our individual 'Course Assessments'. They predicted our chances of passing and gave us a final opportunity to rectify weaknesses. As I stood before them, Mr. Willis said: "We anticipate that you will be Deferred Watch. That means you won't pass, but you'll be encouraged to have another try later on… If you want to."

"Which area do I need to improve upon?" I asked.

Mr. Willis gave an honest appraisal. "Army officers are very conservative by nature. They like everything to be familiar. And in your case, I'm afraid that comes down to reservations about your colour. To be honest, Contractor, you've put us on a spot. You're the first coloured applicant we've had. That's made no difference to us, as I hope you will agree. But we're now passing up the scale … And the further up you go, the more difference it makes. It's not just colour they are prejudiced against. It's difference. Those with regional accents invariably end up with 'Deferred Watch'."

"Then it's a waste of time?"

"Not really. It's important to keep trying … To keep knocking on the door until eventually, one day, it will swing open. And hopefully stay open. They know they can't justify their attitude. Deferred Watch is their way of denying that they are prejudiced."

"So what do you suggest?"

"Just go ahead and see what happens."

So there it was, plain enough. It came as no great surprise. In moments of camaraderie, when playing rugby, or during Sergeant Evans's choral evenings, it was easy to forget colour; but fundamentals don't disappear. Brother Nothing and James had warned me. So had Dad in a more optimistic way. The only surprising thing was that Sergeant Verity, Sergeant Jones, and Mr. Willis had persevered with me. They could so easily have sent me back to basic training and be done with it. Their fairness was something for which I have always been grateful.

When I got to Barton Stacey for the WOSB, I found myself among a great horde of Hooray Henrys. My confidence soared. Surely I would make a better officer than these prats?

As we settled down in our accommodation for our four-day test, I was surprised to find that everyone was terribly friendly towards me. There was a good reason for this. In each Intake 10% were rejected on principle. Consequently, all those who were deemed certain to get the chop (such as me!) were treated with sympathy, as though we had volunteered to make way for others. Cadets seen in the same light as myself included a Jock from the Black Watch who exposed himself momentarily every time he sat down and crossed his legs, an Old Honitonian who chain-smoked Cuban cigars, and a lance-corporal from the Pioneer Corps who must surely have wandered into the camp by accident.

All those I spoke to took it for granted that they were going to pass on account of their breeding, their social background, and their education. Several of them had titles, dozens had double-barrelled names, and one fellow, who was in the same squad as me, had a triple-barrelled name.

WOSB was split into four sections: group discussions, outdoor practical tests, a written examination on the feasibility of a given scheme, and observations of our social behaviour. The practical tests took place in meadow land through which a river meandered. There were several testing stations along the banks and each had an untidy collection of oil drums, wooden planks, jerry cans, lengths of scaffolding, coils of rope, and various other aids for use in the tests. A test everyone had to undergo was to leap from the branch of a tree to a Tarzan rope hanging from another, a distance of several feet with nothing beneath us apart from a pit full of mud. Those who refused to jump were discreetly RTU'd later in the day. Those of us coached by Sergeant Verity knew that it was best to leap without hesitation, deliberately lose one's grip on the Tarzan rope, and fall into the mud, only to emerge bright and cheerful, laughing it off. There was nothing the examining officers liked better than a trier and a good loser.

The practical tests consisted of getting across the river by using the aforementioned aids, all of which were specifically designed not to do the job. The fact that no one succeeded didn't matter. It was the way you went about it that counted: loud, clear, decisive orders and no complaints or excuses about having to try the impossible.

The discussion groups were the main test of our suitability. These were supervised by three officers. A major directed proceedings and two captains took notes. When the major chairing our group suggested that someone should nominate a subject, all but two of us spoke at the same time, a great rush to make a favourable impression. I said nothing, my pre-determined tactics being to come in at number three or four with a gentle, and well-reasoned rebuttal of all that had been said so far. The subject agreed upon was apartheid. That left me in a delicate situation so I delayed my entry. Indeed, I delayed it until eventually I realized that I had to say something or perish. So far, everyone had supported apartheid and I listened in horror to remarks such as:

"Well, I think the blacks are treated pretty well, on the whole. As well as can be expected."

Another was, "After all, that's the life they were brought up to."

A third one said: "The blacks are all communists anyhow."

What finally convinced me to speak up was when a candidate named Huntley-Ross-White told us: "I've actually lived in South Africa, so I can speak with some authority. And I can tell you categorically that South Africa is a great place to live ..."

"Great so long as you're not black," I interjected.

"Well I'm not black, am I!"

"But I am!"

"Then don't go there."

I had no answer to that.

Later on, someone else turned to me and said: "You obviously have an Indian background, old boy, so you should know that apartheid has existed on the sub-continent for yonks. It's called the caste system."

"Same in Japan," volunteered someone else. "There they call it Eta."

"But there is a big difference between those two countries and South Africa," continued Huntley-Ross-White. "In India and Japan it's coloured people discriminating against coloured people. So everyone accepts it. Don't give a monkey's. But in South Africa it's whites discriminating against blacks, and that's something the left wingers can't stand."

At this point the major intervened. "Well, as I'm sure we all agree, in our sadly imperfect world there are all kinds of discrimination ..."

"And why not," laughed Huntley-Ross-White. "After all, officers' messes are a classic example of discrimination and segregation. And thank God for it. Why else are we here?"

That brought the discussion to an end, and also any chances of a commission for Huntley-Ross-White.

By the time WOSB ended I was tired of being observed by officers with notebooks, having my table manners scrutinized by men who cut bread rolls with their knives, and shovelled up peas on their forks. I just wanted to get the final interview over and then decide--- assuming I got Deferred Watch--- whether it was worth trying again.

Our final interviews were with Brigadier Talbot. We assembled in a waiting room and were then called into his office one at a time. The interviews were over in a few minutes and everyone coming out looked puzzled. I asked one of them: "What's he like?"

"Absolutely knackered. Looks as though he's about to fall asleep."

When my turn came, the brigadier was leaning forward, his elbows on his desk, his head resting in his hands. He didn't look up. He was skimming through my dossier. "Signalman Contractor?"

"Sir!"

"Says here you're against apartheid ... That you ride a motor cycle ... You don't hunt ... Don't shoot ... Have never played polo ... Don't row ... Have never been to Ascot or Henley ... Prefer the Oval to Lord's ... And yet you went to Blundell's?"

"Yes, sir."

"Old House?"

"Yes, sir."

"Like it?"

"Yes, sir. Very much."

"Did you last a full five years?"

"Five and a half, sir."

"Good God! I know Old House. My nephew went there. Disgraceful old ruin ... The whole House was once gassed because there were no S-bends in the bogs ..." *

I looked down to see if he was joking. It was impossible to tell. He was still staring at the dossier.

"That's all."

"Thank you, sir."

I saluted and when I reached the door he said: "I'll be recommending you for a commission ... Know why?"

"No, sir."

"As far as I'm concerned, anyone who can last out five years at crumbling wrecks like Eton, Winchester, and Old House becomes commissioned. The army needs people like you. We can send you to any foul, God-forsaken spot on earth and you'll never complain. Good luck."

He still didn't look up, so I saluted again and marched out, light-infantry style.

The Old House gassing incident happened during Tiverton's worst-ever flood. When the Exe and Lowman burst their banks effluent was forced back up the sewage system and, due to there being no S-bends in the OH toilets, toxic fumes filled the House. The House was abandoned and the boys, the housemaster, the hag (matron), and the scutts (maids), were all found lying on Big Field, gasping for fresh air.

5

It Takes All Sort

Our results were confirmed by letters handed round during lunch the following day. I will never forget the amazement of the others when I said: "Ah good! They've put me in the infantry... Eaton Hall for me."

I had another short leave before reporting to Eaton Hall. It gave me a chance to get my ill-fitting uniform altered by Dad's Saville Row tailor. I also had white patches sewn on the lapels of my battle dress tunics--- an Officer Cadet's badge of rank. I then purchased what amounted to our mufti uniform: a long white riding mackintosh, cavalry-twill trousers, a trilby hat, and brown brogues.

I rode to Chester on my Panther motor cycle, another all-day journey. Eaton Hall was a mile or two outside the town with an impressive driveway through pleasant meadows, at the end of which there was a check-point. I was waved to a halt by Company Sergeant-Major Clogg of the Grenadier Guards. He eyed my motor cycle with distaste. When I showed him my orders, he said: "Well, sir, you can't come in here on that stink bomb. Ditch it in town and then proceed back here in an orderly manner. There will be transport waiting for all new gentlemen-cadets at the railway station from 1600 hours."

I was about to follow his instructions when an engine roared behind me. I turned and beheld an open Bentley Tourer, vintage 1928, complete with an outside hand-brake, the battery on the running board, and a leather strap over the bonnet. To me, the finest car ever manufactured. The driver was dressed in a long, leather overcoat, a flying helmet, and goggles. He was invisible under all this, yet he still managed to look like Biggles.

"If you really want transport whilst you're here, sir," added CSM Clogg, as he raised the barrier for the Bentley, "I suggest you get yourself a proper car, like Officer Cadet Lord Hatchleigh."

Lord Hatchleigh removed his goggles and studied me carefully whilst his engine ticked over. Then his interest turned to my Panther. He leaned out of his cockpit and shouted: "Are those hydraulic forks, old boy?"

"Yes."

"Good gracious me! Do they work?"

"Wonderfully..."

"Well, I never did! Are they adjustable?"

"Yes. You just blow them up with a bicycle pump."

"Fantastic! Wish my suspension was like that. Are you new?"

"Yes."

"Follow me then. I'll show you where you can park up."

CSM Clogg tried to assert his authority, but Lord Hatchleigh waved him aside. "It's okay, Sergeant-Major. I know his people from the Raj."

We sped off, much to CSM Clogg's chagrin.

This incident was my first indication that Eaton Hall was the most snobbish establishment in the country. Everything was down to who you knew, what school you'd been to, what regiment you were in, who your father was, and what he had achieved during his military service. Those who did not rate too well by such criteria soon learnt to either keep a low profile or indulge in tactical exaggerations. Lord Hatchleigh was one of the latter. It turned out that far from being a member of the aristocracy with ermine robes moth-balled in his wardrobe, awaiting a life on expenses in the Upper Chamber, he was merely Lord of the Manor of a remote Cornish village, an exaggeration he got away with on the strength of being a Wykehamist and a member of the Green Jackets, his Bentley providing such an aura of class that no one ever doubted him.

As we parked our vehicles in a block of garages at the rear of the main Hall, he quizzed me about my background. "Well if I were you, old boy," he advised, "I'd put it around that your old man is a Maharajah. They'll love that ... Be all over you ... Eaton Hall is ninety per cent bullshit."

"What about the other ten per cent?"

"Keeping your nose clean. Like I do. If they think you're someone of consequence and you don't rock the boat, then bingo! You're in. Choose your own regiment. Better still, your own posting. That's what really counts. Better to be in Kenya with the RASC than Suez with the Royal Scots. Personally, I'm aiming for the West Indies with the Grenadiers. Best of both worlds."

As it turned out, I avoided any dishonesty about my background. It was automatically assumed that my father was either of noble birth or lousy rich. How else could I have passed WOSB? The whole attitude of the Hall was summed up by Major Cox, my company commander. When confronted by a cadet for the first time on CO's Orders, he immediately looked up his father in *Who's Who*. He was rarely disappointed and to Major Cox's credit those whose fathers didn't feature fared no worse than the others. In my case, when he failed to find Dad in *'Who's Who'*, he pulled out a copy of *'International Who's Who'*. Having drawn a blank there as well, he slammed it shut and said: "No trace of your father anywhere, Contractor."

"No, sir. Nor will there be."

"Dead?"

"No, sir. He avoids publicity. Not attracts it. Because of begging letters."

"Ah, yes ... India! Very wise."

Eaton Hall was built in the 19th century, the home of the Duke of Westminster, then Britain's richest man. On seeing it for the first time most people likened it to Euston Station and it certainly had some ostentatious touches, prominent among them being a replica of Big Ben and a tall obelisk. Big Ben was near the main entrance and although about a quarter of the size of the real Big Ben it was reputed to chime just as loudly. The obelisk was at the end of a quarter mile drive leading off the main parade ground and I never did discover what it signified.

During its relatively short existence, Eaton Hall became legendary. It consistently produced more Military Crosses than Sandhurst and Mons combined and it boasted National Service's highest military decoration (DSO) and the most frequently decorated National Serviceman. Cadets became so attached to it that more than half a century later they still hold biennial reunions. I managed a record all of my own: the dubious distinction of spending longer at Eaton Hall than any other cadet, the only one ever to be relegated twice without being RTU'd.* I was also fortunate to be in Baker Company, the only company accommodated in the Hall. All other companies were in flat-roofed, brick-built huts in the grounds. The organization and structure of Eaton Hall was conventional, with a Lt-colonel in command and majors in charge of each company. Course Instructors were captains and under them a company sergeant major and a sergeant as back-up in the way of discipline and drilling.

NCOs at Eaton Hall were drawn from the Brigade of Guards, implying that they were superior to their counterparts in county regiments, which wasn't true: they simply shouted louder and preened themselves more often. The course instructors were generally assumed to be whiz-kids destined for big things, but I can't say I ever heard of any of them in later years. The RSM was Mr. Copp, an enormous man in the Coldstream Guards. On our first parade he explained: "You will call me, 'sir'. And I will call you, 'sir'. The only difference is that you will mean it."

During my 24 weeks at Eaton Hall I got to know RSM Copp well and developed great respect for him, even though he did have one or two blind spots. For example, he could never understand why it is that when a long column of troops is ordered to "Quick March!", those at the front very soon pull away from those at the rear, who then have to run to catch up. No one has ever been able to explain this phenomenon but most

---

Relegated meant being put back a course. RTU'd meant being sent back to your old unit in disgrace. Normally, only one relegation was allowed---- then out!

people don't worry about it too much and accept it as just another of life's little quirks. However, RSM Copp would have none of that. Every morning he tried to achieve the impossible. Time and again he explained that if we all set off in perfect synchronization, acting on the word of command, with a regulation length pace, there couldn't possibly be any need for those at the back to run to catch up with those at the front.

It never worked, no matter how often we tried. RSM Copp would then throw a wobbly and tell us that if we were all that keen on running we could double around the obelisk. This only exaggerated the original problem and those at the rear had to sprint like hell to catch up with those at the front. The whole thing became pure pantomime, known to cadets as, 'Copp's early morning gallop'.

The senior Company Sergeant Major at Eaton Hall was CSM Clogg, who I encountered on my arrival. He was a great rival of Copp's, tipped to take over as RSM when Copp retired. In fact, he didn't. Copp was succeeded by a famous Irish Guardsman, RSM Lynch. RSM Copp and CSM Clogg sounded like a music hall act and they often behaved like one. Their rivalry was highlighted by the many shouted comments they exchanged on the parade ground. Often, they had cadets in fits of laughter. Once, as Copp was about to put us through a morning gallop, he shouted to CSM Clogg at the rear of the column:

"Are you ready, Mr. Clogg?"

"Sir!"

"Well don't let anyone clog things up, Mr. Clogg."

"Sir! If anyone clogs things up I'll cop them, don't you worry."

Compared to their cadets, the education of Copp and Clogg was limited. In late April, several drill parades were lost because of snow, and when things got back to normal, RSM Copp made a remark about making up for lost time now the snow had gone. From out of the ranks a cadet who fancied himself rotten due to his 'First' in English Lit. at Cambridge, couldn't resist an appropriate poetic quote.

"Like an Army defeated,
The snow has retreated..."

"Who said that?" roared Copp.

"Wordsworth, sir."

"Mr. Clogg!"

"I've got his name, sir!"

I had expected to be the only coloured cadet at Eaton Hall but it turned out that there were about thirty or forty, mostly from the Commonwealth or middle-eastern countries such as Jordan and Egypt. The largest number came from Malaya and six of them were in our platoon. This was unfortunate because Captain Rushmoor, our platoon instructor, had no time for any of us. I often encountered mild and fairly harmless racism in the army but Captain Rushmoor was the only one I would classify as an out-and-out racist. He tried to justify his attitude by complaining that the War Office insisted that foreign cadets should be commissioned even if they didn't reach the required standard. If he'd had his way Rushmoor would have RTU'd every one of the Malays, but it was beyond his authority. The only one he had the authority to relegate or RTU was me, and his failure to do so certainly wasn't through any lack of trying. I was lucky, as we shall see. I had an ally who both outranked him and outmanoeuvred him.

Five of our six Malays soon lost confidence because of Rushmoor. They became sullen and morose. It showed up most when we had to deliver mini-lectures. They became self-conscious and mumbled. The exception was a handsome lad named Charlie. He had a great sense of humour and we looked forward to his first lecture, which had the intriguing title of: 'How to Kill Malaya's Deadliest Snake With Your Bare Hands'.

He explained that this snake was about four feet long with bright, circular markings. It was extremely difficult to kill by normal methods. If one cut it in half, the head-end lived on for hours. If one shot it anywhere other than between the eyes it lived on for even longer, and both these methods made it very hostile. It was also very bold and aggressive by nature. It never took evasive action when disturbed but instead allowed the victim to pass over it and then struck from the rear. Its poison killed within twenty seconds. Charlie emphasized that the snake was best dealt with in due military style, by numbers. He then enumerated:

"(1) Grab the snake's tail in the left hand, with an over-the-top grip.
(2) With the right hand, grab the snake adjacent to the left hand but with an underneath grip.
(3) Simultaneously, cock the right-hand thumb and extend it in the direction of the snake's head.
(4) Slide the right hand very rapidly along the snake's body until the protruding right thumb encounters the back of the snake's head.
(5) The snake's neck will then snap, causing instant death."

This fascinated us, but Rushmoor was sceptical. "Have you ever done this?"

"Yes, sir. Just the once."

"And what happened?"

"I found myself with my thumb up a tiger's arse."

Our laughter infuriated Rushmoor. From thereon he separated the Malayan cadets from the rest of the platoon. I was made to join them.

What saved me from Captain Rushmoor's wrath was sport. When I arrived at the Hall I was lucky to get into the rugby XV. The CO took the game so seriously that rugby players were often excused military training in favour of practice, and on match-days we didn't have to report for duty at all. We also enjoyed a high-protein diet. My spasmodic appearances at lectures so infuriated Rushmoor that he found numerous reasons for putting me on CO's Orders, which gave Major Cox no alternative but to give me a long succession of jankers. Rushmoor also piled other duties on me, such as the reception of new cadets every other Sunday afternoon. He made me responsible for completing the paper-work for coloured cadets. "Just the job for you, Contractor ... Look after your own kind."

My main task was to fill in a horrendously long questionnaire for each cadet who in many cases had insufficient English to do it themselves. Complications were frequent. For example, when I asked for their surnames, the Malayan cadets reeled off four or five names, insisting that they were all applicable. Since there was only room on the form for one name, I selected the one which was easiest to spell. Once, I put down Tunku, only to discover later that it was a title, not a name. I had similar difficulties with their places of birth. Many of them had been born in places such as Tangungpinang, Tanahtinggi, Nakhonsithamarat, or Marratgungingi, so I selected well-known places like Penang, Kuala Lumpa, Singapore, George Town, and the Cameroon Highlands and used them instead. (What difference did it make where they were born?)

This questionnaire had obviously been devised by a committee in the War Office bent on covering every eventuality, thereby keeping their collective noses clean. Some of the questions were so embarrassing that I refused to ask them. I just filled in the answers which I knew were required. After all, it wasn't likely that any of them were pregnant, or suffering from syphilis, or drug addiction, or alcoholism, or mental deficiency; nor were they likely to belong to subversive organisations, fathered illegitimate children, or practised sodomy or other related nefarious activities. Even if any of these applied, they were hardly going to own up to them.

Fresh Intakes came up from Chester by Troop Carrying Vehicles. British cadets had already filled in the questionnaire at WOSB so with them it was simply a matter of checking their names against a list and taking them to their quarters. Foreign cadets were directed to a long table in the porch of the Hall where two other cadets and I awaited them with the questionnaires. CSM Clogg was also present. He was there to organize them into queues and yell and scream at them, providing a preview of what was to come.

On the third Sunday there was a surprising development. As the TCVs lumbered up the drive, they were followed by a Daimler limousine such as the Queen uses on state occasions. It was black, highly polished, had flags fluttering front and rear, and a five-star- general's badge attached to its front bumper. When the TCVs pulled up, Sergeant Major Clogg organized the foreign cadets into three queues in front of our table. Meanwhile, the Daimler drove right into the porch, only a few yards from our table. Sergeant Major Clogg marched forward to do the honours, even though he had no idea who was about to emerge. The near-side rear door flew open and three broad-shouldered, hooked-nosed Arabs in smart suits got out. They walked forward briskly, brushing Clogg aside. Then out of the back of the Daimler slid a short, rotund young man in the traditional Arab night shirt and banded head-dress. He looked about sixteen, but it turned out he was twenty-one. As he moved forward rolls of flesh wobbled beneath his close-fitting night shirt. His henchmen stood aside as he sashayed forward. The other foreign cadets made way for him. I was in the middle of the table and he stopped in front of me and greeted me with a salaam and words which sounded like, "Asalaam au lakum," to which I replied: "Hi there!" being unable to think of anything more appropriate.

The cadet on my right was appalled by my familiarity. He made up for my bad manners by rushing round the end of the table with his chair. Once the Arab (Benny as we came to know him) was seated, CSM Clogg reasserted his authority by advising him: "Answer the questions, there's a good gentleman." Then, as I continued to hesitate, Clogg nudged me: "Come along, Mr. Contractor. Ask the gentleman your questions, sir."

From memory, his full name was His Royal Highness, Crown Prince, General El Said Ben Abdullah and his home address was The Royal Palace, Arabica. His father's occupation was Emir and his previous military experience was Commander-in-Chief, Arabican Armed Forces. Things became really complicated when I asked him about his marital status.

"Wife's name?"

"Hala, Mischael, Fatima, Yasmin."

"Just the name you usually use..."

"I use them all. I've got five different wives."

"But you only gave me four names."

"Oh, yes. That's right. I forgot. I've got a new one. Muna, I think."

"Well what is your contact address whilst in the UK?"

"Grosvenor Hotel, Chester."

"Room number?"
"The first two floors."

(A word of explanation. I have invented the name Arabica, but it's real enough, a small Kingdom in the Persian Gulf floating on oil with more hospital beds than people. The only people who worked in Arabica were the foreign employees of oil companies. The indigenous population lived on benefits which would make present-day British spongers, East European cadgers, illegal immigrants, and phoney asylum seekers, swoon with envy. Every family had either a Cadillac, a Rolls Royce, a Jaguar, or a Mercedes, and even though Arabica's road network only led to the frontier and then stopped dead at open desert, they nevertheless made excellent race tracks.

I didn't enquire about the birthplace of Benny's father. This was just as well. It turned out that he was born in a Baghdad slum and acquired his Kingdom by a series of assassinations after acquiring a Tommy gun as a present on his fifteenth birthday. First he fired a magazine into the air to test it. Then he fired another burst by way of celebration. Next he shot dead his greatest enemy to end a family feud, and finally he used his remaining magazines for a series of increasingly ambitious political assassinations that changed the course of history.

Benny's retinue at Eaton Hall and Chester consisted of 65 people, 35 of them concubines. Many cadets who became friendly with him had high hopes of being invited to partake of their pleasures, but they were out of luck. Here endeth the explanation.)

When I had completed Ben Abdullah's questionnaire he salaamed again and said: "Thank you for your discretion. See you in the Naafi, old boy."

As far as I know, members of Royal families attending British Officer Cadet Schools have always behaved, and been treated, in the same way as other cadets and have a record of exemplary behaviour. At Sandhurst, King Hussain of Jordan certainly didn't shirk any duties and he was never known to seek time off to go camel riding; and likewise Prince Khaled Bin Sultan of Saudi Arabia never cut lectures or saddled up one of his Arab stallions when due to go on a route march; and in recent years Prince William and Prince Harry always toed the line, give or take the odd booze-up and roll in a gutter.

However, for some reason Benny did exactly what he liked. He never joined us for drill parades and when he turned up for lectures he was accompanied by two aides. One specialized in academic matters and took notes for Benny and even sat his Military Knowledge exams for him.

The other undertook anything physical that was required of Benny. His course instructor, Captain Rogers, always finished off his field craft lectures by making everyone double round the field twice, and Benny's aide came in first so often that on one occasion Captain Rogers turned to Benny and said: "First again, Your Royal Highness ... Well done!"

Why Benny was allowed to get away with this was a mystery. Perhaps it was because he was so damned fat. Or maybe it was a concession granted by the War Office on economic grounds, since Britain got 90% of its oil from Arabica and sold them armaments by the boat load. Whatever the reason, Eaton Hall staff were under orders not to harass, upset, or unduly inconvenience the Crown Prince.

Benny turned out to be a very pleasant fellow. He had a passion for Naafi breaks and had a favourite corner table with a view of the Hall. Every morning his two aides waited for him with a plate piled high with Cream Slices and Eccles Cakes. On occasions, some of us were invited to join him and our requirements were provided by his aides. After a few weeks, this behaviour became resented by some, especially Captain Rushmoor. He accused Benny of bringing the name of the Hall into disrepute and doing nothing to enhance the future efficiency of the Arabica army. This second point proved purely academic. Years later, when Arabica was invaded by a neighbouring Arab state, Benny surrendered without his men firing a shot, knowing that the UN would take it back again in order to stabilize the world oil market.

6

Affairs of the Heart

There were no female cadets at Eaton Hall, but it could hardly be described as a monastic institution. Most of the cadets were young gentlemen who had great respect for the fair sex, being anxious to cherish them so they didn't lose their inferiority complex; but they were nevertheless at the stage where their sexual yearnings were increasingly demanding attention. A rapid awakening was taking place. The other ranks, with whom they had done their basic training, had made them realize that they were missing out on something rather special, which might be well worth a try. Not that there was any question of trespassing into red-light areas, or availing themselves of Naafi tarts, but the time had dawned when the attraction of respectable, wholesome young ladies within their own social strata was undeniable. They were looking for young ladies who, if anything went wrong, and a hasty marriage became necessary, would not be considered a social disaster.

When cadets of this ilk arrived at Eaton Hall they were amazed to find they had struck lucky. Utopia was sitting there, waiting for them. Chester was renowned for its lovely girls and when the Duke of Westminster so graciously accommodated the future leaders of the country in his stately home, they saw this sudden influx of wealthy, highly eligible young men as the answer to their prayers. The only snag was that each cadet was only in Chester for four months. That made normal courtships (in which girls frustrated boyfriends into submission) out of the question. Speed was of the essence and consensual sexual intercourse was the only answer. So just as their mothers and aunts had abandoned middle-class morality when GIs arrived bearing silk stockings and false promises, this new generation of Chester girls forsook their puritanical morals in order to ensnare a husband of high calibre. Pregnancy became a calculated risk well worth taking. In desperate cases, they even used pregnancy as a deliberate ploy, a last resort.*

On Saturday afternoons, when cadets moseyed into Chester, the girls identified them easily enough by their mufti uniforms. Their riding macs, trilbies, and brogues, were akin to a British Standards Institute kite mark:

---

* *The parents of a cadet who got a girl pregnant exercised their right to forbid a marriage. They offered the girl's parents £20,000 if it was a boy, and £10,000 if it was a girl. "And what happens if my daughter miscarries?" demanded her mother. "Will he give her another chance?"*

young gentlemen who had been exhaustively tested and found worthy. The only trouble was that Chester had no suitable rendezvous where this spark of attraction could be ignited, no equivalent to afternoon tea dances at the Waldorf. However, the solution came in the form of Bollands Tea Rooms on the upper shelf of Chester's famous two-tier shopping street. When it was seen that on Saturdays the cadets flocked to Bollands and lingered over tea and toasted crumpets before going on to a cinema, the bolder young ladies of Chester joined the catering trade as waitresses.

During the early days of Eaton Hall, the waitresses at Bollands were refined old ladies in distressed financial circumstances and physical decline: conscientious old dears who worked until they dropped in order to supplement their meagre pensions. They hid varicose veins in woollen stockings and had arthritic hands that made tea trays rattle like old Ford cars. As they died off, or were forced into retirement by dropping too many trays, they heralded the appearance of bright, long-legged young things who were wonderfully curvaceous and flirtatious, and who bubbled like boiling water. Whilst they lacked the catering expertise of their predecessors, and hardly knew a Bath Bun from a Fairy Cake, their new, figure-hugging black uniforms and saucy little lace caps attracted cadets in droves, and such was the allure of high heels, wasp-waists, bottoms in full bloom, and the smooth curve of thoroughbred flanks, that the cadets were soon convinced that these lovely girls, instead of waiting upon them, should be sitting alongside them, rubbing knees and generating static electricity.

Evening dates soon followed and during the summer months the banks of the River Dee were liberally scattered with courting couples. Cadets with flashy cars boasting ample leg room found it more exciting and romantic to conduct their courting parked in local beauty spots. My friend Lord Hatchleigh started off as one of these, taking full advantage of clear skies and the spaciousness of his King-size rear seat. However, when the weather became inclement and showers exposed the Bentley's one weakness (lack of a hood) the coitus interruptus these downpours caused convinced his Lordship that he would be better off in the shelter of Eaton Hall's stables, despite the risk of being caught with a female on the premises.

If progress between couples proved tardy and time ran out, with a cadet commissioned before a binding arrangement had been made, there was sufficient mutual respect left in the relationship to ensure that the girl was not left stranded. There was a sound and well-tried procedure by which the outgoing cadet introduced the girl to a suitable replacement from a new Intake, thus giving her a full four months in which to exploit her charms. It also gave her the opportunity to specify precisely what sort of partner she desired and she often ended up with someone far more eligible than her first choice, who had, after all, been acquired by the luck of the draw.

When Lord Hatchleigh passed out he was one of the cadets who left things dangling and in order to make up for this, and be the real white-man towards his young lady, the last thing he did before driving off to the Guards Depot at Caterham in his Bentley was burst into the hut of a new Intake and call out: "Anyone here with a place at Oxford? Going to read Law? Wears Wolsey socks? With prospects of a substantial inheritance? And would like a first-rate shag every Saturday night for the price of a dinner at the Grosvenor?"

He had well over a dozen volunteers and the cadet eventually selected, David Milne, won the day on the strength of his Exhibition to Sydney Sussex and his intention to become a barrister; whereas his nearest rival was destined for Economics, Philosophy and Politics at Brasenose, with a view to playing county cricket.

This procedure was sometimes overdone. Some new cadets found that the young ladies they had inherited had done the rounds so often that they were no more than recycled camp bicycles. The signs were obvious enough: the girls expected extravagant tips while waiting on them at Bollands; then an a la carte dinner instead of Menu of the Day; and a visit to the theatre rather than one of the cinemas. Even more telling was that they had long since abandoned the missionary position, knew how to fit a condom without causing a premature ejaculation, and were far too hasty in making introductions to their mummies. When cadets eventually read these signs, and realized that they were the third or fourth suitor in succession, they enjoyed the favours on offer until the novelty wore off and then called it a day, young gentlemen of those days being very wary of soiled goods. On the whole, however, the system worked admirably. Many happy marriages resulted.

I was well aware of all this. I had the same physical yearnings as the other fellows, but there was a complication. The commitment to OCS training was inescapable, which meant that in the limited free time available it was very difficult to indulge in both sport *and* women. The only cadet I knew who managed both was Lord Hatherleigh, but then he didn't have constant jankers to contend with, as I did. Consequently, I concentrated on sport. I knew I could hold my own at rugby and cricket, whereas if I competed with other cadets for the affections of one of the Chester beauties, the chances were that I would come off second best.*

---

* *You're quite right! My colour gave me a huge inferiority complex with girls. Yet, as you will see later in this memoir, when colour was no longer a factor, I was not to be denied, even though I underwent all kinds of vacillations before eventually catching up with the rest of them.*

Whilst at the Hall I had the good fortune to make the first teams in the three major sports: rugby, cricket, and athletics. This certainly broadened my horizons. It took me to parts of the country I had never visited before and enabled me to test myself against players and athletes who were destined to gain distinction at a much higher level. I also kept bumping into men I had either known at school, or competed against in the West Country school circuit. Indeed, the way the paths of various individuals crossed and re-crossed was a feature of National Service. Among those I met were Bleary Morton and Nacker Gilbert, both old school friends.

The winter game was rugby and we produced some of the strongest teams in the three Services which could have taken on most sides in the country. Our side contained three Oxford and two Cambridge Blues and several Public Schools XV players. I managed to establish myself at fly-half, even though the fly-half from the English Public Schools XVs was in residence.

Soon after I arrived at Eaton Hall the rugby season finished and during the short athletics season I concentrated on the javelin and putting the shot. The star turn in our team was Derek Johnson, an Olympic silver medallist. The other great sportsman at Eaton Hall during my time was Mike Campbell-Lamerton who went on to play rugby for Scotland and captained the British Lions. (I later served with him in the Duke of Wellington's Regiment in Korea.) He arrived too late for the rugby season at Eaton Hall but we were paired together in the athletics team as the shot-putting duo. He was a mountain of a man (six foot five tall and around 20 stone) and our opponents would take one look at him and assume that he would win easily; but there is more to shot-putting than brute strength. Speed across the circle and timing are equally as important and these were skills Mike lacked, with the result that he invariably came last.

Our needle match was against Mons OCS in Aldershot and it turned out to be a desperately close contest. The shot putt was the last event and Mike and I only had to come 3rd and 4th to win the match. Bleary Morton was performing for Mons and I knew he was bound to win, always assuming that he did not succumb to his old failing and walk out of the front of the circle. Unfortunately for Mike Campbell-Lamerton, it was a particularly wet day and the 16lb shot had become very greasy. After he'd completed the usual leg-waggling preliminaries, and propelled himself forward in the circle, the shot slipped out of his hand, landed on his foot, and broke his big toe. He was in such pain that he was taken to the Cambridge Hospital in Aldershot and he never did complete a putt. Consequently he got no points and we tied the match instead of winning it.

Cricket at Eaton Hall was taken very seriously. As with all sports, the main concern was to beat Mons OCS, and to achieve this the CO gave the cricket team a week off training in order to prepare for the two-day game. Not being a cricketer, he didn't realize that apart from a net once a day, cricket does not require training. (Not in those days, anyhow.) Consequently, when we were seen drinking at the local pub every lunch hour, and generally lazing about the place for the rest of the day, it didn't go down too well with those who took soldiering seriously; and when we came back from Mons, having lost by an innings and 35 runs, we were really in the dog house.

Earlier in the season, the Western Command trial match was held on Eaton Hall's picturesque ground. That was when I first met Colonel Robins. He was currently employed as a staff officer with Northern Command, in York, with a special responsibility for UK barbed-wire entanglements; but since the demand for these encumbrances had been in steady decline since Hitler cancelled Operation Sea Lion, he was able to devote himself to organizing rugby teams in the winter and cricket teams in the summer. He was a fine cricketer at club level and a member of a famous cricketing family, his elder brother having captained England in the days when the captain had to be an amateur and willing to travel without claiming expenses.

Due to the Colonel's wide variety of army postings, he had played cricket world-wide, alphabetically from Afghanistan to Yugoslavia. In many ways he was ahead of his time, among the first to realize that if you couldn't kill off all the enemy, the next best thing was to win their hearts and minds. His way of doing this was to introduce them to cricket. Sometimes, but very rarely, he was beaten to this, as in the case of Corfu where the Royal Navy introduced cricket in the late 1800s, and where--- to this day--- they still play in the main square of the capital.

By the end of World War II, Colonel Robins was President or Founder of several national cricket clubs. He took local topography in his stride and frequently created suitable flat spaces by utilizing bull-dozers of the Royal Engineers. Even the fiercest equatorial heat didn't deter him. The only time he ever made a concession to local conditions was in the Highlands of Papua New Guinea. There, the Methodist Missionary (an elderly lady who had survived head-hunters, cholera, typhoid, typhus, typhoons, and even Nips heading for the Kokoda Track) objected to the natives playing in the nude, even though they had lived in the nude for centuries. She maintained that all the bending down in the slips, and the leaping about after appeals, was positively indecent, so to keep the peace the Colonel told the natives it was traditional for everyone to wear strap-on boxes throughout the game, and not just when batting; and that remains their custom to this very day. Even the umpires and scorers wear boxes.*

Four of us from Eaton Hall were selected for the Western Command trial match and we all performed well: David Milne made 75, Campbell-Lamerton hit a bright and breezy 30, Lord Hatchleigh kept wicket like Godfrey Evans, and I chipped in with five expensive wickets. On the strength of our efforts we were selected for Western Command's first fixture against Southern Command, to be played at Aldershot adjacent to the tennis courts where the Aldershot sun burnished Miss J. Hunter Dunn. This we won with some ease and all four of us kept our places for the next game against Northern Command at York.

In the meantime, we had had our first Military Knowledge written examination and I did not do very well. I came last in the platoon with only fifteen marks out of a hundred. I soon discovered that this was Captain Rushmoor's way of making sure I played no more cricket.

When I was selected to play against Eastern Command at Colchester, it was arranged that the team would travel in convoy, with Colonel Robins and other members of the team calling in at Eaton Hall for the four of us travelling in Lord Hatchleigh's Bentley. We were actually sitting in the Bentley, waiting for them to turn up, when Captain Rushmoor approached us. He told me that my selection had been cancelled and that I was to rejoin the rest of my platoon in the gym. Naturally, I protested and pointed out that my selection was on Part II Orders. He said he had sufficient authority to override such orders and that if I did not obey immediately I would be placed on a charge.

I was actually removing my kit from the Bentley when Colonel Robins and the rest of the team arrived. When I explained what had happened, the Colonel was so furious that he called after Captain Rushmoor. "You there! Come back here!"

There followed an unseemly argument which should never have been enacted in front of junior ranks. Both officers expressed their views succinctly and forcefully. When Rushmoor explained my incompetence, idleness, and general disrespect, Colonel Robins counter-attacked by stating that since I turned it both ways and had a loop that troubled all but

---

Colonel Robins was the best known of these cricket pioneers. He was very proud that when Noel Coward once entertained the troops he added a special verse to his famous song, 'Mad Dogs and Englishmen'.

> *'While goatherds in Crete deplore the heat*
> *And make a dash for the nearest thicket*
> *Only a few yards away, in the heat of day,*
> *Major Robins and his men play cricket ...'*

the best batsmen, he didn't give a damn if I was as useless as the Good Soldier Svejk.

Insults flew back and forth and when Colonel Robins pulled rank, Rushmoor used his trump-card. "Unless Contractor obeys me I will have no alternative but to relegate him forthwith."

There was a stunned silence. That really was nasty. Relegation was the penultimate disgrace, only exceeded by being RTU'd. Whilst my fellow cadets and I reeled in shock, Colonel Robins astounded us by taking an opposite view.

"I say! What a splendid idea, Captain. Problem solved. Get back in that Bentley, Contractor. Consider yourself relegated. You're going to play cricket."

I was duly relegated. My new course instructor was Captain Rogers and one of my new comrades was the Crown Prince of Arabica (Benny), and it was at this point that I furthered my friendship with him and enjoyed special treatment in the Naafi. Indeed, I was much happier in Captain Rogers's platoon. He had no objection to me playing cricket and all through June and July I had the best of all worlds. Yet between Western Command fixtures I worked hard. I had no intention of being RTU'd. The prospect of going back to Catterick and starting all over again was too horrendous for words. My weak link was written exams, but my salvation came when the questions in my second Military Knowledge exam turned out to be exactly the same as in the first, thus enabling me to come a commendable fourth in the results.

Two weeks before I was due to pass out I played in what I imagined would be my last game for Western Command. I mentioned this to Colonel Robins as we sat in deck chairs in the United Services ground, Portsmouth, watching Milne and Campbell-Lamerton piling on the runs against the Home Fleet. "You can't leave yet," he declared. "August is absolutely vital. Leave it to me ... I'll sort things out ..."

Once back at Eaton Hall I was summoned before the CO. He gave me a lecture on the army's many diverse functions and how, in peacetime, sport assumed a greater significance due to the effect upon morale and the honour of the unit; and how rivalry between commands was an excellent thing. He concluded: "So, Contractor, I'm going to relegate you for another four weeks."

"But what about 'one relegation and out', sir? Won't I be RTU'd?"

"Ignore that. And I'll make sure you get the regiment you want. The fact is, we have a duty to Western Command to retain the Army Cup."

So I was relegated for a second time.

We retained the Army Cup and when our cricket fixtures ended I got down to some serious soldiering. My efforts were rewarded when I was made an Under Officer. Like everyone else, I was well aware that I didn't deserve the promotion and that it was an early example of positive discrimination. I found it most embarrassing and even today, sixty years on, whenever I hear of a coloured nonentity heading a Quango, or an insignificant and gormless Muslim becoming a Lord, or a second-rate Negro actress becoming a Dame, or a Nigerian playing Hamlet, or a thick woman backbencher being elevated to the Cabinet, I know that in their hearts they realize what frauds they are, just as I did. Unfortunately, and unlike the aforementioned, my positive discrimination brought no advantages. For me, there was no high salary or limitless expenses, or attendance money, or cushy directorships: it brought only trouble. Two days before our passing out parade, the Senior Under Officer, who was to have commanded the parade, was struck down by appendicitis. I was ordered to replace him. It was to be one of the most important parades in years, with General Sir Gerald Templer taking the salute. On the big day, with the School's turn-out impeccable, all went well until I marched the parade up in front of the Hall and alongside Big Ben for General Templer's address. He was well into his speech when Big Ben started to chime 12 noon. It made such a colossal din that General Sir Gerald Templer couldn't make himself heard, so he stopped speaking.

I hadn't been listening to a word of his speech. I was far too busy rehearsing in my mind the next orders I would have to give the parade. When Big Ben stopped chiming, there was silence and I assumed Sir Gerald had finished, so I called the parade to attention and was just about to order them to slope arms, turn right, and march off, when General Templer yelled: "What are you doing? I haven't finished yet!"

After the parade there was a big reception. I was introduced to Sir Gerald. He didn't say a word, just looked at me with contempt. It was not an auspicious start to my life as a commissioned officer.

PART TWO

HANGING ON THE

OLD BARBED WIRE

8

I Meet Earl Gray

As promised, I was granted the regiment of my choice: The Duke of Wellington's. As I approached their main depot in Halifax I had never felt so nervous. Hitherto, whether at Hill Head Prep School, Blundell's, Catterick, or Eaton Hall, I was still learning, an apprentice. Now, I was qualified, someone who was supposed to know what I was doing and would be in command of 40 men on active service. One wrong decision and there could be all sorts of tragedies: an awesome responsibility.

My confidence was also eroded by the reputation of my new regiment. They were second to none. They had been a star turn at Waterloo and seen some of the hardest fighting along the Somme. Dad had served alongside them in Flanders and was full of praise for them, relating how, whenever he had cause to pass through their lines, he was confronted by lines of hardened Tykes ('e by gums' to him) sharpening their bayonets.

Dad further dented my confidence when he reminded me that the job of platoon commander was the most difficult, demanding, and dangerous in the army, and it was only delegated to the least experienced and qualified on the grounds that they were the most expendable, with never a shortage of young idiots queuing up as replacements. His only useful tip was: "Never salute the RSM before he salutes you."

As it happened, when I reported to the Guard Room, the Guard Commander was a corporal, so I didn't feel too intimidated. He directed me to the officers' mess where the Mess Sergeant was equally as helpful. He showed me to a small bedroom, empty apart from a bed and a dilapidated wardrobe, and then advised me to report to the adjutant.

The adjutant was an over-bred young aristocrat: from his natty little moustache down to the suede desert boots, via his silk shirt and gleaming Sam Browne, he was a superior being. As I stood before him, he studied me in silence. This was by no means contrived. He was genuinely staggered by what confronted him. "So what do we have here?"

"Second-Lieutenant Contractor, sir."

He ran his finger down a list of names. "Ah, yes! Mr. Contractor ... So, you've passed through that sausage machine they call Eaton Hall and now you're all set?"

"Hopefully, sir."

"Good. Well we'll soon see, won't we. How old are you?"

"Coming up for nineteen, sir."

"You'll be old enough to serve in Korea? You have to be nineteen..."

"Yes, sir. I'll make it by a week."

"Good show! A very wise ruling by all accounts. It won't be all tea and crumpets…"

"No, sir. I was aware of that when I volunteered."

He ignored my piece of self-promotion. His attention settled on my cap. "In this regiment we wear hats. Not caps. Schoolboys wear caps. We wear hats which are specially designed and made for us by Messrs. Herbert Johnson of Saville Row."

"Yes, sir."

"May I suggest, Mr. Contractor, that you go away and consult the battalion's senior subaltern, Mr. Blakey. He will advise you on how to present yourself whilst properly dressed. Come back after lunch … And don't salute … Not until you are wearing a Herbert Johnson."

I marched from the room with a burning dislike for the man. I returned to the officers' mess and more by luck than judgement located the senior subaltern, Bill Blakey. He listened sympathetically, knowing that for the rest of the day he would be kept fully occupied sorting out similar problems with other newly arrived subalterns. He suggested an early lunch so that he could explain things at his leisure. A large buffet was laid out in the enormous dining room and I was delighted to see several types of soup on offer, including Brown Windsor, a favourite of mine which had disappeared with Civic Restaurants.

"What can I do about a Herbert Johnson hat?" I asked.

"No problem. I'll lend you mine."

"Won't he realize?"

"Of course. I'm size eight so it'll probably fall over your ears. But it doesn't matter. You are the first of the new subalterns to arrive, so you get the hat treatment. Others will get something different. Hawthorn has a list of faults to pull you up on. If you're wearing boots, why aren't you wearing shoes? And if you're wearing shoes, why aren't you wearing boots? And all sorts of other things. Belt, lanyard, buttons, badges. The best advice for you is 'Illigitimus nil carborundum'. Don't let the bastards grind you down!"

As we progressed through lunch, Bill Blakey became quite loquacious about life in the regiment. "We're an odd lot, but no more so than other regiments. We all consider ourselves unique. And we all have absurd traditions and trophies. Like the $14^{th}/20^{th}$ with Napoleon's chamber pot, and the Cherry Pickers with their scarlet trousers. And the Glosters with their two cap badges."

When we left the table, Blakey asked: "Did you enjoy your soup?"

"Great! I haven't had Brown Windsor for years. Why?"

"Well, if you don't mind me saying …" He hesitated, his smile signifying that he intended no offence. "You start life in the regiment with a very distinct disadvantage so don't make things worse for yourself. If you go on sinking half a boat of gravy under the impression that it's Brown Windsor soup, your fellow officers will be fully justified in having misgivings about you."

I waited for some time after lunch before re-presenting myself to Captain Hawthorn, this time wearing Bill Blakey's Herbert Johnson. As he had feared, it fell over my ears, but since it was a genuine Herbert Johnson Hawthorn was satisfied.

"You are to be 12 Platoon commander. Report to Major Gray at the Dog Company orderly room. The major is a charming fellow. One of the Old Brigade. Earl Gray, actually. But naturally you will simply address him as 'Sir!' His family goes way back with the regiment. Both his father and grandfather were Dukes."

"Dukes! My word!"

"We're all Dukes, you idiot. Even you are, now ... And Major Gray isn't really an 'Earl'. It's his nick-name."

"I see ... As in tea."

"Don't converse. Just Keep a low profile. Especially in the mess."

"Seen and not heard ..."

"Precisely! And never forget that you are now the LFL in the PBI. Understand?"

"No, sir."

"The lowest form of life in the poor bloody infantry. Now clear off."

I located Dog Company orderly room easily enough. Several men were standing outside. A corporal brought them to attention and saluted. As I returned it, I stopped dead in my tracks. There were six of them. Four of them I knew. Indeed, I knew them so well that I could hardly believe my eyes. On the end was Rupert Sandwitch. Beside him was Animal Evans. Then Fletcher, and finally Bertie Mee. I realized straight away that their presence might cause complications, but I couldn't help being delighted to see them all the same. I just couldn't fathom how they came to be there.

(A word of explanation. Their presence was simple enough. After the cupboard incident, and their transfer to the Yorkshire Infantry Brigade training depot at Strensall, they got into further trouble. The Brigade ran an annual assault course competition between the various trades--- drivers, batmen, latrine orderlies, mess waiters, clerks, storemen, and those doing basic training--- and because basic training were the fittest, they always won. However, on this occasion Fletcher persuaded his comrades to save themselves a lot of hassle by throwing the competition in the first round. This was normally the prerogative of the Mess Waiters,

so when they met in the first round it turned out to be a titanic struggle, the slowest assault course race ever known. At one stage, the Mess Waiters came to a halt, but Basic Training went one better and started going backwards on the pretext of helping stragglers. In fact, they went backwards far faster than they ever did forwards. Then, when one of the Mess Waiters staged a heart attack, Basic Training retaliated with a broken leg. In the end, by utilizing their superior cunning, Fletcher and his gang triumphed and lost handsomely.

Not that it did them any good. The CO was so furious that as soon as they completed their basic training he had them posted en bloc to the 1st Battalion The Duke of Wellington's Regiment, knowing that within a few days they would be embarking for Korea where he assured them they would get their just desserts. Here endeth the explanation.)

They were all staring straight ahead in the correct manner but I could see they were finding it difficult to contain their laughter. I had no idea what to say, so I hurried into the company orderly room. Just inside, an unkempt youth with ginger hair was sitting behind a desk piled high with papers. He greeted me in a broad Yorkshire accent. "Owt I can do to help?"

"I'm looking for Major Gray."

"He won't be long. Gone for a Jimmy Riddle. Not holding his ale too well these days. Hard to tell if it's old age or over-indulgence."

"A bit of both perhaps?"

"Aye, you could be reet, sir. You must be one of the new officers from Eaton Hall? I'm Hurst. Company clerk."

Hurst suddenly leapt to his feet and stood to attention. I turned and saw Major Gray for the first time. He was tall and very solidly built. Touches of grey hair peeped out from beneath his Herbert Johnson, making him look more like a general than a major. I jerked to attention and saluted. He ignored me and turned on Hurst. "Why are you still sitting on your arse? I told you to get this place cleaned up. It's a damn disgrace."

"Reet, sir!"

"Never mind 'Reet, sir'. You've said 'Reet, sir' five times now and still not done a damn thing. Anyhow, there's a section of men outside. Get their documentation sorted out. They will be the start of 12 platoon. And when you've got all their paperwork done, join them. I've had enough of your idleness."

"Reet, sir. Suits me fine. It's a bit of action I'm after."

"Really," sneered Major Gray. "Well when we're up to our necks in muck and bullets, to say nothing of great hordes of screaming Chinese charging at us like a football crowd, I'll remember that, Hurst. My God, I will."

74

"Won't worry me, sir."

Major Gray turned away and stared at me as though I was something the cat had dragged in.

"Contractor, sir. The adjutant told me to report."

"Really! Come through to my office." He sat down behind his desk. I stood to attention in front of it. "Ready to leave?"

"Yes, sir."

"You will command 12 platoon. Those men standing outside are the start of your platoon ... Plus Hurst. And don't take any nonsense from him. When he says 'Reet, sir!' don't for one moment imagine that it'll make the slightest difference."

"Reet, sir!"

I thought he might find that amusing, but he didn't. He eyed me distastefully. "What is your Christian name? If you are a Christian?"

"Yes, sir. C of E. Sajit."

"Bajit?"

"Sajit, sir."

"Savit?"

"Sajit!"

"Very well ... In that case, Contractor, I suggest you introduce yourself to your platoon, such as they are."

"When do I get the rest of my platoon, sir?"

"Christ knows! Just be thankful that you've got anyone at all at this stage."

I saluted and marched through the orderly room, more concerned as to how to handle my new platoon than with Earl Gray's hostility.

Outside, the corporal in charge called the men to attention.

"Don't bother with all that, corporal," I said. "Stand easy." I went to the end of the rank and faced my old pals. "I never expected to see you fellows here."

"Ditto," replied Rupert Sandwitch.

"You're going to be in my platoon. 12 platoon. Do you mind?"

"Is there a choice?" asked Fletcher.

"None at all."

We laughed and for a couple of seconds my eyes lingered on Rupert's. Memories of Catterick flooded back. He knew what I was waiting for and he duly obliged.

> *"Trust the army to have a surprise in store!*
> *And just our luck to draw the short straw."*

There was more laughter, but the corporal wasn't amused. He still didn't know Bloody Sand Witch. "Silence in the ranks!"

"It's all right, corporal. I know these men of old." Then I added, in an attempt to strike common ground, "Let's hope Korea doesn't turn out to be a short straw. By all accounts it's pretty rough out there."

No one contradicted this. Then one of the men I didn't know took a pace forward and saluted. He was a short, weedy youth with flat feet pointing at ten-to-two.

"Permission to speak, sir?"

"Certainly ... Name?"

"Wilmott, sir."

"Carry on."

"I been giving Korea some reckoning, sir. And to be honest--- and all things considered, like--- I don't reckon I'm cut out for this malarkey. I'm not the gung-ho type, sir. I thought perhaps a posting to Gibraltar would be better ... In fact, that would be fooking perr---fect."

The others watched Wilmott with amusement, obviously accustomed to such outbursts. No doubt they were also intrigued as to how I would respond to such a blatant lack of enthusiasm. "Tough luck, Wilmott," I replied. "I feel exactly the same way myself. And if I can't get out of it, I'm damn sure you can't. But if you find a way, let me know."

As hoped, my response amused them. Even Wilmott laughed. He seemed delighted that his protest had been lodged and noted, even though dismissed. He saluted again and then, on account of his flat feet, made a pig's ear out of another about-turn before returning to the ranks. He then saluted again. Animal Evans muttered: "Bloody roll on!"

"Silence in the ranks," yelled the corporal.

"Thank you, corporal," I said. "Dismiss the men." As they broke away I called the corporal back. Despite his officiousness, he was a smart and intelligent-looking fellow. "Your name, corporal?"

"Holroyd, sir."

"Is that man Wilmott all right?"

"Nay, sir! He's a reet bloody half-wit."

"Oh ..."

"Thems all bloody half-wits, sir."

"All of them?"

"Aye, sir. Especially Wilmott and bloody Shakespeare."

"Oh ..."

"But nowt to be done about it, sir. If we got rid of the bloody half-wits there'd be no buggers left."

I made no attempt to contact Rupert or the others after our initial meeting. I judged it best for all of us to grow accustomed to the situation gradually. The trip to Korea was due to take six weeks, ample time in which to adjust to any problems. During the rest of the day several National Service subalterns reported for duty, all of whom I'd known at Eaton Hall: David Gascoyne, Peter Chester, Arthur Finch, Peter Gutherie, Ernest Kirk, Simon Berry, Mike Campbell-Lamerton, and Ralf Waugh. It was quite like old times and our mass posting to the Dukes proved very helpful. In the officers' mess it was normal to ostracize new subalterns, to make them feel as uncomfortable and insignificant as possible; but our arrival en masse made it impossible. We had strength in numbers and weren't in the least intimidated by any childish 'new boy' treatment. I became involved in two faux pas which would normally have left me mortified, but instead I simply told the others about them and we all had a good laugh.

I dropped my first brick during afternoon tea. This was taken in the mess at 16.30 hours, and it was a ritual as sacred as any Japanese Honourable Tea Ceremony, the only difference being that whereas the Japanese incorporate the art of intelligent conversation, afternoon tea at the Duke's officers' mess was taken in silence, as though they were trapist monks. Each officer was completely self-contained. He had his own pot of tea, his own hot-water jug, his own strainer, his own slop basin, his own sugar bowl, and his own dinky little milk jug bearing the Duke's badge. Unfortunately I assumed that tea pots followed the same custom as wine glasses and were placed on one's right, but when I seized upon the tea pot on my right my neighbouring officer, Major Ince, watched me with incredulity. He made no effort to correct my error, or request my tea pot in exchange; he simply raised his right hand above his head and clicked his fingers. A mess waiter came running and Major Ince then broke the traditional silence by declaring: "This officer has used my tea pot."

"I'm extremely sorry about that, sir," said the waiter, as though it was his fault and not mine. He then hurried off to the kitchen and supplied Major Ince with a fresh pot of tea. He then turned to me and, with great politeness and not a hint of reprimand, said: "If you require more tea, sir, the custom is to utilize your hot water, as supplied in your hot-water jug on your left-hand side, next to your slop basin."

My second faux pas concerned our mufti turn-out. After tea one was expected to change into civilian clothes until it was time to change into one's No 1 mess kit for dinner. The frequency with which the Dukes officers changed their clothes made life reminiscent of a fashion parade, and the pleasure they derived from this was unnerving, as though an effeminate influence was abroad.

Mufti dress fell into three categories: Optional (any old thing), Casual (sports jackets and cavalry-twill trousers) and Official (lounge suit with regimental tie). However, all these codes of dress were heavily qualified. When Peter Guthrie, Ernest Kirk, and I entered the mess we made the mistake of being in Optional Mufti when we should have been in Casual Mufti. We were confronted by Captain Kavanagh, of Charlie Company. He was a portly, moustachioed, plumy-mouthed caricature of a young Colonel Blimp. Being a third generation Duke, he had taken it upon himself to uphold various regimental traditions, the most notable being mess etiquette, with special reference to regimental haute couture. When the three of us entered the mess lounge, he took one look at us and let out a cry of: "Oh, no! We can't have this."

We stopped and looked at each other, wondering which of us had left our flies open. Captain Kavanagh picked on me first, the obvious target. "Young man, you can't wear a striped shirt and a striped tie." He then pointed at Peter Guthrie and said: "And you can't wear a plain shirt and striped collar with a patterned tie." Finally he switched his attention to Ernest Kirk: "And you, young man, will have to come up with something better than a plain shirt, a plain collar, and a plain tie. What I suggest is that you all go away and change into plain shirts with detached white collars, and regimental ties."

As we left to take appropriate action, Simon Berry entered. Since he was an immaculate dresser and was sporting a plain shirt, a white detachable collar, and a regimental tie, we paused to see if he passed muster. Captain Kavanagh immediately summoned him. "Young man, do you intend to frequent the pubs and clubs of Halifax later tonight?"

"Good Lord no! "

It was the last thing Simon would ever have done.

"Then why are you wearing brothel creepers? One can wear brown brogues with rubber soles whilst sporting cavalry-twill trousers. Or one can wear black brogues with leather soles with practically anything … But two things you can never do is wear brown boots on parade and blue suede shoes with crepe soles in broad daylight."

Since we were due to embark for the Far East the following day, a formal "Guest Night" was held. Numerous distinguished regimental figures were present and they turned out to be marvellous old buffers. Unlike the serving officers, they were delighted to see so many new, youthful faces and they gave us an unequivocal welcome to Dukes. The evening was a great success and by the time the guests thinned out there was a feeling among us that once away from the formalities of the Depot we would fit in without trouble.

Fairly late in the evening, Bill Blakey joined our group and we picked his brains as to why the Dukes were so desperately short of men. He explained that the size of the regular army was totally inadequate and without National Servicemen it would be unable to support the UN in Korea with a battalion, let alone two brigades, armour and supporting arms. "It's the reason they've increased National Service from eighteen months to two years," he explained. "To start with, they even had to call up reservists... Poor devils who'd already fought one war."

He went on to explain another reason for our depleted numbers. The War office, in its wisdom, had decided it could increase the size of the regular army by enticing National Servicemen to sign-on for a third year on the promise of extra pay (roughly double) and the choice of the unit they served in. The decision was made a week before the Dukes were posted to Korea and within hours most National Servicemen in the battalion had signed-on and demanded transfers to either the West Yorks, who were in Cyprus, or the York and Lancs, bound for the West Indies.*

By midnight there were only a few left in the officers' mess, mostly our Eaton Hall gang. For some reason Captain Hawthorn was mooching about as though he was responsible for locking up, and in a far corner of the mess a small clique of field officers was centred around Earl Gray. His voice dominated their conversation and as time passed, and he sank more whiskies, it became more strident. Very soon those around him drifted away until he was on his own. He was staring straight ahead, as though deep in thought. Occasionally he would mumble to himself. Then, for no apparent reason, he suddenly yelled out at the top of his voice: *"Bastards!"*

We pretended we hadn't heard, but surreptitiously we watched for further developments. When he let out another yell of *"Bastards!"*, Hawthorn went over to him. He leaned down and had quiet words with him. Then he helped him to his feet and escorted him out of the mess. As they walked past us, the Earl's tall figure was stooped and crumpled, age suddenly apparent, and once through the double doors and in the ante room, he let out a third echoing yell of *"Bastards!"*

Bill Blakey turned to Ralf Waugh and me, knowing that we were in the Earl's Company. "Don't worry about your lack of numbers. That's your real problem."

"How do you mean?" I asked.

"You'll find out soon enough."

---

* *This was news to me. Later on, I checked with Corporal Holroyd. He confirmed it. When I asked him why he hadn't signed on, he said it was a matter of principle. He saw it as cheap blackmail and wanted no part of it. Others, such as Rupert Sandwitch and his mates, had been denied the chance with their hasty posting.*

9

Getting Ready for Battle

We had a great send off from Southampton. Hundreds of relatives, friends, well-wishers, and regimental notables cheered and waved as the Devonshire caught the evening tide. On board we threw down streamers, making a last, lingering contact.

My family was not well represented. James was still in Cyprus and Brother Nothing declined to disturb his studies at Oxford on the grounds that I was hardly heading for the Somme or Passchendaele and would inevitably reappear like the proverbial bad penny. Mum was also absent. Dad persuaded her that her presence would only embarrass me, just as it always had at school. Furthermore, he reminded her that since she was President of the Blindley Heath Women's Institute, with a General Purposes Committee Meeting on the same day, it would be a gross dereliction of duty to miss it in order to see her son off to the flesh pots of the Far East. This was, of course, a deliberate ploy on Dad's part. He was keeping Mum away so that he could turn up with Miss Beaumont, and although it might reflect very poorly on me and my relationship with Mum, I preferred it that way. I introduced Dad and Miss Beaumont to several of my Eaton Hall friends, all of whom were dazzled by Miss Beaumont and highly amused by the way Dad kept referring to me as 'Din'.* They realized it was derived from Gunga Din and since my father saw no harm in it, they took their lead from him and all my fellow subalterns were soon calling me 'Din'.

The highlight of our departure was the performance of the Regimental Band. They were immaculate on the quayside and played patriotic military marches with gusto, culminating with the Dukes' Regimental march, 'On Ilkley Moor Bar Tat'. The singing that accompanied it was tremendous and those who have never experienced going off to war on a trooper have missed one of life's most emotional moments. It was certainly something I never forget, especially since the Duke's band had a big influence on my life over the next year.

I thought I had seen the last of the band as we disappeared down the Solent, but two days later, as we drew into Gibraltar, I was amazed to to see it on the quayside, playing us into port with 'On Ilkley Moor Bar Tat.' On leaving the Rock, there they were again, going through what was swiftly becoming a ritual. So it went on. Every time we called in at

---

* *For the origins of this, see Volumes I, the Blitz episode.*

a port, the band was on the quayside, playing us in, and every time we departed, there they were again, playing us off.

As we drew away from Aden, I asked Earl Gray about it. He said it was perfectly simple and blindingly obvious. The band was on the trooper the whole time, but they took a tender into the ports as we approached, and then caught up with us again later by the same means. He explained this as though I was an idiot, and I suppose I was pretty thick not to have worked it out for myself. He later used my interest in the band to pull a flanker on me. In the Yellow Sea, he summoned me to his cabin and said: "You're always very interested in the band and you're always moaning about your platoon being under strength. So you will be pleased to hear that now the band has done its last ceremonial at Hong Kong, all of its eighteen privates will be transferred to your platoon."

"But bandsmen are only ever trained as stretcher-bearers, sir. We'll have more stretcher-bearers than riflemen."

"Well if things turn nasty, you'll be bloody lucky then, won't you?"

The Earl grinned, but to me the whole thing stank. Some of the bandsmen were still only eighteen; others had signed on for another six months purely for ceremonial purposes and were due to be demobilised early in the New Year; and others were National Servicemen who had extended their service by a year and then been denied a transfer to another unit on the grounds that there were no band vacancies. When I pointed out these injustices to Earl Gray he told me to stop making trouble and get on with things. Amazingly, when I told the bandsmen of the Earl's response, they accepted it. Their natural leader, Ron Jenkins, merely shrugged his shoulders and said: "You can't win in the army, sir."

A highlight of the voyage was Animal Evans winning the boxing championship. This was really a platoon effort. Fletcher was the chief organizer. He declared himself to be Animal's manager and spent his whole time going around the place referring to Animal as "My boy!" and how "My boy!" was going to mash everyone up. Fletcher appointed Harry Wilmott as "My Boy's" second, and Harry specialized in waving a huge bath towel about between rounds until his arms grew tired, at which point the would sit on a stool beside Animal and revert to verbal advice.

Mike Campbell-Lamerton was expected to win the championship on account of being twice the size of anyone else; but it turned out that there was a diminutive sergeant in the Welch Regiment who was a latter day Tommy Farr. His technique was to launch himself like a rocket at his opponent in the first seconds of the contest and at the same time swing a right hook to their jaw which laid them out flat. Campbell-Lamerton went down like a felled ox and after that no one thought Animal had a chance; but they hadn't reckoned with Fletcher's expertise at fisticuffs.

He advised "My Boy!" to back pedal the whole time and concentrate on throwing out straight lefts. This worked perfectly and every time the Welshman launched himself bodily he encountered "My Boy's!" straight left and very soon found himself sitting on the canvas taking a count, with his nose resembling a squashed tomato.

About this time, 12 Platoon at last got a platoon sergeant. He was the oldest soldier in the battalion and his recent promotion to sergeant was in line with the old dictum, 'set a thief to catch a thief'. Having run out of any ideas of what to do with the poor old sod, Colonel Banbury decided he might just as well be 12 Platoon's sergeant. His name was Brummell, known throughout the battalion as Beau Brummell, even though he was far from being a dandy. In army vernacular, he was in perpetual shit order and although, with his appointment to sergeant, he tried to do something about it, he failed conspicuously.

Beau Brummell was the only one in the platoon to have been outside Europe and whilst he took everything in his stride, the rest of us were fascinated by the world that opened up before us. First there was the blue calmness of the Mediterranean and then the human upheaval at Suez with bumboats surrounding us and gully-gully men swarming on board to stagger us with their magic. Next came the arid bleakness of Aden, succeeded by the contrast of Ceylon and a visit to the famous Mount Lavinia Hotel. Finally, the Far East with the poverty, squalor, and the packed humanity in Singapore and Hong Kong. At each port we spent at least eight hours ashore and we had no trouble in entertaining ourselves. The only man to show disappointment in these outings was Fletcher. When he returned from 24 hours in Hong Kong he was in a foul temper, swearing that he would never trust his brother again. His ire arose from that fact that the three 'taxi girls' he'd sampled were just as vertical as any other females.

Pusan came as a shock. There were hardly any proper buildings left standing. It was just a vast, sprawling slum; a conglomeration of shacks constructed from planks of wood, cardboard packing cases, sheets of plastic, ammunition boxes, and old crates. We filed down the gangplank in silence and marched off to the railway station for our journey north. We reached the end of the line two days later and were bussed to a tented camp adjacent to the reserve 'Kansas' line. Here, there had been abortive attempts at sabotage by communist infiltrators and security was tight, with every company area surrounded by barbed wire.

We had two weeks in which to train before going into the front line. We needed it. Our ignorance of soldiering was incredible. Apart from Animal Evans and Beau Brummell, no one had the faintest idea about warfare. Whilst basic training was second to none at teaching saluting, arms-drill, turning to the left and right, and instilling an instinctive response to orders, it made no mention of a platoon in attack, nor any reference to the vital role of covering fire; and when I explained the principle of fire and movement the lads were full of wonder, astounded by the army's ingenuity. When I went on to extol the virtues of DFs, supporting fire, stonks, inter-locking fields of fire, and air-burst shells, their amazement became wide-eyed, having always assumed that fighting the enemy consisted of leaping over the top and charging at them in the manner of the American Marines.

When our training got underway, elementary mistakes abounded. Men could never resist walking along skylines, and during night exercises, whenever a flare went up, they ran for cover instead of freezing like statues. They had no idea of the importance of staying in visual contact with each other on night patrols, and the normal technique of moving in staccato bursts, and going to earth to listen for enemy movement, was another revelation to them. At first, they thought we were stopping to have a rest, including a smoke-oh! They had no idea that grenades had a fuse-time of seven seconds and phosphorous grenades were completely unknown to them. If their Bren gun stopped firing they discarded it in the hope that Sergeant Brummell or I would sort it out later, or better still, that they would be able to trade it in at the QM Stores for one that wasn't clapped out. The news that stoppages on Brens were quite frequent, and could happen any time during an attack, and that they were expected to sort them out with 'immediate actions', terrified them.

As their platoon commander, I found all this disconcerting. As their company commander, Earl Gray found it appalling. I felt sorry for him. After all, he had once commanded a column of Chindits behind Japanese lines. They had been the elite of the 14th Army; but now, at the crunch moment of his career, when he so desperately needed success, he was landed with a company of men who were about as much use as a troop of boy scouts.

Not that he was deterred. It simply made him all the more determined to lick us into shape. To use the American expression, he 'kicked ass!'. Each morning, after an exhausting session of PT, we did section and platoon attacks up the steepest hills in the neighbourhood. He doubled us everywhere. We were never allowed a moment's rest. There were no breaks for smoke-ohs and we didn't even get lunch breaks. We snatched our C-ration meals in odd moments; and all the time the Earl strode about with CSM Howard at his side, castigating us unmercifully, with the continual cry going up: "Take that man's name, Sergeant-Major."

I came in for the severest criticism. My fellow platoon commanders, Ralf Waugh and Stan Bennett, were lucky in that they had young and active platoon sergeants, whereas Beau Brummell had been clapped out for years and was always left miles behind the rest of the platoon, a sort of perpetual rear-guard to be pitied rather than criticized.

The main complaint levelled at me was that I wasn't assertive enough. I lacked a dominant personality, and my half-hearted orders brought half-hearted responses. When we did platoon attacks, with the assault group charging up steep hills, we automatically split into three groups. At the rear would be the idle and unfit, one step ahead of Beau Brummell. They usually clustered around Fletcher and Bertie Mee, with all of them stumbling about, gasping for breath and using their weapons as walking sticks. In the middle group there would be Corporal Holroyd, Animal Evans, the bandsmen, and myself, all doing our mediocre best. Finally, way out in front, bounding up the hill a good 30 yards ahead of everyone else, would be the Buckpass ex-captain of cross-country running, Rupert Sandwitch. Once he reached the skyline he assumed a triumphant pose with his Sten held high in the air. Then he would look down on us and give us the benefit of another verse, such as:

> *"All speed you Britannic soldiers,*
> *You few, you shagged-out few.*
> *Make haste before the sun goes in*
> *And spoils a splendiferous view."*

Earl Gray and CSM Howard, for all their experience, had never known anything like it. CSM Howard expressed his anger by beating hell out of small bushes with his pace stick and Earl Gray's language went from the highly respectable to a stream of swear words. After one of our greater disasters, Earl Gray treated me to an eyeball-to-eyeball confrontation in the manner of Sergeant Gough. "Contractor! If I hear another word out of that bloody wireless operator of yours, I'll bloody well ..." The Earl's voice trailed away in despair before turning to CSM Howard with his usual: "Take his name, Sergeant-Major."

"Sandwitch's or Mr. Contractor's, sir?"

"Both of them."

After another mock attack, Earl Gray shouted: "Contractor! That stupid bugger Sandwitch can't take every hill all by himself. You're supposed to attack as a bloody unit ... All together."

"Right, sir! I'll tell him to slow down ... Wait for the rest of us."

"No you bloody won't. You'll tell those other idle buggers, including yourself, to keep up with him. And who is in command of the covering fire section?"

"Corporal Jackman, sir."

"Well tell him to pull his bloody finger out. They're there to fire their weapons on rapid. And who was that man at the back who stopped for a pee?"

"Fletcher, sir."

"I thought so! Get his name, Sergeant-Major. Right, Contractor! Take your pathetic platoon back down the hill and start again. And this time--- when you go into the charge--- bloody well charge!"

"Yes, sir."

"And the order is, 'Charge!' Not 'Right lads, let them have it!'"

"Very good, sir."

"And when you've taken the position you don't stand around smoking bloody fags. You get ready for a counter-attack … Adopt a position of all-round defence. The golden rule is to watch for the enemy's next move … Anticipate!"

"Okay, sir."

The Earl's emphasis on anticipating soon became beyond a joke. Even when we began to improve, he was so determined to deny us any credit that he adopted another tactic, to which there was no answer. Under the guise of anticipation, he invented tactical situations of which we had no warning. Whatever happened, we were promptly declared to have been annihilated by some new and unexpected manoeuvre by the imaginary enemy.

"Contractor, you have just been wiped out by mortar fire," became a favourite cry. Or, "Contractor, that stream you've just come through just happens to be a raging torrent. Since your weapons weren't at the high port they are now useless."

At the end of each new imaginary scenario, came the Earl's golden rule: anticipate!

Once, when we were in a good position of all round defence, behind boulders, digging-in frantically, he strode up to us and shouted: "You're all as dead as mutton … Know why?"

"Mortars, sir?"

"Rubbish! Chinese machine guns. You've been caught in enfilade fire. Do you know what enfilade fire is?

"Of course, sir. But do you think we could have prior notice of these unexpected developments?"

"Oh yes, Contractor. Good idea! I'll get the Chinese to send you a post card. Think in advance, man … Anticipate!"

Eventually, a rebellious spirit reared-up in the platoon and found expression through Sandwitch. After another debacle, Earl Gray stormed over to us and demanded: "Don't you ever learn? You're all as dead as mutton. Know why?"

"No idea, sir," I replied.

"Can't any of you ever anticipate anything?"

No one answered.

In desperation Earl Gray turned to the nearest man: "Don't you know?"

Sandwitch was not one to shirk a challenge. "I would be happy to venture a suggestion, sir. Off the top of my head, that is.

"Either a counter-attack by Field-Marshal Earl Haig
Or an unprecedented outbreak of bubonic plague."

The Earl was stunned into silence. Eventually, but still speechless, he turned to CSM Howard.

"I've got his name, sir."

The man who gained the Earl's greatest contempt was Hurst. His ambition to become an ace Bren-gunner in the Errol Flynn mould still stood, but he had assumed that we would always be in defence, not charging up and down hills. He was so unfit that he was a regular member of the Fletcher/Bertie Mee rear-gang and only reached the summit while the rest of us were lying in our position of all-round defence. He would stumble over the crest of the hill and then, realizing that he'd at last made it, and was once again on flat ground, he was rejuvenated. All his aggression returned and he let out ferocious screams and rushed around, going through the motions of bayoneting the enemy. Having watched this pathetic performance twice, Earl Gray shouted: "For God's sake control that idiot Hurst. Tell him that Brens aren't fitted with bayonets."

Our greatest disaster was Harry Wilmott. Because of his flat feet, he rarely made the summit at all. He even lurked behind Beau Brummell. Halfway up the hills he would decide that the whole thing was quite beyond him and he would either find a convenient bush to hide behind, or dead ground in which to lie doggo. He had a natural talent for disappearing and he was the sort of character whose presence was rarely missed.

Hence, I knew nothing of what he was up to until the sharp-eyed CSM Howard spotted him and brought him to Earl Gray's attention.

"Contractor! One of your men is halfway down the hill, sitting behind a bloody bush, smoking a bloody fag. What the devil does he think he's doing?"

I did my best to cover-up for Harry. "I think you'll find that he is anticipating... Watching for an attack from the rear ... Or maybe he's anticipated a wound and is waiting for stretcher-bearers."

"Rubbish! He's a bloody shirker. And if I catch him shirking again he won't have to assume he's a casualty. He'll bloody soon be one. And he won't be 'walking wounded'. Do I make myself clear?"

Poetically, this was one of Rupert Sandwitch's most productive periods.

Whenever he came up with a new ditty, the Earl put him on a charge, then docked him a week's pay, thinking that would very soon curb him, but it didn't. The Sandwitch family was lousy rich and the loss of a pound a week meant nothing to Rupert.

So the ditties continued and on two occasions he caused so much laughter that our platoon attacks simply stuttered to a halt. The first occasion was when, having gained the top of the hill well ahead of us, he called down:

> *"Cannons to your left! Cannons to your right!*
> *Unfortunately they are invisible*
> *So they'll be bloody hard to fight."*

The second outburst of laughter heralded the greatest fiasco of our training. The Earl was so fed up with us that he decided to make an example of us in front of the rest of the company. He got CSM Howard to form the company into a three-sided square at the base of his favourite training hill (gradient 1 in 5) and gave 12 Platoon a fearful dressing down. He then announced that we would do an assault to demonstrate to the rest of the company that we were perfectly capable of doing things properly if we only tried.

"12 Platoon will reach the peak as one man," he declared. "And there will be no stragglers. No stopping for a smoke. No knocking off for a pee. Or sitting behind bushes. This time it will be done properly."

We were called forward and lined up by CSM Howard. I was at the front, Rupert beside me. "When CSM Howard gives the order," shouted the Earl, "12 Platoon will do a frontal assault and capture the peak."

Before CSM Howard could give the order, Rupert dashed several yards up the hill, then turned back to everyone. He raised his Sten above his head and in true Shakespearean style, he cried out:

> *The peak! The peak!*
> *Onwards Brothers to the peak!*
> *Though legs grow weary and straining tendons ache,*
> *Let no man falter at what we so nobly undertake.*
> *Yon slope of gravel upon which we slip and slide*
> *Is but a challenge we'll overcome in our stride.*
> *Onwards Brothers!*
> *Onwards to the peak!*

For a moment there was silence. Then came the gurgling sound of strangulated laughter. It came from CSM Howard. He did his best to keep a straight face but as everyone watched him, waiting for him to unleash a tirade of foul abuse at Rupert, his features twitched and then crumbled. Eventually, and before Rupert could start his lone assault, he collapsed in uncontrollable laughter. The rest of us joined in. It was impossible to do otherwise. Only the Earl remained unamused.

When training finished I stood to attention in front of the Earl.
"So what have you got to say for yourself?"
"I'm sorry, sir. I had no idea he was going to do that."
"What's the matter with the stupid bastard?"
"A sort of Shakespearean complex, I think, sir."
There was a long silence between us.
"I won't be made a laughing stock of, Contractor."
"No, sir. Of course not."
"And don't think you're going to get away with this. You've got to get a grip. I could easily replace you. Get you thrown out of the Dukes without any trouble. But I'm not going to. This is now personal. I'll make damn sure you and your miserable platoon see this campaign through to the bitter end. Or die in the attempt. Am I quite clear?"
"Yes, sir."
"Dismiss!"

Increasing animosity between 12 Platoon and the Earl came as no surprise and the platoon took a perverse delight in fighting against what it considered to be unfair treatment. I did my best to jolly them along. I kept calling out: "Now come on, you chaps!" and I clapped my hands together briskly, like a cricket captain encouraging his fielders to walk in smartly. They took no notice. Even when the Colonel and the Brigadier came round it made no difference. It just made my efforts at being assertive look all the more pathetic.

In the evenings, the lads loved to gather around their camp fire. Our progress--- or our lack of it--- was their favourite topic. Fletcher came out with a theory that the worse we were, the less responsibilities we would get. Rupert put forward an alternative theory: that having reached the nadir of incompetence, we could only get better. Since none of us knew what 'nadir' meant he got no arguments and, as events turned out, he was probably right.

What saved us was that we were involved in a purely defensive war in which the overriding requirement was an abundance of guts, the ability to sit tight through endless shelling, and to stand and fight and not run away. In those qualities 12 Platoon--- inspired by a large dose of Yorkshire cussedness--- was not found wanting.

Before long, we had our first pay parade: it was routine, but it still managed to cause trouble. We assembled in the open in platoons with our new company 2 i/c, Captain Copper Bowden in charge. Being the last to be paid, 12 Platoon had the opportunity for a quiet natter whilst others marched to and fro receiving their pay. We noticed that everyone got slightly less than a quid, instead of slightly more. This was due to a deduction for 'barrack-room damages'. Whilst that may have been justified at Catterick or Strensall, none of the lads thought it justified in Korea. Something needed to be said, so Rupert said it. He strode up to Captain Bowden, gave a sloppy salute, and then, when he palmed the grand sum of 19 shillings and 8 pence, he looked down at it, poked through it to make sure nothing was hidden, then said:

> *"My goodness, sir!*
> *I'm amazed by how much Her Majesty can afford,*
> *Especially when it includes full bed and board."*

Copper Bowden put him on a charge and when his case came up, Earl Gray said: "You shouldn't have been getting any pay, anyhow. You've been docked a month's pay already. And now there's another week to add on to that. The rate you're going, Sandwitch, you're going to have to ask the Paymaster General for a mortgage."

"No problem, sir. I've got plenty of collateral."

Our most memorable incident during training concerned passwords. Devising the passwords was the responsibility of the Company Clerk, and this vital post was now in the hands of Corporal Bridges, late of the Royal Fusiliers. Bridges was a Cockney and when he joined us everyone was suspicious of him because he was a friend of Fletcher, indeed he was Fletcher's only friend, and vice versa. Physically, Bridges was tall, fat, and flabby, a man who had grown to enormous proportions (nearly 20 stone) due to his addiction to Bridges Ready Salted Potato Crisps.* Mentally, he was shifty, conniving, cunning, and two-faced, guided by a one-track mind so foul that most people likened it to a cesspit, or a soot-laden chimney in dire need of sweeping.

---

* Bridges father produced the UK's first-ever ready salted crisps, and it brought him great commercial success. Until his entry into the market, each bag of crisp had a small twist of blue paper in it containing salt. One had to disentangle this and apply it oneself, which meant that the crisps on top became inedible and those at the bottom remained as before. Bridges had regular supplies of his father's crisps sent out to Korea, but he never shared them with anyone, apart from Fletcher.

Among other things, he was a natural barrack room lawyer. He had the ability to talk himself out of anything, which was how he managed to avoid any blame in the incident I am about to relate, even though it was his ridiculous passwords that caused all the trouble. When he made them up he reasoned that the cruder they were, the more likely men were to remember them. The previous passwords during the week had been: "Bugger --- Off" "Balls --- Up" "Up ---- Yours" "Piss ---- Off" and "Shagged ---- Out"

Apart from Harry Wilmott, no one in the company took any notice of passwords. Earl Gray and Copper Bowden considered themselves way above such trivialities, and it wasn't until 12 Platoon mounted the evening guard on the barbed wire barrier surrounding the company lines that trouble struck. By appointing Harry to be the evening sentry I made a big mistake. I didn't realize it, but it was the first time in his life that he had ever been entrusted with any responsibility, and he was so proud of this that he was determined to justify the confidence I'd put in him.

Earl Gray and Copper Bowden were the only two out of company lines that night. They had been at Battalion HQ playing bridge with the Colonel and Hawthorn. When they returned--- rather late and pleasantly intoxicated--- they were confronted by Harry at the barrier. His Sten was at the ready, his bayonet was fixed, his safety catch off. He was prowling up and down like a caged tiger, albeit a flat-footed tiger, if there ever was such a creature. He was desperate to do his duty. When he saw Earl Gray and Bowden approaching he saluted. Then he levelled his Sten at them and challenged: "Halt! Advance and be recognized. Bull ..."

"Since you've just saluted us, you know damn well who we are."

"Aye, sir. But I must have the password .... Bull!"

"Just let us in!"

"Nowt doing, sir ... Bull! Can't come in without it."

"Don't be damn silly. Let us through."

"Orders are orders, sir. No one comes in without the password."

"I gave those orders."

"That's why I'm obeying them. Can't catch me out. Bull!"

Earl Gray turned to Bowden, but he merely shrugged. Earl Gray became sterner: "Look here, this is your last chance. Let us in."

"Nay, sir! I know the punishment for disobeying orders ... Bull!"

"Dozer," guessed Gray.

"That's not it."

"Cow."

"No."

"Eye."

"Not even warm, sir."

"Ring."

"Nowhere near. "

"China shop?"

"Getting colder, sir."

Copper Bowden was so sick of the whole thing that he exclaimed: "Oh shit!"

"You got it, sir!" cried Harry. "Fooking perr---fect! 'Bull ---- Shit!' Well done, sir. Come on in." Harry laughed like a drain and opened up the barrier, ushering them in. "Like I say, sir. Bloody good try. But you can't catch old 'Arry out like that."

The following morning Wilmott was charged with insolence. CSM Howard marched him into the marquee amid a plethora of shouting and stamping. Copper Bowden was the witness and I was there to give a character reference for Harry. Bowden related what had happened and Earl Gray found Wilmott guilty. "You will be transferred," said Gray. "You are not fit for a rifle company. Anything to say?"

Wilmott stepped forward, did his usual atrocious and unnecessary salute, and replied: "Aye, sir. Thanks a million. I told Mr Contractor weeks ago that I wasn't cut out for this fighting malarkey."

"Did you, indeed!" Earl Gray eyed him with disgust. "In that case, the sentence is suspended. Dismiss."

A very puzzled Wilmott was marched away by CSM Howard. I turned to Earl Gray. "What about my character reference, sir?"

"His character speaks for itself, Contractor."

"That's hardly fair, sir. The fact is, Wilmott is a few bullets short of a full magazine."

"He's what?"

"Simple, sir."

"Rubbish! He's just trying to work his ticket. He's no more simple than you are."

"Thank you very much, sir."

"Don't be insolent. And give Wilmott extra fatigues."

"Yes, sir." Then I added: "By the way, sir. Wilmott does have a point. We are expected to know the password. And since you'll no doubt be at battalion HQ again tonight, playing bridge, it might be a good idea to make a note of it."

"Really? All right ... What is it?"

" 'Get --- Stuffed', sir."

10

Into the Line

We concluded our training with a battalion exercise. We acquitted ourselves well, inasmuch as we didn't louse things up. Then, on the morning of September 30th 1952, we assembled in full battle order for the march to the front line. As usual, Dog Company was at the rear, 12 Platoon last of all. We marched in silence, apart from the rhythmic beat of our footsteps and the jangling of loose sling swivels and other pieces of equipment. An ominous feeling gripped us: here at last was the real thing. Now, the larking about had to stop.

After marching for several miles our bandsmen, headed by Ron Jenkins, decided to liven things up with some well-known bugle calls and marches. It was their sole skill so they were keen to make the most of it. I expected a runner to appear from company HQ with a message from Earl Gray telling them to pipe down, but although the runner duly arrived, his message was: 'Well done, Contractor. Keep it up!' It was the first praise I had ever received from him. As far as I can remember, it was also the last.

Our bugles were a siren call to the locals. They streamed out of the villages and the thatched huts lining the MSR. Others abandoned their work in the paddy fields to cheer us on. Our greatest admirers were small boys. They marched alongside us, arms swinging, generally mimicking us, calling out remarks we didn't understand, apart from the inevitable, 'Chinky number ten!' How time repeats itself, I reflected. It was only a few years ago that I was doing exactly the same thing during WWII, marching alongside Guardsmen heading up Caterham's Harestone Valley Road to their training areas in the North Downs.

The gangs of small boys stayed with us until we reached the combat zone, the presence of which was announced by a roadside hoarding stating:

> *'You are now entering the battle zone courtesy*
> *of the road-making skills of the US 35th*
> *Engineering Regiment.'*

Korea was full of bullshit like that.

Entering the war zone was an unnerving experience. Exploding shells became threateningly near. Before long we could feel the earth vibrating beneath our feet. We seemed to be heading straight for trouble and concern in the company became so palpable that Earl Gray sent a message back, reassuring us that the area receiving so much attention was the Hook, whereas we would soon turn eastwards for Yong Dong on the other side of the River Samichon.

That was my introduction to the Hook. During my service in Korea I was never more than a few miles from it and I never knew it when it wasn't being shelled or when there weren't ambulances buzzing around the jeep-head, evacuating wounded. Now, the hill itself was etched against the skyline. Yet it wasn't monolithic as I had expected. There was no touch of the Matterhorn about it. It was no more than a high ridge dominating the countryside for miles around. It was completely bald, every scrap of vegetation having been blown away,

We soon veered off to the east, on the far side of the Samichion valley. Here, things were very different--- no shelling and all the hills covered by bushes and stunted trees. At the base of the Yong Dong position was a large, open area. It had been flattened and cleared by bulldozers and it was bustling with activity, a marshalling yard with Jeeps and 15cwt trucks scurrying around. Above, in the hills, men of the 3rd Battalion Royal Australian Regiment were making their way down deep trenches. Some were already formed up at the bottom in platoons, waiting for the order to board TVCs some distance down the road. Nearby was a large compound wired off from the road. In it, squatting on their haunches, looking dejected and miserable, were the battalion's Korean porters. They were waiting to take supplies up the hills. More dramatic were three Centurion tanks, rumbling and clattering about as they prepared to mount the hills allocated to them.

Regimental police guided each company to the base of the hill it was due to occupy. Dog Company was on the left flank, neighbouring the Samichon River. At the bottom of our hill was a sign which proclaimed:

'Welcome to Rat Castle'

It was a warning as much as a name. In the early days of the war our hill had been the site of a stand by American troops. Outnumbered and surrounded, they were wiped out to a man, and the North Koreans had been in such haste to exploit their victory that they swept on, leaving the dead to rot where they fell; and that was when the rats took control and multiplied copiously.

We had to wait for darkness before the take-over could take place, so

whilst waiting I went around the platoon to check that everything was in order. They were strung along the roadside and when I came to Animal Evans I was amazed to see that he had a young Korean boy sitting on his shoulders. The lad's head was shaven, his features sunken and scrawny. He was clearly half-starved. Yet he was full of spirit and when he saw me approaching his face broke into a cheeky smile. He recognized me as the officer and saluted, American style.

"What's he doing here?"

"Picked him up on the way, sir," said Animal. "I've tried to get rid of him but he won't go."

"He'll have to. Give him something to eat and tell him to go home."

"He's already had a tin of chicken hash. And he hasn't got a home."

I ordered the boy to the ground. His eyes glistened with fear. He grabbed Animal's hand and clung to it. I told him to go away and pointed back down the road, but he wouldn't budge. I called Fletcher over. Already, he was our expert at pidgin Korean, boasting an assortment of army slang, genuine Korean and Japanese words, and a few phrases of well-known international abuse. He kept telling the kid to 'vamoose', 'scarper', and 'bugger off', but the boy refused to budge. He clung all the harder to Animal's hand. Animal encouraged him and even Fletcher spoke up for him. "The poor little bastard's been wandering around the countryside for years, sir."

"I can't help that. Get rid of him. Take him to the Korean porters' camp. They'll help him."

Darkness closed in. Australian guides appeared and led us up the hill to show us around the position. They waved airily in various directions and nodded to bunkers lurking down narrow and winding trenches. We were shown everything, but absorbed nothing. The trench system was like a maze to us and when my opposite number suddenly said: "Orl right, mate? Good on yer!" I didn't have the nerve to tell him I was still in the dark, literally and metaphorically.

Left on our own, we floundered around, not infrequently bumping into each other in the trenches. Beau Brummell and I managed to allocate each man to a bunker and then the section commanders allotted each man a weapon pit on the forward slope. I turned my attention to platoon headquarters. This consisted of two large bunkers, one of which I shared with Rupert Sandwitch (batman and wireless operator) and Beau Brummell. The other was occupied by Animal Evans (platoon runner) and Bertie Mee (2-inch mortar man). Both bunkers were neat and tidy and quite well appointed with rough-hewn tables and chairs and a primitive space-heater in each.

As I stored my kit under the bottom bunk, I saw Rupert rummaging about in his kitbag. He pulled out an assortment of books. I knew he carried some around with him, but I had never imagined it amounted to a small reference library, including *The Complete Shakespeare, The Collected Works of Keats, Machiavelli's Il Principe,* and a thick leather-bound volume of Sun Tzu's *The Art of War.* Once he had them arranged at the back of the table, using unprimed grenades as book-ends, he reported to company HQ over the 88-set that we had settled in. He was premature. Almost immediately men began to appear in the doorway, complaining about their bunkers. When I inspected a few of them I sympathized. They were in a disgusting state. The Australians were undoubtedly the best fighting troops in Korea, but they would never have got the Queen's Award for Good Housekeeping.

Beau Brummell accompanied me on my inspections and every time I sympathized he muttered to me out the corner of his mouth: "Don't be so bloody soft, sir." Then he would turn on the men and yell: "What the hell do you expect? A bloody sea view? Get back in there and make the most of it. You're hairy-arsed soldiers in the front line, so bloody well grow up."

Fletcher and Harry Wilmott were among those who complained but they were in a different category. They refused point-blank to occupy the bunkers allocated to them. Fletcher was positively mutinous, arguing fiercely with Beau Brummell. Beside him, Harry Wilmott gave him close support, only this time, instead of it being "Fooking perr---fect!" it was "Fooking diss---goosting!"

They claimed their bunkers stank to high heaven and were lousy with rats. Fletcher related how, on entering his bunker he struck a match and found himself surrounded by scores of tiny pink specks, all apparently suspended in midair. He ran off and it was only when he returned, armed with a torch, that he realized that the pink specks were rats' eyes. They were poking their heads out of their holes in the mud walls to see what all the new commotion was about. Fletcher further claimed that when he managed to light his candle, there were four rats sitting on a table eating the remains of a loaf of bread. "Just like bloody toffs having a dinner party," he said.

Wilmott rounded off their complaints by saying: "Where I bloody come from, us lives like human beings ... Not bloody animals."

"Bollocks!" said Beau Brummell. "You come from Bradford."

Before the argument got any further a large rat scurried along a wooden beam near the roof. We all turned and watched it. I pretended it didn't unnerve me. Beau Brummell was less successful. He drew back in alarm and was so shaken by the size of the brute that he became far more conciliatory. "Right, sir. I'll see what alternative accommodation I can offer these lads."

Within half an hour everything was resolved. Beau Brummell took them at their word--- that their bunker was the worst in the platoon. He promised them something better. Nothing grand, but something better. He told them to collect their kit, bring it round to the CP, and to wait outside. He then disappeared for several minutes and on his return claimed to have everything organized. In fact, all he did was switch them over. When he showed Fletcher's bunker to Wilmott, he said: "There you are. That's better than your old bunker, isn't it?" and Harry had no option but to agree. Then Beau Brummell gave Fletcher the same treatment and his final sarcastic remark to both of them was: "Your Teas-Maid will be here in the morning."

When dawn broke we realized why Yong Dong was regarded as an ideal position for new units. No man's land was nearly a mile wide. Nor were there any signs of life on the Chinese hills.

The first thing I did was lay down a daily routine. I ordered that every third weapon pit along the front trench should be manned all night and that from dusk to dawn two standing patrols were to be sited in the valley, ahead of our barbed wire entanglements and minefields and well to the flanks of our concealed path into the valley. Each patrol had an 88-set, with the patrol commander obliged to send back reports to platoon HQ every hour. I also made a point of ensuring that every man in the platoon was familiar with using the 88-sets and the field telephones. Most of them took to them easily enough, but it was difficult to stop Bertie Mee from arsing about. Earl Gray wasn't at all amused when Bertie answered one of his calls with: "Hello! Bridgend Coal Gas and Coke Company ..."

For two days we settled into our subterranean existence. I held my first orders group and gave the section commanders our priorities. Our first task was to prop up sagging bunkers, strengthen their roofs, and clear out the filth and muck the Australians had left behind. Then we fitted out every bunker with some form of heating, modelled on the space-heater already in the platoon CP. In most cases this meant putting a 42 gallon drum of petrol on the roof with rubber tubing running down inside and ending up in an old ammunition box filled with earth. At the end of the rubber tubing was a metal clip which regulated the flow of petrol, the aim being to get a steady drip, which set the soil alight in a controlled manner and provided reasonable warmth.

The platoon latrines were our greatest problem. We inherited three deep holes with two planks of wood laid over the top. The gap between the planks allowed a man to sit on them and answer a call of nature with what was commonly referred to as the big drop. The only snag was that there was no longer any big drop. The Aussies had left the latrines chock full. One more crap and they would have overflowed. I put Corporal

Holroyd in charge of sealing them off and told his section to dig fresh ones some way down the reverse slope. This vital work had only just got under way when I heard Harry Wilmott's flat feet plodding towards the CP. Eventually, he poked his head round the corner and saluted. "Permission to speak, sir?"

"Of course, Harry. You don't need permission."

"Aye, well, sir. This is official business, like. I've just been helping to dig new latrines. And I was wondering if you'd ever read a book called *The Specialist*?"

"No. Why?"

"Well neither have I, sir. Not proper, like. 'Cause as you know, I can't read. But we had a teacher at school and he used to read it to us last lesson of every term, like."

"The whole book in a lesson?"

"Aye, sir. It's only about fifteen pages. But it's a reet good laugh. All about a fellow called Lem Putt who specialized in building outside loos. Just like what we need out here. At one stage, old Lem Putt pulls his car up some way off, on top of a hill so his family can admire his handiwork. So he puts his car into mutual ..."

"Mutual?"

"Aye, mutual! Not neutral." Harry chuckled gleefully. "It really is a reet good laugh, sir. By heck, if only Lem Putt was in the platoon ... In another part of the book ..."

"What's your point, Harry?"

"Well, sir, I'm volunteering to be the platoon Specialist. To be the Lem Putt of 12 Platoon. Not so much digging the holes, sir. The lads can do that. But finishing off work ... Making seats on top, like."

"Good idea. By all means."

"And what I thought, sir ... Since this'll be reet hard work and very important ... Perhaps I could be excused patrols and all that lark."

I smiled inwardly. I hadn't the slightest intention of sending Wilmott out on patrols to crash around with his great flat feet. I valued the lives of others far too much. However, I hummed and hawed for a bit, making him feel that he had struck a hard bargain. As it turned out, it was a good appointment. To Harry's credit, he realized the importance of modifying Lem Putt's techniques, especially with the use of sandbags rather than tongue and groove planking. Nor was there any question of our latrines having a security latch or inward-opening doors to let in sunlight. Where Harry outshone Lem Putt was in the seats. Harry made the most comfortable lavatory seats I've ever encountered. They were specially shaped so that they gave support and comfort on both the sides and the rear. He even lined them with foam rubber for softness and warmth. As one of the lads remarked after using Harry's latrine for the first time: "By heck, Harry, men have been given medals for less than that!"

Our next task was to improve our general living conditions. Rats were our biggest problem but at that early stage it was left to men to adopt their own solutions, usually killing them with their bayonets. Another problem was the inadequate supply of candles. Even though most hours of darkness were spent on standing patrols or in weapon pits, our method of rotating these duties meant that men spent quite a few hours of darkness in their bunkers, and our ration of one candle a week was pathetically inadequate. Even when used sparingly, a candle never lasted more than two days. I indented for more but was refused. The QM sent back a rude message asking if I intended to set up in competition with Blackpool Illuminations. I complained to Earl Gray but all he did was accuse us of taking candles into our weapon pits, which was strictly forbidden. As our wireless operator, Rupert spent the whole of every night in the CP and he was so enraged by such a meagre ration that he posted the first of his verses on the platoon notice board.

The Good Lord ordained: 'Let there be light'
So man be not condemned to eternal night.
But due to another botched-up military scandal,
We flounder about for want of a flaming candle.

It was Animal Evans who came to the rescue. "Nowt to worry about, sir," he said with great confidence. "I'll soon get you more candles than we'll ever need."

I didn't question how he was going to achieve this, knowing that with the golden thread of thievery running through the army, the less queries the better. Within an hour, Animal reappeared. He had Kim with him, the young Korean boy. They were smiling and without a word of explanation the youngster turned out his pockets, producing candles by the dozens. It was like a conjuring act when one wonders when the unveiling of rabbits, pigeons, and artificial flowers will ever cease.

Candles were merely the start of their activities. In the following months, whenever we were in need of something, Animal Evans and Kim were invariably able to oblige. Some things they got for us were vital. Other things were less so, even verging on the trivial; but even trivial comforts and supplies were not be scoffed at in the front line. For example, Harry Wilmott soon had all the foam rubber and toilet roll holders he needed and Geordie Graham (our Catering Corps cook) soon had plentiful supplies of plastic bowls, saucepans, and buckets. Rubber tubing for space-heaters was also supplied and incidental things such as matches, torches, and spare batteries. The most prized items they procured were tins of self-heating tomato soup, made by Heinz--- their 58th Variety. They were delicious and a great comfort to men when on stag or standing patrols. However, they did pose a grave danger. Lighting the fuse of the internal element was easy enough (usually done with a fag), but if one forgot to punch a hole in the tin (and there were no instructions to remind one to do so) they exploded like hand grenades. It happened first to Fletcher. A loud explosion came from his bunker, followed by frantic screams. Harry Wilmott and Bertie Mee dashed out of their bunkers to see what had happened. They saw rats scattering in all directions and then Fletcher emerge from his bunker, staggering down the trench towards them. He was saturated in blood. They couldn't understand how a man could bleed so profusely yet still be alive, let alone able to walk. Then, working on a hunch, Harry Wilmott went up to him, drew a finger across Fletcher's face and examined his finger closely. He smelt it and then tasted it.

"That's bloody tomato sauce," Harry declared. "Not blood."

"Tomato soup, you twat," corrected Bertie Mee.

All Fletcher said was: "I'll get some bastard at Heinz if it's the last thing I do."

At first, I assumed the supplies obtained by Animal Evans and Kim were due to their personal cunning, but it soon transpired that they were mere pawns in something that went much deeper. In Korea, corruption ruled supreme. Every strata of society was riddled with it, and the Korean porters formed the bedrock of it in the battle zone. They carried all the supplies up to the forward combat areas and it was estimated that 40% of what they set out with disappeared en route. These porters were such maggoty-looking cut-throats that their dishonesty should never have surprised anyone. There were approximately 150 of them in each infantry battalion. Theoretically, they were too old for army service but in reality their average age was around thirty. They just looked old because of their addiction to opium and the dissolute lives they led. Most of them had been rounded up by South Korean police during raids on brothels and opium dens and they were little more than slave labour, paid an irregular pittance. This meant they either went hungry or stole wholesale, and since they carried all the necessities of human survival, including food, drink, and medical supplies such as morphine phials and anti-malarial Paladrine tablets, the temptation to capitalize on their cargoes was too much for them.

In the Dukes we soon had a mafia-like organization the same as everyone else, the brains behind it all being a fat, ugly porter known to everyone as 'Number One Man'. He had his own hut in the porters' compound and could often be seen sitting in a dilapidated armchair with his feet on a 42 gallon petrol drum, smoking a Cuban cigar. The likes of Animal Evans and Kim were a vital link in the set-up. They were the ones who knew exactly what was needed and where they were able to secure cash payments.

Before long, Kim was spending so much time in Dog Company that he moved in with Animal Evans and became part of the platoon. His instinctive commercial acumen was vital to us, but this never went to his head and he loved to act as a general factotum within the platoon. It became his home and we became his family. He was forever brewing up in the cookhouse and supplying men with cups of hot, sweet tea laced with rum, especially when they returned from night patrols. He became our collective houseboy and the speed with which he picked up English was amazing, with his use of Yorkshire expressions endearing him to everyone.

We came to value him so much that everyone chipped in a shilling a week by way of pay, a gesture that not only delighted him but made him a relatively rich young man, earning more than those pay-rolling him. We kitted him out with a cut-down uniform and a beret and cap badge, and the only proviso about his presence was that at the first signs of action he returned to the porters' unit. In fact, he never did. Instead, he went down to the Company Aid Post and made himself useful with Corporal Benson of the RMAC, a good friend of his from whom he pilfered Paladrine tablets, the antidote for malaria.

(A word of explanation: Kim's background. His parents had been farmers, fifty miles or so south of the Yalu River. They lived off a few acres, their traditional crops being rice in the valley, and ginseng on a south-facing slope. Kim was the only child, two elder sisters having died in childbirth. When the war started his family was unaffected by the fighting. It wasn't until the UN advanced north that they realized they were going to be drawn into the conflict, especially when there were rumours of a Chinese invasion.

To the majority of North Koreans, the Chinese were unacceptable. They meant murder and mass slavery and rather than face that the locals ran for their lives. During the shameful UN retreat from the Yalu, all roads heading south became clogged with refugees. Frequently they were shelled by the Chinese to get them off the roads. Tens of thousands were killed and many murdered in cold blood. Others were abandoned on the roadside to freeze to death. No one knows how many perished. Yet some survived and eventually reached the UN's new front line. There, they thought they were safe, but they weren't. The party which included Kim and his parents were taken aside by a South Korean Colonel and shot as North Korean infiltrators. Kim survived because he hid behind his father and, being short, the bullets passed over his head. He was the only one to escape. After that, he spent eighteen months wandering the land, fighting off starvation and hypothermia in the winter. It wasn't until he heard the buglers of 12 Platoon, as we marched off to Yong Dong, that he saw a chance to re-establish himself by attaching himself to us. Here endeth the explanation.)

11

A Narrow Escape

Our baptism under fire came on our seventh night on Yong Dong. Inevitably, it involved the Hook. The Black Watch had recently taken over from the American Marines who had suffered a torrid time for the best part of a year. The ridge had changed hands dozens of times with horrific casualties on both sides. When the Black Watch moved onto the hill, Chinese pressure increased even more. They shelled hell out of the Jocks and it soon became obvious that it was all part of a softening up process prior to another major attack.

On our fourth morning in the line, Earl Gray summoned an orders group. Stan Bennett (10 Platoon), Ralf Waugh (11 Platoon) myself, Corporal Bridges and CSM Howard attended. He explained that a spotter plane had reported Chinese troops massing in front of the Hook in awesome numbers. The Dukes had been ordered to stand by to give support with our Vickers Machine Guns and 3-inch mortars, and Dog Company had been detailed to send out a patrol to cover the ground on the Hook's right flank, in case the Chinese tried to infiltrate along the Samichon valley.

The Chinese had never done this before, which convinced the Earl that they might well do it now. He therefore proposed to send out no less than three fighting patrols, one from each platoon. For two nights we stood-by, all blacked-up, weapons well-oiled and inspected, ammunition levels checked, every man well- briefed.

Eventually, the order came through to be ready to move within the hour. The Hook had been shelled all day and it was now reaching an unprecedented crescendo: an attack was imminent. The 10 and 11 Platoon patrols went out first and we followed. Going 'over the top' in Korea lacked the drama of the Great War, except on the Hook. There was no question of being picked off as soon as our heads poked over the parapet. We just hopped over the trench wall and walked slowly and calmly down the narrow pathway between the minefields, and then through the zigzag gap in the broad belt of barbed wire. In the valley, we followed the line of paddy bunds and waded across the Samichon, getting soaked to the waist in the process. Then we followed along the northern bank of a stream that fed into the Samichon. This was an area of greater risk. The shelling ahead of us grew heavier and the flares soaring into the sky gave good visibility. We moved forward smoothly: arrow-head formation, moving in bounds of approximately thirty yards, staying in visual contact with each other and facing outwards in all directions when we went to ground. We listened for two or three minutes and then, when satisfied there was nothing suspicious ahead of us, off we went again.

The other patrols were well away from us, on the far side of the stream, nearer to the Hook. Our final position was on the slopes of a small hill. I arranged the lads behind some boulders, excellent cover if anything happened. Below us several small bushes were growing out of the top of a paddy field bund, or embankment. They were swaying in the wind. I counted them, knowing that later on in the night my imagination might mistake them for Chinese.

We settled down to wait for the battle to erupt. Ice formed on our soaked uniforms. We were soon shivering convulsively. It was our introduction to the agonies of winter patrolling in Korea, hours and hours of lying on the frozen ground, getting colder and colder and more and more bored out of our minds, agony that seemed to stretch on without end, which to start with we thought we would never be able to endure.

When the 2nd Battle of the Hook came it was a relief. It was at least a fascinating spectacle. First came a long roar of explosions, an artillery concentration far in excess of anything the Chinese had produced before. The hill became a kaleidoscope of weird flashes, orange-coloured spots, flying stars, and zigzag patterns caused by the might of high explosives. Distant guns barked at each other in a ferocious duel and American 155mm guns joined in like guard dogs roused in the night, once started, reluctant ever to stop. The machine guns and 3-inch mortars of the Dukes gave their full support and the tracer bullets of the Vickers seared over our heads before disappearing into the holocaust developing on the Hook. Small-arms fire shrieked out above everything and we heard human cries of warning and despair, terror-stricken voices of dying men. We even picked out the wavering notes of bagpipes as the Jocks rallied in the face of overwhelming odds. Then searchlights, manipulated by distant engineers, sprang into life, pin-pointing the Hook and beating against low clouds to create artificial moonlight. Three Centurion tanks, sitting on the peaks of neighbouring hills, fired their 20-pounders, their shells cracking like whips as they streaked across the valley and crunched into the enemy hills and forming-up areas.

In the light of the searchlights we saw Chinese infantry swarming up the steep slopes, struggling to get through the barbed wire entanglements, beavering away like battalions of ants. We could see them falling in droves but fresh waves of them kept appearing, apparently without end. They surged forward regardless, never giving their dead a second glance. They just ploughed on until they too dropped and lay still or slithered back down the hill.

We watched, aghast at such butchery.

It lasted three or four hours. Then things cooled down, soon to die away altogether apart from occasional single shots as survivors were spotted and finished off. We went on waiting. Our shivering was more pronounced than ever. Eventually, Rupert contacted Company HQ and asked for permission to return. It was refused. Earl Gray said the danger had not passed. The Chinese might still try a wide flanking movement.

Another hour passed and I could feel the patrol growing restless. They started talking among themselves and someone stood up and had a pee. Then someone developed a persistent cough and I had to hiss at him to keep quiet. Fletcher swore back, saying it didn't make any fucking difference and we were just wasting our bloody time.

The spirit of bolshiness increased as we became even colder. Men started to blow into their hands and flap their arms. One idiot stood up and stamped his feet. For the first time we came to appreciate the difference of being in the shelter of hills and the exposure in an open valley, down which the wind blew without let-up.

Eventually, Corporal Holroyd and Fletcher came crawling over to me. "See those bushes growing out of the tops of the bund over there…"

"Yes."

"Well we reckon there are more now than there were before. We counted them earlier on."

"So did I."

"Well how many were there?"

"I've forgotten."

"So have we. But they keep moving. Bobbing about like heads."

I could see the bushes clearly and they were right. They were moving. One of them stood up and there was a distinct outline of a weapon. This was no hallucination brought on by the severity of the cold. It was the Chinese, and no mistake. Fletcher wasn't one to hesitate. He didn't wait for an order. He swore: "I'll get that bastard!" and let rip with a long burst on his Sten. He missed by a mile. We saw his bullets kicking up earth well in front of the bund. The man ducked down behind it, out of sight. Then Fletcher's fire was returned. Bullets cracked around us and ricocheted off the rocks, pinging and zinging everywhere. We were soon involved in a fierce fire-fight. Everyone was blazing away. Then weapons opened up on us from our right. Bullets were suddenly coming from all angles. With horror, I realized we were three-parts surrounded. I yelled at everyone to keep firing.

"Rapid bursts! Rapid bursts!"

I yelled it repeatedly, urging them on. Each time I replaced a magazine in my Sten I looked around for a means of escape but we were trapped. The only route open to us was to go up the hill to a dead end at the top. All around me men were putting down an impressive volume of fire, but without any evidence of results. The enemy stayed secure behind their bunds, obviously intending to finish us off one by one without the risk of charging us.

Then a flare went up. A small one from a 2-inch mortar. Above all the noise I recognized its peculiar 'popping' sound, and its feeble light. I wondered where it came from. It certainly wasn't from Bertie Mee, our 2 inch mortar man. He was right beside me, firing his Sten.

A penetrating scream suddenly came from those we were firing at.

"Stop firing, you stupid bastards! It's us! Ten platoon. Stop firing!"

In the morning, Stan Bennett, Ralf Waugh, and I stood to attention in front of Earl Gray and Copper Bowden in the company CP. For what seemed like minutes the Earl regarded us in silent disgust. Eventually, he said: "I'm not going to ask any of you what happened because I am quite sure none of you has the faintest idea. If I asked for an explanation you'd only start blaming each other."

He was dead right. We'd already done that out in the valley, directly after we'd stopped firing at each other.

"I could understand two patrols exchanging a few shots," continued the Earl. "Or a nervous sentry firing at a returning patrol ... But for three fighting patrols of sixteen men each, all from the same company, to have a pitch battle that lasted ten minutes is something .... Well, only you lot could ever have done that.

"Captain Bowden and I watched from the front trench. Even from that distance it was obvious what was happening. Not a single Chinese weapon was heard. No Chinese bugles. Nothing! Just Brens and Stens. I watched helplessly as half my company did its best to wipe itself out. I stood there, knowing that I was the commander of the biggest rabble I have ever known."

He broke off, apparently speechless. Then he produced a piece of paper bearing notes. "Since you came back, Sergeant-Major Howard has checked your ammunition levels. You used two thirds of your Bren magazines and all but a dozen Sten magazines. You fired damn nearly five thousands rounds." Then he turned on me. "How many grenades did you use, Contractor?"

"None, sir."

"Mr. Bennett?"

"None, sir."

"Mr. Waugh?"

"None, sir."

"And none of your men did. You came back with a full complement of grenades. In God's name, how many more times do I have to tell you? If men are sheltering behind a bund, or behind any other kind of cover, you've got no chance of shooting them. Your bullets either go over their heads or into the bund. Which is why they get behind the bloody thing in the first place. So you have to attack from the rear. If you attack from the rear, they have no cover. So you throw grenades. They land behind them, at their rear, where they have no cover. So the grenades will blow them to bits. Can't you understand that? Well can't you?"

None of us replied.

"So you've got nothing to say? Any of you?"

"It could have happened to anyone," said Stan. "We'd been out there for five or six hours and we were frozen stiff and ..."

"Bollocks! It could only have happened to you lot."

"Well at least there weren't any casualties," I said.

The Earl swivelled round on me. For a moment I thought he was going to hit me. "No casualties!" he exploded. "No casualties! By Christ, Contractor, that's rich. That's the worst thing of all! I'd rather you'd come back with half your men dead, riddled with bullets, than for you to come back with the ignominy of having fired five thousand rounds without hitting a bloody thing. You're so utterly useless that you're no danger to anyone, least of all the Chinese. Clear out of here. You make me sick. And if you ever shoot each other up again--- which I've no doubt you will--- don't come crawling back to me unless you've got some dead bodies to show for it. You can shoot as many of each other as you like. You're all useless. Bloody useless. Not one of you worth a shit. Clear off!"

We saluted and departed.

When I got back to 12 Platoon I paused outside the CP. Rupert had posted another verse on the notice board.

'We're three raw platoons that went astray,
Woe! Woe! Woe!
We're three raw platoons that blazed away,
Woe! Woe! Woe!
How the hell we all missed we'll never know,
Ho! Ho! Ho!'

12

The Taste of Blood

Our blue-on-blue incident was followed by an event that confirmed our incompetence but which--- by pure luck--- turned out to our advantage. For a short time it made us the blue-eyed boys of the battalion.

It started as pure farce. Earl Gray ordered me to take out a patrol to check the minefields in front of the company, to make sure that they were properly marked by a continuous strand of barbed wire bearing red triangles at regular intervals. It was not an easy assignment. The company frontage was nearly a mile long, with dozens of small re-entrants and an abundance of dense undergrowth, all on a night which was inky black, with no moonlight.

I took twelve men and we progressed well to start with. The strand of barbed wire was in good order and we only had to replenish sections twice. When we completed our task we were on the far right flank of the company, with still an hour before dawn. That seemed ample time, until we got lost. The narrow pathway leading through our barbed wire disappeared without trace. We kept going backwards and forwards where we felt sure it should be, but we still couldn't find it. Normally, it would have been easy enough on account of the standing patrols posted approximately fifty yards either side of the gap, but both standing patrols had been withdrawn early through fear that they might fire on us as we headed back in.

Before long, we began to doubt if we were even in front of our company position. The more we scanned the outline of the hills towering above us, the more confused and doubtful we became. It never occurred to me to contact Rupert Sandwitch on the 88-set and get him to fire a Verey light to pinpoint the platoon position. The result was that we were still wandering about in the valley when dawn broke.

The lighter it became, the more I panicked. I was entirely responsible. I could feel the eyes of the patrol on me, cursing me for my incompetence. Within minutes it would be broad daylight and the Chinese would be bound to see us. I told everyone to go to ground and I at last got round to contacting platoon HQ on the 88-set. When they sent up a Verey light it showed us to be three hundred yards away from the pathway.

I should have ordered everyone to crawl back to the gap, but I decided against it. Because of our tiredness and desperation, I decided to make a dash for it. It was a big mistake. We had only gone twenty or thirty yards when Chinese shells screeched in and landed around us. Most of the patrol vanished amid smoke and flying earth. I saw several men blown off their feet and things appeared to be even worse when shells landed in the minefields and caused further detonations.

Miraculously, no one was hit and once we had regrouped and the smoke had cleared, I ordered everyone to await my command and then sprint for the minefield gap, only this time split into groups of three.. I was due to go with the last group, together with two bandsmen carrying a stretcher.

I gave the order for the first group to go. They made good progress but as they got near our pathway the shelling started again. It was like a scene out of a war film, with the heroes dodging through a storm of flying metal. The second group started off, regardless. They made it as well, and so did my third group. Soon, we were all running up the concealed path. Then two shells landed alongside the group directly ahead of me. An agonizing cry went up, the like of which I had hoped never to hear, a cry that struck terror into my heart.

"I'm hit! I'm hit! I've fucking had it!"

It was Fletcher.

The other two men in his group kept running. I dashed forward with the stretcher bearers. Fletcher was lying on the ground, his head rolling from side to side, his face contorted in pain. I was amazed not to see blood flowing freely and guts lying around the place. Then I saw he'd been hit in the foot. His right boot was torn and mangled-up, with blood coming from it. I did my best to reassure him but we didn't have time to remove his boot and apply a dressing. With shells still screaming in all around us, we simply grabbed him, dumped him on the stretcher, and made a run for it.

I was on the rear end of the stretcher and as we started up the hill the narrowness of the path slowed us right down. The Chinese shelling followed us with uncanny accuracy. I kept yelling at the man at the front to go faster, and Fletcher was urging him on even more desperately. Before long, he sat bolt upright, twisted his head around, and screamed at the man to pull his finger out. Then he turned on me, shouting insults of a very personal nature. Finally, he sat bolt upright and yelled: "Get fucking moving! Get on with it, you bastards!"

We did our best, but it was impossible to go any faster. Fletcher continued to shout. "Get bloody moving! What's the matter with you, you bastards! Move! Move!"

Perspiration was pouring down my face, flooding into my eyes so that I could hardly see. I felt sure that at any second someone would be hit by shrapnel, or simply blown away. Our luck couldn't last. We were bound to be hit. Fletcher thought so as well. Suddenly, he declared: "I'm not waiting for you bastards!"

With that, he leapt off the stretcher and sprinted up the hill. We were left with an empty stretcher and the sight of Fletcher streaking towards safety as though he was Jesse Owens.

I was none too pleased. When I reached the top of the hill I couldn't get at Fletcher fast enough. I rushed at him, as though I was about to clonk him one, and he cowed against the trench wall, obviously thinking that I was going to. Somehow I restrained myself. You don't call them bastards and you don't clonk them one either. All I could do was make my feelings known with some very down to earth language, much to the amusement of those who hadn't been directly involved.

Fletcher's wound turned out to be a deep scratch, even though his boot was a total write-off and his foot bled copiously. At the CAP, Corporal Benson put a bandage on it and he was back with us within an hour.

"Hey, Fletch!" called out Bertie Mee as he saw him approaching, "how come you didn't come back on a stretcher?"

The only good thing about the incident was that no one outside the platoon realized what had happened. Rupert reported the shelling to company HQ, but he assured Corporal Bridges that it was nothing more than 'spasmodic harassing fire' and nothing to worry about, so the Earl never knew that we had once again proved ourselves to be completely useless.

That was the first half of the incident. The second half came three nights later and was a resounding success.

The credit for this was Corporal Holroyd's. He was in command of one of the standing patrols. As he led his patrol back in just before dawn, he noticed a piece of white cloth hanging on the barbed wire at the entrance to our pathway. It had been tied securely, leaving no doubt that it had been placed there as a marker. It even had Chinese writing on it, like a laundry mark. How they'd managed to put it there without either of the standing patrols spotting them was a mystery, and pretty alarming, for the standing patrols had been no more than fifty yards away from the entrance all night. It would have been easy for Holroyd to have ignored it, or to have destroyed it to make sure his patrol wasn't blamed for not spotting the Chinese; but he left it exactly where it was and reported it to me.

My immediate reaction was to inform company headquarters, but Rupert dissuaded me. "Just wait to see what happens, Saj. It's a direct result of you getting lost the other day. And Earl Gray knows nothing about that. If he gets to know, you'll only get another bollocking."

"But this marker is bound to have some significance."

"Naturally. They now know exactly where we come in and go out.

And by putting the marker there, they obviously intend to do something about it."

"You mean come up the path?"

"Of course. Probably a raid. Saj, they're not playing games."

"All the more reason to report it."

"I don't see why. If we report it and nothing happens, we get two more rockets. One for getting lost in the first place, and another for letting the Chinese slip past our standing patrols. And if we tell the Earl, he'll make us set up an ambush out in the valley. And that's the last thing we should do. We must draw them in like a magnet, not go out there to meet them."

So I kept quiet about it. In the meantime, I saw Rupert refer to one of his books. He kept flipping through the pages, desperate to find something he could quote at me. Eventually, he found it. "Sun Tzu says here, 'Always read the signs the enemy leaves'. He also says, 'To wait for the enemy on your own ground is better than seeking him out on his ground'."

"So what are you suggesting?"

"Set an ambush halfway up the minefield path. Where the path opens up after the minefields and the barbed wire. If they try something and get that far, they'll be strung out in single file, going up a strange path which isn't easy at the best of times. A perfect spot for us to form a large semi-circle and get them from various angles. The wire and the minefields will have them trapped. And if they turn and run, the standing patrols can get them as they go back into the valley."

"Bit risky, surely …"

Rupert gave me a sideways glance, as though I was a hopeless case. "We've got nothing to lose. And if they don't come, no one will be any the wiser. But if they do come, we'll be a damn site better off trusting to our judgement than let a thick regular like the Earl muck it up."

"But the Earl will do his nut if we never say anything to him."

"To hell with him. We'll say we caught them from the weapon pits. Let's do it our way for a change."

I selected a dozen men for the ambush and sent a message to company HQ that we would be testing weapons that afternoon on the reverse slope. The real purpose of that was to have some target practice, during which I emphasized that they must resist the tendency to fire high. Also, I put far more emphasis on Brens than Stens, the latter being notorious for jerking upwards when on rapid. The other essential was to be properly blacked-up and camouflaged. Then, under cover of darkness, I was confident we could achieve surprise. Another thing I did (which will probably make

professional soldiers laugh), was to connect every man by pieces of string, so that as soon as anyone heard enemy movement he could raise the alarm with sharp tugs on his string rather than whisper and thereby run the risk of being heard.

When it was dark I sent out just one standing patrol. I ordered them to take up a position well away from the entrance to the path and turn a blind eye to any Chinese they saw, unless they walked straight into them. It wasn't an easy assignment so I put Corporal Holroyd in charge.

Once they'd gone out I did a final inspection of weapons. Then we went over the top and adopted our ambush position, knowing that we might have to lie there for hours. However, this time we were much better prepared for the cold with extra clothing piled on, including pyjama trousers as additional long johns.

They came just after 0200 hours.

Hurst heard them first and alerted everyone by pulling on his string. A second or two later I saw them. Then they were unmistakable: short and squat, in padded uniforms and peaked caps, their Burp guns thrust forward in readiness. They were moving slowly, intent on silence, watching their footsteps rather than looking ahead. Their leader kept half-turning, checking that everyone was following on.

I knew the lads were ready. Everyone had been tugging like mad on their bits of string. I felt like yelling out: "All right! All right! I know!", but of course I didn't. It was simply a matter of how close I should let them get. There were at least thirty of them, more than I had expected: a major raid rather than a simple intrusion or prisoner-snatch. I waited until their leading man was fifteen yards away. His face was flat and round, his features screwed up in concentration. When those at the rear were in sight, with their leader now not ten yards away, I yelled: "Rapid fire!"

The reaction was instantaneous. Brens and Stens spat out a lethal spray of bullets. My Sten vibrated violently in my hands and I was gripped by a feeling of power and omnipotence. I could see the effect of my bullets. The man I had selected kept shuddering and jerking about. Then he fell backwards and squirmed about on the ground.

The Chinese stood no chance. It was a massacre. They might just as well have been unarmed. Each one was taken out, just as planned. One or two at the front fired back, but to no effect. Those further behind couldn't fire on account of their comrades being directly in front of them. As their leaders fell to the ground, so the others were exposed before us, waiting to be flattened like targets popping up in a shooting gallery.

Later, we confirmed that each of the Chinese had been shot numerous times. In all probability the Brens' .303 bullets tore straight through the leaders and then killed those behind them.

It was over very quickly. A few of the Chinese at the rear, realising that their only chance was to break out of single-file, leapt over or ducked under the single-strand minefield wire and made a run for it. They disappeared from our sight, straight into the minefield. Above the sound of our small-arms fire, the general hullabaloo, and cries of alarm and exaltation, we heard them being blown up. In all, there were eight explosions. Then silence. There were no more left to kill.

The pungent smell of cordite hung heavily over the ground like heavy gas. Bodies lay before us in grotesque postures. None of us moved or made a sound, as though we expected something else to happen, a disaster we hadn't thought of, amazed that killing could be as simple as that. A gunnery flare went up and illuminated everything, breaking the trance. I turned to Fletcher and Animal Evans and motioned them to go forward to make sure the Chinese were all dead. Beside me, Rupert was lying flat on the ground, his face buried in his arms. Smoke was still curling away from the barrel of his Sten. I pulled on his piece of string. "Call up the standing patrol. Tell them to come back in. But be careful."

Soon, we heard them coming. I recognized the tall figure of Holroyd. I went forward to meet him. "Get everyone back to the platoon. The Chinese might start shelling. We'll sort out the bodies shortly."

The lads ran back up the hill to our trenches and assembled around the CP. It was as though they were expecting fresh orders to be issued. They were chatting and laughing excitedly. Beau Brummell was delighted, passing among them, slapping each man on the back in turn. He couldn't credit what we'd done without sustaining any casualties. Kim appeared with mugs of strong coffee. Beau Brummel went round them again, this time pouring out generous tots of rum which only exaggerated their excitement, with everyone speaking but no one listening.

I went into the CP and found Rupert sitting at the table, staring straight ahead, wanting nothing to do with the celebrations. "Call up company HQ and tell them what happened," I said.

He used the field telephone. Bridges answered and demanded: "What the fuck have you lot been up to now? Bloody woken us all up, you bastards. Earl's going spare. Not another cock-up, surely?"

"Of sorts," replied Rupert. "We caught a group of Chinese trying to raid our position."

"So what happened?"

"We shot them."

"How many?"

"About thirty."

"Dead?"

"As door nails ..."

"You're joking?"
"No I'm not."
"Fucking hell!"

We dragged the dead bodies to the top of the hill and took a closer look at what we'd done. Some wounds were raw and repulsive, others mere red splodges on their quilted uniforms. Some skulls were split wide open whilst others were unmarked with facial expressions betraying surprise and panic. As we made our morbid inspection, the full significance of what we had done struck home. There was a split reaction among us. Most men remained in a state of euphoria. They went by the old dictum, 'them or us', and this time it had been them. I'd never seen Fletcher so elated. "Better than a good fuck," he kept joking.

The bastard felt no compassion or remorse, only gloating. He kept going around the bodies to give them a kick, or prodding them with his Sten, as if to make sure they really were dead. Other men in the platoon (his sycophantic followers) were wandering around, making jokes about what ugly devils they were and how one had fouled himself.

I watched from a distance. I felt ashamed. Only a few moments before these lifeless lumps of flesh had been human beings, yet here we were crowing triumphantly. I said nothing, knowing how hypocritical it would be to start passing judgements. With the firing at its height, I had enjoyed it. I had been possessed by a sensation of power and pride: the vibrations of my Sten created within me a feeling of demented glee, driving me on ruthlessly. I was the one who'd kept screaming at them to pump more bullets into them; and with each man I saw go down and die, so my sense of fulfilment increased.

Now, looking around, the hardest thing to bear were the moans and screams of the Chinese who had been mutilated but not killed in the minefields. My mind throbbed with the same, repetitive wish: for God's sake stop howling and die.

I ordered the Chinese to be loaded on to stretchers and then Beau Brummell and I searched them for documents. It was a messy job which produced very little information. Rupert emerged from the CP and watched us. When we finished he said: "We're all killers now."

"I know that."

"Once you've joined the club, it's life membership."

"I know ..."

"Our only excuse is that we were made to do it."

I didn't reply. He had an excuse. He was in Korea under duress. I had no excuse. I volunteered. This was the writing material I was so keen to gather. Now I could tell the world what it was like to kill other human beings: complete strangers against whom I had no grudge. If I described it well, made it highly dramatic without being too callous, it would no doubt earn me good money. It might even be the basis of a writing career, even gain me a reputation, never mind that it would haunt me for the rest of my life.

When all the stretchers were on their way, a few of us were left standing around. Bertie Mee nodded towards the noises coming from the minefield. "What about them blokes, sir?"

I didn't know what to say. I wasn't going to order anyone to risk his life by trying to extract them, but something would have to be done. I decided to refer the matter to Earl Gray. I went round to company HQ and found him in the doorway of the CP, watching the stretchers trailing past. His face was a treat: flabbergasted was the only word for it. I went up to him and saluted.

"Dead bodies, Contractor. First you've ever seen?"

"No, sir. But the first Chinese."

"Right, you'd better tell me all about it. I've already told the Colonel that Dog Company has scored a major success."

When I asked him about the wounded in the minefields, he replied: "Well you can't do anything until daylight. By then they'll probably be dead. But if any are still alive, put them out of their misery."

"Shoot them?"

"What else? You shot the others. What's the difference?"

"These men are wounded and helpless."

"Contractor, spare us your grammar school scruples. After a night of suffering they'll be only too pleased to be put out of their misery."

When daylight came we had no difficulty in locating the Chinese in the minefields. Several were still alive, making pitiful noises. One was trying to crawl. His arms and legs were moving but nothing else. Hurst pointed out that if he succeeded in moving he would only blow himself up for a second time. Animal Evans replied: "That's what he's trying to do."

I called for volunteers. Fletcher stepped forward. He finished them off quickly and cleanly with single shots from a Bren gun.

Later that morning Earl Gray and I were de-briefed by Colonel Bunbury. Gray told me to leave all the talking to him, so I listened like a dumb cluck whilst he made out the whole thing was a well-planned and well-rehearsed Dog Company effort. Instead of "they" (12 Platoon) it became "we" (Dog Company), with our success attributed to our training before going into the line. Our ability to anticipate.

The Colonel was delighted. He led us from the CP to the officers mess where the Earl went through the whole thing again for the benefit of his fellow field officers who had gash jobs just sitting around under the guise of controlling things. The Colonel insisted that we should stay for lunch. As we made towards the dining tent, Captain Hawthorn sidled up to me and advised me that it was time I went back to my platoon.

13

A'hunting We Will Go

The killing didn't stop there. This time it wasn't the Chinese. It was the rats. Of the two, we regarded the rats as the greater menace. Stories about them abounded. Some were comical, just so long as they happened to someone else. It wasn't at all uncommon for the rats to gather round men whilst they were eating, like dogs anticipating tasty morsels. They loved American C-rations, especially chicken hash. Also, they had a weakness for tomato soup and would lick discarded soup cans so clean they were almost polished.

Most men tried their own methods of dealing with them. Harry Wilmott got Animal Evans and Kim to supply him with dozens of toilet rolls and stuffed reams of paper into the holes in the walls of his bunker; but the rats munched up the bog paper as though it was caviar and were soon watching Harry's every move again. Bertie Mee kept a bayonet fixed on his Sten and used the rats for bayonet practice. He rarely spiked one and when he did it made such a mess that he decided it wasn't worth the bother.

One of the most gruesome experiences befell Earl Gray. He was a natural snorer and spent his hours of slumber flat on his back with his mouth wide open. One of the rats found this intriguing and crawled up his body, on to his face, and then peered into his mouth to investigate. Every time the Earl let out another snore, the rat jumped back in alarm. When the rat's movements eventually woke the Earl he had hysterics. He flung the rat aside and then spent at least half an hour gargling with whisky.

To prevent any repetitions, he got Bridges and some of the Korean porters to build him a bunk on stilts, and as a further precaution he made them take it in turns to sit on guard at his bunk-side all night to prevent any more nasty experiences.

A favourite trick of the rats--- who had a definite sense of humour--- was to scramble along overhead beams and knock down pieces of earth on to sleeping men. They also liked to get inside sleeping bags and anyone who took his boots off, to give his feet an airing, soon learnt to give them a good shake before trying to put them back on. When Fletcher was issued with new boots after his 'wound' he left his spare boot lying around in his bunker and soon found that rats were nesting in it.

"The buggers must be fitted out with gas masks," said Harry Wilmott.

Eventually, the rats got so bad that Earl Gray called a special orders group. He divulged a master plan to sort things out. We would poison the rats; but the QM greeted his request for poison with his usual derisive laugh. "Earl! Rat poison is not budgeted for by the War Office. They would have kittens if they realized we were spending tax payers' money on killing rats."

The Earl called another orders group. This time he informed us that whilst the platoons would have to grin and bear the situation, he would send Bridges and his Korean interpreter (another Kim) back down the MSR in the company jeep to purchase a dog from a village, preferably a Terrier, a breed renowned as ratters. Earl Gray concluded that once the dog had done its duty and killed all the rats in company HQ it would be passed round the platoons on a rota basis.

(A word of explanation. Some may find the details of what follows distasteful, even un-British. Nevertheless, it happened, so there is no point in pretending otherwise. Just bear in mind that other nations have very different standards to us, especially with regard to animals, and that many British villains (like Bridges and Fletcher) are only too willing to adopt taboo foreign practices so long as there is money in it for them. Anyhow, I make no excuses. The rats were such a problem, and we were so desperate to get rid of them, that the ends justified the means. Here endeth the explanation.)

The following day, Bridges and Kim returned to Dog Company with an enormous, shaggy, young dog. He was more a cross between an Old English Sheep Dog and a St Bernard than a Terrier. As they entered company lines the dog was sitting on the back seat of the jeep, very upright and dignified, looking around with great interest as though he was an inspecting general. Occasionally he barked, as though by way of announcing himself. As is often the case with large dogs, he turned out to be extremely docile; a lovable old softy, with a tail that rarely stopped wagging and with an endearing habit of raising a front paw to shake hands with men. Earl Gray was delighted. He named him 'Rex' and declared Bridges to be Corporal i/c canine affairs.

Rex soon regarded Bridges as his new master and this pleased Bridges no end. Apart from Fletcher, Rex was the first real friend he'd ever had. The only trouble with Rex was that when Bridges pushed him towards the rats, he got down on his haunches, humped his backside in the air, wagged his tail furiously, uttered a few falsetto yelps, and tried to play with them, jumping first one way and then the other.

As a ratter, he was a total write-off. At first men were happy to accept this, regarding it as a joke, especially since Bridges had told the Earl that

Rex had cost £15-15-0, whereas in fact he'd only cost £2-2-0, with Bridges pocketing the difference.

However, men soon grew tired of Rex. He was a persistent cadger and was forever stealing food. Nothing edible was safe from him, not even Bridges's ready-salted crisps, bags and all. Before long he was eating everyone out of house and home and still regarding the rats as playmates. Mostly, he just sat around the place, only stirring himself to have another crap. Some of his bowel movements were the most prolific ever seen and Beau Brummell, who had served in East Africa and India, said they were on a par with elephant droppings.

What vexed the men most was that it was soon impossible to walk down a trench without being confronted by a pile of dog shit. Company headquarters began to stink so badly that men found it difficult to sleep, whereas the rats found it a fascinating aroma and large gangs of them would crowd around the piles as though they were tucking into a Sunday roast.

Very soon, Rex was re-named. He became 'Big Dolloper!' and stories of his nauseating habits became so legendary that no one doubted Bridges when he claimed that Big Dolloper! evacuated at least twice as much as he consumed. What was beyond dispute was the number of accidents caused by Big Dolloper! Ironically, the first to suffer was Earl Gray. On one of his rare night-time excursions into the trenches, he put his foot right in it. He skidded, went arse over tit, and ended up sitting in it. This so infuriated him that he added yet another task to Bridges's rapidly increasing responsibilities: corporal i/c trench cleanliness. He also ruled that since Big Dolloper! had turned out to be so useless, Bridges and Kim were to make another trip down the MSR in order to purchase a cat, which the Korean porters claimed were much better at killing rats.

This time they came up trumps. They returned with a large wooden box on the back seat of the jeep which housed a ferocious, semi-wild cat. It had dagger-like teeth and spat and hissed at anyone who went near it. It clearly had Lynx connections and given half a chance would have returned to the wilds. In fact, it was such a vicious creature that it came with a tight-fitting collar, to which a long wooden stick had been attached so that it could be held-off at a safe distance.

The cat's name was Tiddles. This suggested that in the fullness of time it might become a lovable little pussy, but Bridges took no chances. His technique with Tiddles was to attach its long lead to a substantial metal stake driven into the ground and then let it wander in a wide radius, having first declared the area strictly out of bounds to all ranks.

Soon there were dead rats all over the place. Or, to be more accurate, half-eaten dead rats. Tiddles turned out to be extremely fastidious when it came to devouring heads, legs, feet, and tails, and these remains added so heavily to Bridges mopping-up duties that he became distinctly bolshy. He even threatened to go on strike, claiming that a court-martial, on being told that he was company clerk, signaller, mess waiter, dog-handler, dog-shit warden, cat-operative, and also responsible for clearing up rat remains, working in an environment reeking of canine excrement and feline piss, would acquit him without hesitation. "In fact," declared Bridges to a group of men he was haranguing, "they'd probably strike a new fucking medal for me."

Eventually, Bridges had the last laugh. Late one afternoon he roused the Earl from his rat-proof bunk. With a wide grin, he announced: "Good news and bad news, sir. You know that dog you bought ... Big Dolloper! The one so useless at killing rats ..."

"Yes."

"Well he's turned out to be a killer after all, sir."

"Excellent. How many rats has he got?"

"No rats, sir. But he's killed the cat which kills the rats."

Like Bridges, everyone--- apart from Earl Gray--- thought this was hilarious. For days the Earl stomped around in a foul temper. He got no sympathy from anyone and eventually even Copper Bowden got fed up with him and was heard to say: "Earl, for goodness sake! Where's your sense of humour? You're losing the respect of your men."

This accusation struck home and the Earl decided to reassert his sense of humour, on which he had always prided himself. He put Big Dolloper! on company orders and charged him with first degree murder.

Big Dolloper! was placed under arrest and in due course CSM Howard marched him in front of his company commander. When he raised a paw, offering to shake hands, CSM Howard shrieked, "Stand still that man!" The charge against Big Dolloper was then read out and when he didn't reply it was interpreted as an acceptance of guilt and willingness to accept his OC's punishment. Eventually, having gone through all due legal procedures, the Earl found Big Dolloper! guilty and sentenced him to death.

This all added to the fun. The saga was getting better and better. It was even boosting the company's morale. Indubitably the British love of the ridiculous had triumphed and the Earl's sense of humour was restored. The news of Big Dolloper's trial spread around the battalion and became a highlight of the Dukes Korean campaign, recalled with delight at Regimental Dinners for generations to come.

However, no one reckoned on the reaction of the Korean porters. From the moment they'd first seen Big Dolloper! they'd eyed him with greed, their mouths salivating, dogs being a culinary luxury in Korea. When Big Dolloper! was charged with murder and found guilty their hopes and expectations soared. They saw nothing humorous about his trial. How could they? They had no sense of humour. They simply saw it as typically British. It confirmed just how detached we were from reality. It didn't surprise them a bit that people who opposed torture and demanded fair trials for North Korean infiltrators, and regarded Syngman Rhee as a villain simply because he looked after Number One, should extend their perverse sense of justice to a dog and go through the farce of trying it for murder instead of simply slaughtering the beast and eating it.

What surprised them even more was that Big Dolloper!, having been convicted of first degree murder, was put under open arrest, without bail, and allowed to wander around the company lines, a free man. At first the Koreans assumed this was because Dig Dolloper!'s case was under review by the Chief of the Imperial General Staff in London, but when Bridges laughed at this and assured them dogs had no right of appeal, the Koreans saw an opportunity that was too good to miss. Ever since Corporal Carver of the Army Catering Corps had gone sick with food poisoning, they had been in control of the company HQ cookhouse, so all they had to do was secure Bridges's silence with a bribe (he held out for the Korean equivalent of ten guineas) and then despatch Big Dolloper!, using the slow, drip-drip bleeding method favoured by the Arabs, thus ensuring that his flesh became tender and all the tastier.*

Once Big Dolloper's fate had been sealed, the Koreans sold his scrag-ends in villages along the MSR, and in deference to their British masters they retained the choice cuts (rump and fillet steaks and chops) for Earl Gray and Copper Bowden, with Bridges and the other mess waiters serving them up with relish.

The two officers would never have known the difference had not CSM Howard noticed the absence of Big Dolloper! and instigated a search. When he discovered a dog collar hanging on a hook in the corner of the cookhouse, he became suspicious. Although there were denials and protests of innocence all round, he soon unearthed the truth, as he always did. He then judged it to be his duty to inform Earl Gray and Copper Bowden of what had happened: that for the past few days they had been dining off the dog that killed the cat that ate the rats.

On being told this, they were both as sick as dogs.

In the end, the rat problem in 12 Platoon was solved by Animal Evans. He was the only man in 12 Platoon not worried by the rats. He often caught hold of them and talked to them as though they were pets and when I queried this odd behaviour he told me that his father had been head rat-catcher for the Leeds Municipal Council for over thirty years.

---

* *Dog tastes like horse, but more tender and a touch sweeter.*

"My father spent his whole life keeping them in check in the Leeds sewers. And when I got expelled from school, instead of doing what my Mum favoured and reading Law and becoming a barrister, I became an apprentice rat-catcher with Dad. It's a highly respected trade up north. "

"So how do we handle our situation?"

"Not by buggering about as we are now, sir. There are only two ways to get rid of rats en masse. You either drown them or you incinerate them. What you have to understand about rats is that there's nowt wrong with them. It's their fleas that are the danger. They carry the diseases. That's why it's fatal to kill a rat and then just leave it lying around. As soon as you do that, the fleas look for a new host body. And if they can't find another rat they are quite happy to settle for humans. That's when you're in trouble. When you get Songo fever."

"So we're best off just leaving them alone?"

"Unless you can drown them or burn them, like I said."

"Well we can hardly do either."

"We could burn them, sir. No problem."

Animal's idea was to dig a deep pit with sheer sides so that once in it the rats couldn't easily climb out. The pit would also have a cover over it which could be pulled back very suddenly, like a sideways-operating trapdoor. We would then entice the rats on to the cover by smothering it with chicken hash. A quarter of an inch above the cover would be a wooden bar to ensure that when the cover was pulled back the rats were pushed into the pit.

Animal assured me that rats would soon be attracted by the food. He said they were like sharks: one whiff of what they fancied and they appeared from nowhere in droves.

"And how exactly do we incinerate them?"

"Easy, sir. Once they're in the pit, we lob in phosphorous grenades."

So that's what we did. There was no shortage of volunteers to dig the pit, nor to chip in with tins of chicken hash. We had a couple of dry runs and then went ahead with the real thing. It took about twenty minutes for the rats to smell the great heap of chicken hash and then, just as Animal Evans had predicted, they came in droves. Frankly, rats moving en bloc (whole battalions of them) is about the most revolting sight I've ever seen. They thundered down the hill like a herd of miniature buffaloes.

Once they were scoffing the chicken hash, Animal ordered the cover to be withdrawn. The ropes were pulled and every last one of them was swept into the pit, whereupon Holroyd and Hurst lobbed phosphorous grenades into the pit. The result was staggering, like a fireworks display, with lumps of phosphorus leaping into the air. They burnt for several minutes and when all was still again, and the smoke had cleared, we went forward to inspect the damage. There was an appalling smell, but no sign of any live rats.

We repeated this procedure three times. It would be an exaggeration to say that we got rid of them all because the odd rat did appear from time to time. Animal wrote these off as visitors from other platoons, explaining that rats had friends, neighbours, and relatives, just like humans. We did, however, feel justified in following the Korean War tradition by erecting a large notice on the side of the trench approaching 12 Platoon which said:

> *"You are now entering a rat-free zone.*
> *Courtesy of Animal Evans."*

Ten days after the final cremation, we were ordered to move along the front line to a more active area, so I don't suppose the hill at Yong Dong stayed rat-free for long. A couple of times, while occupying other positions overrun by rats, 12 Platoon did a similar exercise, but where it mattered most, on the Hook, the close proximity of the Chinese made it impossible. On the Hook, we just had to live with them.

14

The Korean Winter Strikes

The position we moved to was in the middle of the Commonwealth Division, known as Chaktong-Ni (or Nae Chon). On our left flank was The King's Regiment and on our right the Durham Light Infantry. Dog Company occupied the right, forward position, directly opposite a notorious Chinese hill known as The Boot. The Boot jutted out into the valley and for over a year a succession of UN units had assumed that its isolation would make it easy pickings for raids and capturing prisoners. The opposite had proved the case. All those who ventured on to the Boot had received a bloody nose.

We knew that wouldn't deter the Earl; indeed, only make him more determined to show that we could succeed where others had failed.

We'd been on Chaktong-Ni two weeks when the weather turned really nasty: winter arrived with a vengeance, and there are few winters like a North Korean winter. We'd been warned about them, especially that they had been getting worse every year, with eminent world meteorologists forecasting the start of a new ice-age. We were soon only too willing to believe them. By God it was cold! Winds screamed and howled off the wastelands of Mongolia and blizzards blotted out everything, leaving four or five feet of snow and drifts into which one could disappear for good. At one point temperatures went to 44 degrees below freezing. Everything that was liquid froze solid. At times our eyes seemed about to seize up in their sockets.

Battalion transport was severely affected. Engine oil proved useless, anti-freeze failed utterly, and batteries froze so hard that the cases cracked wide open. From a personal standpoint it was even worse. We were reduced to moving around the place in slow motion, our movements deliberate and ponderous, as though we were zombies. Food became a major problem. The cookhouses were nothing more than open lean-tos and it was impossible to serve up hot food. Only the Heinz self-heating tomato soup proved up to it. They became so popular that Kim and Animal Evans spent most of their time cajoling Korean porters to risk broken legs and ankles on the icy and snow-bound tracks to bring up new supplies. The price went sky-high--- a tanner a tin--- but they were well worth it.

Harry Wilmott had all kinds of trouble with his latrines, especially the urinals. These were no more than wide diameter pipes stuck into soak-aways in the open, with sacking wrapped around them to form a filter.

When men used them their urine froze all around the sacking and stalagmites immediately formed, advancing back towards the man urinating. Fletcher claimed that because the length of his organ was so much above average, every time he peed an icicle formed on the end of it, and once he'd emptied his bladder he had to snap it off (the icicle, that is). No one believed him so he offered to demonstrate this phenomenon, but no one took him up on it.

Where the cold hit men hardest was on patrols. As we had discovered at Yong Dong, the valley was like a wind tunnel and no man's land was where temperatures plunged lowest of all. We changed the standing patrols every hour, but for men who went out on the ambush patrols there was no such relief. We pleaded with Earl Gray to suspend them but he wouldn't hear of it. He wasn't going to let the Chinese gain the initiative just because we felt cold. On these patrols time stood still. Our bodies shivered convulsively and we literally froze to the ground. When it snowed (as it did most nights) we became nothing but white mounds scattered about the paddy; and when it was eventually time to return, we had to prise ourselves off the ground into a standing position.

We were issued with white cotton overalls for patrolling, which made us look like troops out of the Russo/Finnish war of 1939/40. We just thanked God for our string vests, long johns, cold wet-weather boots, and especially the individually constructed space-heaters in our bunkers. Without these (highly dangerous though they were) we would never have survived. The trouble with them was that they were improvised, not made to a proper standard. More elaborate and properly designed models existed, but they were only ever seen in the rear echelons, confined to officers' messes and the elaborate CPs inhabited by the top brass.

Our contraptions had an additional problem. As the weather grew colder, and men turned them up as high as they could, so thick clouds of soot were thrown out and men soon resembled negro-minstrels. They were required to wash and shave every morning but no one ever succeeded in the battle against the soot. Tell-tale tide-marks were always left behind. Senior officers on visits from the rear were appalled, but no matter how irate they became it made no difference. Nothing was ever going to stop men sitting around their fires in search of warmth.

When the cold spell reached its peak, the heaters were incapable of throwing out enough heat, and there was a constant temptation for men to increase the flow of the petrol ad nauseam. Inevitably, when the drips gave way to a continuous flow, flames leapt out of the ammunition box and back up the tubing, and disaster was only a split second away. With luck, and swift action, the flames could be controlled, but when men were slow, or too bemused by the cold to care, fires frequently roared out of control, bunkers would suddenly be engulfed in flames and all men could do was abandon them, dash for safety, and disconnect the tubing leading from the 42 gallon drum as quickly as possible.

Usually, men got out in time, but not always. Once, on a visit to Stan Bennett's platoon, I witnessed a bunker going up in flames. The alarm went up very quickly and two of the men inside were able to escape, but two others, who had been asleep, were trapped inside. Their shouts and cries on awakening brought everyone running, only to find that there was very little that could be done. First of all they yanked the rubber tubing from the 42 gallon drum, but those trying to fight the flames to get into the bunker to drag the men out, were beaten back by the intense heat.

Then came a new type of cry from within. Not a shriek of pain, or one seeking help, not even one of fear; but a shriek of resignation to a horrible fate. A second or two later a man burst out of the bunker. He was ablaze from head to foot, his hair fizzing like the head of a newly struck match. The circle of men outside parted instinctively and he dashed through them, heading down the trench. When he reached the gap in the trench wall he plunged down the reverse slope, not knowing what he was doing, just running in blind panic. Men rushed after him. He began to slow down with every step, but his impetus kept him going, with parts of his clothing falling away. Before the others reached him he stumbled into the belt of barbed wire near the bottom of the slope. Then he lay there, motionless, still blazing, stretched across a single strand of barbed wire. Blankets, coats and other articles of clothing were produced and wrapped around him in an effort to extinguish the flames feasting on his flesh; but they were too late. Already there was the smell of roasting flesh and he had ceased to cry out in protest. Apart from the slight heaving of his chest and the quivering of his raw hands he might just as well have been dead. Men hesitated, waiting for someone else to lift him from the wire and expose what they all knew would be a horrifying sight. The strand of wire had sunk deep into his mouth, cutting through his cheeks to the back of his jaw, almost splitting his head in two. Men pulled him away as gently as they could but flesh from his jaw and cheeks slipped away and was left dangling on the wire. On the lower half of his face bone was exposed, shining with smoothness, only a thin film of watery blood giving them any protection.

I watched from a distance as he was placed on a stretcher and rushed back along the trench. He was dead before they got him to the Company Aid Post.

The weather wasn't our only problem. Due to the height of the Boot, parts of our rear slopes were under Chinese observation. The MSR approaching the position was so exposed that a long stretch of it was covered by camouflage netting. This afforded some protection, but many of our larger trucks gave off tell-tale exhaust fumes and became favourite targets for the Chinese artillery. Not a day went by when we weren't shelled or mortared.

In 12 Platoon mortar bombs were the greatest threat. The Chinese loved to lob them over indiscriminately and it was during this period that we grew accustomed to taking casualties and coping with death. When the first man died it was especially traumatic. He was a Bradford lad named Brown. He was some way from a mortar bomb when it landed and when he went down there was no initial indication of where he had been hit. Eventually, it was found that a tiny sliver of shrapnel had gone into his brain via his temple.

Men soon got used to moving about with one eye on the next piece of cover. Some had amazing escapes. Jimmy Birch had a mortar bomb go off right beside him. He disappeared in smoke and we were certain he'd perished, but when the smoke cleared he was unharmed, still standing upright. He looked down at himself in disbelief. Apart from his boots, socks, and steel helmet he was stark naked, his clothes scattered around him. All he said was: "The cheeky bastards."

During our first week on the hill we lost seven men. We accepted it as best we could, but our devastation must have shown. Copper Bowden made a point of coming round to see us. I had never rated him highly, but after these visits I revised my opinion. He had been at Arnhem so he knew all about death. On his visits he spoke to men individually, explaining that in war one just had to accept such things. It was no good feeling mawkish or hard done by. We had to realize that it could, and would, happen time and time again, that any one of us might be the next; and that the best way to deal with it was to get on with the next job as though nothing had happened. Never discuss it, never indulge in fond memories, never hark on about the waste, and never indulge in cursing the enemy.

Some may claim that this was an early form of counselling, but it wasn't. He offered no cure, no solace, only acceptance. He invariably finished his little pep-talks by saying: "You are about to discover the true value of a stiff upper lip. Apart from your rifle, it's a soldier's best friend."

(A word of explanation. He was right and we accepted his advice. It wasn't that we were indifferent or callous. Deep regret and sadness were always there, but we kept our emotions under control. Not for us the modern wailing and gnashing of teeth. We never allowed it to get the better of us. There were no outbursts of copious weeping, nor any desire to promote a single death into a national disaster. There was no mawkish day by day totting up of how many were dead. Above all, no one

attempted to promote the deceased from ordinary private soldiers into supermen who inspired everyone with their dedication and leadership. No one was made out to be an inspiration to the entire division and a legend in his own lunchtime.

We kept our grief private and would have been mortified if the media had orchestrated endless photographs of dipping Colours and newsreel shots of females in mini dresses dashing out into the road to throw wreaths on to a passing hearse. The battlefield has never been a place for banality and angst. It is a place where death is best accepted quietly and with dignity. True soldiers want to be remembered for the exploits of their unit, not personal glorification. Their stock-in-trade is, always has been, and should always remain, killing and being killed. To pretend otherwise helps no one. There was the case of a female protester at the time of the Falklands who carried a banner demanding: 'What good will my boyfriend be dead?' She needed to be told that he wasn't any damn good to anyone unless he was prepared to die. Here endeth the explanation.)

Our concern for our mates was best exemplified when one was wounded. As soon as someone was hit there was a stampede to give first aid, to stem the bleeding as quickly as possible. It was also a point of honour to minimize the wound, no matter how bad it was. It was routine to pretend that every wound was a Blighty touch; and incredibly even victims who had previously perpetrated this lie to others believed it implicitly when they were wounded. Mostly, as they lay on a stretcher, they welcomed their luck and joked about going home, even fantasizing about nurses and clean sheets. Yet so often they were dead before they got to the Regimental Aid Post or the local MASH unit. When a man died, Rupert gathered his personal effects together to make sure no trace was left of him before his replacement moved in. My job was to write to the next of kin. I aimed to be truthful, kind, and appreciative; and I had several letters back thanking me for having told them exactly what happened. Not one of them demanded a public enquiry, a written apology from the Prime Minister, enormous compensation, and least of all a demand that a medal be struck for his next of kin.

* * * * * * *

It was at this point that we had the curious case of Bill Oglethorpe. He was a jovial character who, on the troopship, had been one of the leading lights in our 'entertainments' and a rival of Bertie Mee's when it came to singing modern hits, except that he was a forerunner to Adam Faith in that you couldn't understand a word of his lyrics. We first noted his odd behaviour during our ambush on Yong Dong. He was one of the Bren gunners who helped to demolish the Chinese. After it was all over I noticed he was played no part in retrieving the dead bodies. He refused to go near them. He just stared at them. By the time we had them all piled up, he had disappeared. I sensed it was best to leave him in peace, assuming that the sight of so much blood and torn flesh had sent him into shock.

He managed the rest of Yong Dong without incident, but as soon as the shelling and mortaring started on Chaktong-Ni he showed increasing nervousness. He was always first under good cover and screwed himself into a tight ball and never emerged until everything was over. I kept an eye on him and when I mentioned it to Rupert he laughed scornfully. He claimed it was all an act and that there was nothing wrong with him. So I had a word with Brummell and he agreed with me. Eventually I tackled Oglethorpe and recommended that he went sick. I telephoned the MO, Doc Mackie, and explained the situation, requesting that he should arrange to have Oglethorpe transferred to a rear echelon. To my surprise, he returned to the platoon two hours later, together with a sealed note from Doc Mackie. In it, he said it was all an act, that there was nothing wrong with Oglethorpe. Whilst he was waiting his turn to be examined at the RAP they had been shelled and Oglethorpe had shown no signs of concern, not realizing that he was being watched. Rupert refrained from saying 'I told you so'.

About a week later, in the middle of the cold spell, I was amazed when Oglethorpe volunteered for one of Earl Gray's madcap ambush patrols. The night was one of the coldest ever and we went halfway across no man's land and lay there for over six hours. Nothing happened. For hour after hour our agony increased as we got colder and colder and colder. We shivered as though attached to pneumatic drills and we became caked in snow and ice.

When Earl Gray's order eventually came to return, it took us several minutes to unfreeze ourselves from the ground. Then we moved so slowly that it took us the best part of an hour to reach our bunkers. Later in the morning Bill Oglethorpe came round to the CP to see me. He said he was experiencing trouble with his feet. They had gone an odd colour and were numb. I had no hesitation in sending him back to Doc Mackie. This time he didn't return. He had frost bite. He was evacuated to the base hospital in Kure, but by the time he got there, gangrene had set in and they had to amputate one of his big toes.

It was a long time afterwards that I discovered Oglethorpe had worked his ticket. He had gone out on patrol without any socks on, knowing that that was a sure way to get frost bite.

When Harry Wilmott heard about this (much sooner than I did) he exclaimed: "Fooking perr---fect! That's the way to go!" and from thereon Harry never wore socks or gloves; but all he ever got were chilblains and blisters. He never even got 'Excused boots'. Poor old Harry. He was a born loser.

15

The Tuesday Morning Club

The cold spell had one blessing. We were able to take stock and reflect; and after Oglethorpe suffered frost bite Earl Gray relented and called a temporary halt to the ambush patrols. We even began to master our space-heaters and life settled into a steady routine. We learnt to tolerate our comrades' ugly mugs and their sundry unpleasant habits and characteristics, ranging from their smelly feet, to spitting and hawking, blowing their noses without a handkerchief, and priding themselves on thunderous farts and belches. There were petty differences among us, of course. Several men made a point of disappearing every time Bertie Mee pulled out his harmonica and both Rupert and I found Fletcher's repetitive threats highly irritating; and for his part Fletcher made it clear that he regarded us as a couple of stuck-up snobs.

One of the hardest things was the integration of more Korean labourers assigned to the platoon. Unlike Kim, who had become one of us because of his impishness, his willingness to be a general factotum, and his black market contributions, the other Koreans were dour, humourless, unattractive, and very often slow on the uptake. We found it impossible to feel any crusading spirit on their behalf. They were totally ignorant of democracy. To them, it was a sign of weakness. They took it for granted that anyone who ended up on top of the pile was going to make damn sure he stayed there. On one occasion our Koreans were trucked to Seoul for the day to vote in a general election. With Kim, I went to the jeep-head to make sure they got off okay. They were being organized by Yong Po, the senior company porter. He was an ex-Japanese POW guard and an arrogant bully. When I arrived on the scene he was shouting at a group of about 20. Every now and then he pushed in among them, kicked them, and slapped them. I called him over and gave him a good telling-off. Then, thinking I might have overdone it a little, I sought to appease him by asking him who he was going to vote for when he got to Seoul. He greeted this enquiry with blank amazement and replied: "How should I know? They'll tell us who to vote for when we get there."

Another thing to climax around this time was Rupert's verses on the platoon notice board. Earl Gray told me he'd had enough of them. I objected and pointed out that the platoon notice board was my concern and that Sandwitch's verses maintained good morale. We argued about it for some time, but I refused to give way. "After all, sir," I said. "Free speech is one of the things we are fighting for."

"Then I will do similar things and we'll see what the men think of it."

Nothing happened until St Crispin's Day. Then the Earl posted a message on all platoon notice boards.

'Today is St Crispin's Day. It was immortalized by Shakespeare. In one of his plays he emphasized the good fortune all soldiers have in serving their country, and how the idle men left at home come to rue not having served their country.

> *'And gentlemen in England now abed*
> *Shall think themselves accursed they were not here*
> *And hold their manhoods cheap whilst any speaks*
> *That fought with us upon St Crispin's Day.'*

On the 12 Platoon notice board Rupert responded:

> *'Behold!*
> *Yon shimmering dawn doth herald once more*
> *St Crispin's day!*
> *The day whereon the Bard, through noble Harry,*
> *extolled us on high*
> *To gather up proud English wounds*
> *And then plug up a hole and die.*
> *Hark Tommy!*
> *With mighty impudence I doth say:*
> *Stuff St Crispin's Day!*

> *Those whingeing Union bastards now abed*
> *Won't curse they missed St Crispin's Day.*
> *More likely, in some fag-bespattered loco-shed*
> *They'll convene a meeting and grab more pay.'*

This time Earl Gray deducted a month's pay.

The most unifying thing among the platoon was mail from home. This was delivered regularly every Tuesday morning and it sent morale soaring. Dour faces burst into smiles, and laughter could be heard throughout the platoon. Corporal Bridges brought the letters round and the platoon would be waiting for him, crowded around the CP. Bridges would climb on to the trench wall and sort through the envelopes and then call out the names and make pertinent comments as he handed them round. Like professional postmen, he was a past-master at deciphering outside clues as to the contents, but unlike his professional counterparts he loved to air his knowledge.

"Animal! Your Blossom's in full bloom again, mate ... Weighs a ton ... Sent you more dirty postcards, I'll bet."

"Fletch ... Three for you. Two from crumpet and one from Doolittle, Dally and Dawdle ... Another bun in the oven, is it?"

"Harry! Feels as though you've got another photograph ..."

"Mr. Contractor ... Your old man's on his travels again. Brighton this time ... Another Saturday morning post mark ... He's up to something, no doubt about it."

"Holroyd! Your old man has promoted you to sergeant. Been bull-shitting him again?"

None of us minded. It gave us all a good laugh.

We had five men in 12 Platoon who were illiterate, so either Rupert or I wrote their letters for them and then read out the replies they received. When our mail was delivered, they waited patiently so that Rupert and I could read our own letters first. With most of them they were the only letters they had ever received and they were so proud of them, and so tickled by the novelty of them, that they weren't bothered about privacy. As we read a man's letter out the others listened-in and the man concerned would interrupt with explanatory comments, such as: "That's my uncle Albert ... A right grumpy old bastard!" or "Eddie is Aunt Mabel's fiancé. He's forty years younger than her. When they announced their engagement Mum had instant diarrhoea."

These interjections made the letters all the more enjoyable for the rest of us. We became part of them. At times, the laughter over the illiterates letters became so raucous that other men drifted in to the CP to find out what it was going on, and after a few weeks this became so routine that we formed what we later called 'The Tuesday Morning Mail Club'. It was a gathering at which we exchanged chit-chat from our letters and, as far as I know, we were the only platoon ever to do it. It certainly drew us closer together. It was a good excuse to get everyone away from the confines of their squalid bunkers and enjoy a couple of hours of communal life, with everyone crowded into the CP drinking beer and smoking free-issue fags. News from home put us all on equal terms, away from rank and discipline. Camaraderie flourished and inhibitions were cast aside. The quieter, more timid members of the platoon were drawn out in a remarkable way. A good example was Willy Enright. For weeks he was a docile little bandsman, still only eighteen, never known to contribute anything to platoon banter. Yet on his first visit to the Tuesday Morning Mail Club he came out with a witticism which so amused the others that it transformed him. Fletcher read an extract from his brother's letter in which he sang the praises of his latest girlfriend. He claimed she had such enormously long legs that she was able to generate tremendous vaginal suction during intercourse. This was greeted by cries of derision, but Willy Enright amazed everyone by sticking up for Fletcher's brother.

"Aye, it's possible all right," he declared. "I remember seeing a film starring Cyd Charisse and she had such long legs I could feel the suction from where I was in the back row of the stalls."

From thereon he was one of the lads. He rolled off droll remarks at regular intervals.

Many of the letters we shared linger with me to this day. Others were very mundane, merely cataloguing what various relatives had been doing. Corporal Jackman's widowed mother only ever wrote about her cats and when her ginger tom died she insisted that he should apply for compassionate leave.

Joe Fairweather exchanged letters with his Dad that were the essence of brevity. His father's letters were never more than five or six lines and always started. "Are thee reet, lad?"

In reply, Joe rarely wrote anything but, "Aye, Dad. I'm grand. How's mother? Is she reet?"

Other letters were so full of lurid derring-do and jiggery-pokery that they were more entertaining than the letter column out of the Mayfair Magazine. Bertie Mee's sister featured every week. According to Bertie, she was a rebellious young tart with an enormous backside and boobs like gooseberries, in that they were covered in fine down. She was at war with her father, a miner down the Maerdy pit. He was a drunkard and a lecher, yet when it came to his daughter, Old Man Mee assumed very strict Victorian principles. He had a deep loathing and mistrust of her boyfriend, a Scottish train-driver named Jimmy who came from the Gorbals. He was so untrained in the niceties of life that he disposed of his French letters in their outside loo without even bothering to pull the chain.

Old Man Mee's letters were full of bile against the bastard and, since Bertie was his son and heir, his Old Man considered he had every right to know the intimate details of his sister's love life. In one letter, he wrote: "It's bad enough that the heathen bastard doesn't wear anything under his kilt, but he bloody near lives in Doreen's room. I reckon he's in and out of her more often than he is Cardiff Central."

In the end, Bertie's sister got pregnant and for a couple of weeks we were on tenterhooks, wondering if an engagement was about to be announced; but all Old Man Mee's predictions about the bastard proved correct. Doreen got a note from him stating that he had a new job driving the flag-ship train of the London Midland and Scottish, and after that he was always referred to in the Mee family as 'The Flying Scotsman'. His disappearance didn't matter much. Doreen (like the rest of the Mee family) had great ingenuity and at the Cardiff Shunters' and Wheeltappers' Christmas Party, she had a one-night stand with a fireman from Porth and persuaded him that he was responsible, so wedding bells rang after all.

My favourite illiterate was Harry Wilmott. Despite being the runt of the platoon, Harry had a girl-friend who was the envy of us all. She was not only beautiful but an intelligent, fun-loving extrovert. She gave Harry hilarious descriptions of what she and her girlfriends got up to at their hen parties and she always included a glamour photograph of herself which Harry handed around with great pride. It soon became obvious to everyone except Harry that she was discarding an item of clothing each week and was systematically treating him to a strip-tease; and being the lecherous young sods that we were, we never said a word, hoping that if we kept quiet we might eventually be treated to the full monty. Unfortunately, when she got down to her panties and bra, Fletcher got over-excited and spilt the beans. "Two more weeks and we're fucking there!" he exclaimed.

"Where?" queried Harry.

"Alice in all her glory ..."

"What glory?"

"Stark bollock naked, you pillock. "

"Nay, she'd never do that ..."

"Of course she will, Harry. She's sending you a fucking message, isn't she?"

"What message?"

"For you to give her one, you dope."

"Nay, she's not like that."

"Harry, they're all bloody like that."

From thereon, Harry slipped the photos into his map pocket before any of us could get a glimpse of them.

The ignorance of those at home was incredible. They had no idea what we were up to. Fathers who'd had military experience were determined to minimize our adventures and even those who had never known a bullet fired in anger insisted that we were on a soft posting compared with what they'd been through. Most of the Mums closed their minds to the risks of war. They dismissed the dangers facing their darling little boys by immersing themselves in voluntary work. Fletcher's mother join the Hackney Wick Town Women's Guild, a most patriotic group who knitted endlessly for the troops in Korea. We soon had so many baggy pullovers and ten-foot long scarves that Fletcher wrote to his Mum telling her that what we needed were garments to keep our extremities warm, so why not divert their mass production to nose caps and willie-warmers. His Mum wrote back telling him not to be so cheeky. "Anyhow," she added, "we've been in touch with Paton and Baldwin and they say there are no such things as nose warmers and patterns for willie-warmers were discontinued after the Crimea war when a Scotsman invented Jock Straps."

Some of the best letters came from girlfriends who thought they were the ones suffering hardships, not us. They were convinced that because cease-fire negotiations were underway the war was over and we had nothing to do but go on five days R and R in Tokyo, something that caused all of them great concern, having heard all about the Geisha system and nubile young girls who were an integral part of the famous Japanese steam baths. When writing on behalf of his illiterates, Rupert dismissed their forebodings by writing: 'Oh ye of little faith!' One of them wrote back incredulously: "'Oh ye of little faith?', surely you don't have Jehovah Witnesses out there as well?"

Ron Jenkins's recently-wed wife moaned about everything. She had no washing machine, no vacuum cleaner, not even a radio. To cap it all she had to do an eight-hour night shift at the Rowntree's chocolate factory and had put on 20 lbs and needed new clothes. Her greatest moan was about having to live with her in-laws, which meant being woken up five times a night by Ron's Grandad going to the loo. Once, after cataloguing the chores expected of her, she ended up by demanding: "So what the hell do you do all day?"

Ron, a soft, unimaginative soul, asked our advice. Unanimously we told him to tell her the truth. Next week, he read out his reply. It went:

Dear Mavis,

What do I do all day? Not a lot, really. Try to get warm, mostly. I keep an eye on the space-heater in case it plays up, goes out, or blows up. I get through 50 fags a day, and sup a dozen bottles of beer a day. And I read magazines I get them from a bloke called Bridges whose friend nicks them off the top shelf at his local Smith's. And at night we wander into no man's land where nothing happens, except that we get so perishing cold that we have to spend the rest of the next day trying to get warm, like what I just said to start with."

Corporal Holroyd's girlfriend was the naïve one among them. "It must have been a very big boat to take all you lads? I've always wanted to go on a luxury liner like that." On another occasion she wrote: "What was Pusan, like? All palm trees and golden beaches, I'll bet. You lads have all the luck!" Another of her misconceptions was how we lived. "I hope your barrack rooms are better than those at Halifax. Now you're a corporal, I expect you get a room all to yourself. And why do you want a hurricane lamp? Is it for when you're out in nobody's land looking for the Japanese?"

Because Rupert and I were privy to the correspondence of the illiterates, we felt it only right to let them have an insight into our letters. Rupert came from an interesting family of intellectuals. All of them, apart from his Uncle Jasper, had been to university, and his father (a lecturer at the University of the South West) would cover at least two sides of foolscap paper in tiny writing. Yet it was letters from his Uncle Jasper that caught everyone's attention. He was some kind of adventurer, currently employed in the winter as a harpoonist on a Japanese whaling ship, earning enough money to allow him to spend his summers as a cricket umpire with Sidmouth and the Old Honitonians. Originally, he had been in the Royal Navy and had served in Flanders as a member of the Royal Navy Infantry Battalion. This, he considered, qualified him to give advice on how to survive in the trenches. In the second world war he had reverted to naval duties and spent four years on Corvettes doing Atlantic convoys.

My own letters? Well, like Rupert's, they seemed very odd to the others. Most of them were from Dad and the thing that caused greatest surprise was his habit of calling me by my nick-name, the one I'd picked up during the London Blitz. All his letters started, 'Dear Din...' and when I explained that this was short for Gunga Din, Harry Wilmott was scandalized. "That's nowt but bloody racial prejudice," he declared. "You can't go around t' place saying things like that ... It's not reet ..."

"He's my father, Harry."

"I don't give a fuck what he is. It's not reet to treat coloured people like that."

"But he's coloured as well... An Indian. And Gunga Din was a hero."

"Like hell! He was a fucking wog. It's not reet, sir. You deserve more respect."

Other than that, Dad's letters aroused very little interest due to his preoccupation with the price of scrap lead. They only came alive when he mentioned the Jag, with descriptions of how he'd twice cracked 100 mph on the straight stretch at Lower Dicker whilst taking Miss Beaumont to a slap up lunch at the Café Royal at Bexhill. When he referred to Miss Beaumont too frequently I made a point of passing on quickly to Mum's letters. Predictably, her tomes were a long list of household chores she had recently undertaken, something which would have bored the others stiff had she not reverted to Spoonerisms--- the only person I've ever known to use spoonerism in writing as well as verbally. It took me some time to convince them that when she wrote, 'I spent all morning legging the washing on the pine', what she really meant that she'd spent all day pegging the washing on the line. Once, when enquiring if I was eating properly, she offered to 'cake me a bake'. She was also very critical of our maid. She said that despite paying her two pounds a week she was useless and spent her whole time skipping around the place 'dicking her fluster'.

The fact that the Contractor household had a maid brought a hush to the gathering. They became convinced that I lived in a different world to them. They were even more amazed when it came to light that Rupert's parents employed a butler, and the irony that Rupert was now my batman didn't escape them.

When all the letters had been read out, and it was time to disperse, we went off happy. Home no longer seemed quite so distant.

16

Back to Patrols

Once the cold spell was over, Earl Gray's thoughts turned again to patrolling. Throughout our 'hibernation' he made it clear that as soon as conditions improved, we were going to snatch a prisoner. This had nothing to do with the need for greater intelligence. It was simply that no Commonwealth unit had succeeded in landing one for over a year, so if we succeeded it would be a great feather in our cap.

Like a true professional, he went about things in a very methodical manner. He didn't intend to take any chances, knowing that if we fouled up we would never get another chance. The first thing he did was build a new bunker in company headquarters, adjacent to the existing CP. The Royal Engineers turned down his request for help, ruling that it was totally superfluous, so instead he organized the company into labourer gangs and worked us around the clock. It was, he declared, to be both shell-proof and rat-proof. He needed security and peace of mind if he was to master-mind a Dog Company triumph. Once the bunker was completed he used it as a patrol control-centre.

In the middle of the bunker was an operations table covered by a large-scale map of no man's land. Superimposed over the map were superb china graph tracings on which all standing patrols were shown, together with patrol routes--- be they recce, ambush, or fighting. Also recorded, in varying colours, were the suspected routes and destinations of Chinese ambush patrols. As Bridges put it: "All we need now is radar and asdic and we'll be well away."

The Earl spent hours poring over his map and referring to intelligence reports which indicated that in recent encounters the Chinese had come off best and were now dominating the valley--- something the Earl intended to reverse. After the control-centre had been up and running for a week, he called an orders group and told us he was now ready to proceed with the snatching of a prisoner. It would, he said, take at least half a dozen recce patrols behind enemy lines to find out how the Chinese organized themselves on the Boot. Only then would we be ready to pounce and cover ourselves in glory.

Stan Bennett was detailed for the first recce patrol. He was to be responsible for surveying the forward trenches of the Boot. Ralf Waugh was due out next and he was expected to find out exactly what happened on the rear, left-hand side of the Boot. I was then to sally forth and do the same on the rear, right-hand, side.

This gave me plenty of time to mull over matters and decide on who to take with me. As it turned out, I was saved the embarrassment of having to nominate someone. Animal Evans volunteered on the grounds that if I was to start wandering around behind enemy lines, I would need someone with his experience and capabilities to look after me.

Stan went out into the valley under a full moon. I watched from our forward trench as he and his companion strode through the barbed wire. They soon disappeared. Then it was a matter of waiting, constantly visiting our standing patrols to make sure they were alert for his return in case he wandered slightly off course. He came back six hours later. I was present at his debriefing. He had crossed no man's land without incident and when he climbed the Boot there was no barbed wire or minefields. When he reached the lateral trench near the top of the hill he discovered a series of open weapon pits, well-spaced out, about 30 yards between each. He crawled along the hill above the weapon pits and established that each one was manned by two men. His most significant discovery was a telephone wire connecting all these weapon pits. It was pinned into the ground on the top of the rear wall of the trench. Stan also established that the Chinese were never relieved and there was no evidence of any wireless communications.

Earl Gray considered the patrol a great success. It gave him an excellent picture of how the Chinese were organized and enabled him to make all kinds of fancy, coloured alterations and additions to his china graph overlays.

Ralf's patrol went out the following night. He also took several hours. On his way out he came across two men patrolling in front of the Boot. Every thirty yards or so they went to ground to listen and observe, before completing another stretch. He watched their movements closely and discovered that there were in fact two pairs, one pair based on the left of the Boot and the other on the right, and that every now and then they met up in the centre of the hill. When they joined forces they disappeared into the undergrowth for anything up to twenty minutes, obviously having a smoke. This probably accounted for Stan not having seen them.

Ralf slipped past them easily enough and went round the back of the Boot. Here, he found one broad trench stretching down from the lateral trench to the base of the hill, indicating that the Chinese, instead of living in individual bunkers on the rear slope, as we did, lived in a large cave they had created at the bottom of the hill. He saw plenty of movement with men passing up and down the central trench and going in and out of their cave.

On the right hand side of the cave (which I was due to investigate) he saw sandbag structures and a crudely-made lean-to surrounded by sheets of canvas: also, what appeared to be a cookhouse, due to the presence of a metal chimney. On the way back, he again saw the men patrolling in front of the Boot but had no trouble avoiding them.

Earl Gray regarded this as another success and marked up his maps accordingly. My patrol turned out to be an all-night effort. We crossed the valley slowly, crouching low, using the cover of the paddy bunds. We came across the Chinese 'warning' patrols and watched them long enough to confirm that they spent most of their times with their mates, enjoying a smoke. When we got around the back of the Boot there were no surprises. As Ralf had stated, there was frequent noise and movement from the cave area. The out-houses he'd described, and which I was to investigate further, were equally clear. The undergrowth was fairly dense so we had no trouble moving right up to the lean-tos for a closer look. The one surrounded by canvas sheets was a latrine. It smelt vile, pungent enough to excuse any closer examination; but Animal wasn't worried and insisted that we kept it under surveillance for half an hour.

During that time, three men walked over to it and relieved themselves behind the canvas, their grunts and farts putting its usage beyond doubt. When the last of them went back to the cave, Animal crawled up to the rear of the latrine and poked his head under the canvas. He came back grinning broadly. "Three thunder boxes in a row," he whispered.

We hung around for a little longer, until a fourth man came wandering over. We heard his Burp gun clatter to the ground. "I'll get the bastard now," hissed Animal. "Slip in behind. Clonk him one, and then bugger off with him."

I was sorely tempted. It would have saved an awful lot of time and trouble; and I knew Animal was perfectly capable of it. Then all kinds of complications occurred to me. We had no stretcher on which to strap him, which would have meant a fireman's lift all the way, something even Animal would find exhausting. Also, we had no back-up patrol waiting in the valley in case we ran into the two warning patrols. Most of all, if we made a cock-up of it and the man got away, the Earl would go ballistic.

Much to Animal's disappointment I shook my head and mimed that it was time to return to base. Our mission was complete.

The success of these recce patrols stirred up great interest in Dog Company, with everyone keen to see how things would develop. Stan, Ralf and I accompanied the Earl to battalion headquarters and had a lengthy meeting with the Colonel and the IO. We were questioned closely and the Colonel couldn't have been more fulsome in his praise.

At the Earl's next orders group a curious thing happened. He came over all democratic. He told each of us to make out a plan for the snatch of a prisoner, with particular attention to timings, numbers on the snatch party, and the role and strength of a firm base. Why he did this, we never discovered. It was so out of character that we assumed it was on the insistence of the Colonel, all part of his attempts to make his subalterns more assertive.

Anyhow, two days later we met again, together with Copper Bowden, CSM Howard, and all three platoon sergeants. We then presented our plans. Stan went first. His idea was to snatch one of the Chinese patrolling in front of the Boot. He suggested a snatch party of four men. They would wait until the two patrolling Chinese reached the extreme left of the Boot. They would then kill one and snatch the other. If the other two Chinese from the right intervened, they would be shot dead. He said the Chinese prisoner would be easy to deal with since the distance back to our own lines would be minimal.

Ralf put forward a plan which no one understood. It was more of a full-scale company attack than anything else. It included an initial air reconnaissance, an outflanking movement, covering fire, diversions, several artillery patterns, and the final snatch accomplished by means of a lasso. A horse and a dog also featured in it. Although their roles were somewhat ambiguous, it was assumed that the horse had something to do with the lassoing. When he concluded, Earl Gray asked a pertinent question. "Mr. Waugh, this dog you mentioned ... Do you want a Sniffer Dog or a Guide Dog for the Blind?"

There were times when one had to admire the Earl's cutting remarks.

After that, I presented my plan full of confidence. It would be difficult to beat the simplicity of Stan's idea, but it certainly had more originality. Indeed, it was breath-taking in its audacity. It had five great advantages: it only involved one Chinaman; there was no need to kill anyone; there would be no noise or commotion; we would be grabbing someone unarmed when they were least expecting it; and finally the prisoner would not be missed for some time, thereby giving us a good chance of escaping before any alarm was raised. (All in line with principles straight out of Sun Tzu, thanks to Rupert.)

I suggested that our snatch party (Animal Evans, Holroyd and myself) should proceed across the valley with a firm base. They would stop some way short of the patrolling Chinese and the three of us would then slip round the back of the Boot. We would head straight for the Chinese latrine and if it was occupied we would wait until the incumbent(s) had completed his (their) mission. Then, once the latrine was vacant, Animal Evans and Holroyd would slip under the rear canvas and take up suitable postures on the two end thunder boxes, complete with a disguise of Chinese-style caps borrowed from Korean porters.

When the next Chinaman approached, I would alert Animal Evans and Holroyd by means of our usual lengths of string. As the newcomer arrived, Animal and Holroyd would make a big business of tearing-up lavatory paper, thus giving the impression of being far too busy to enter into any social chit-chat with the newcomer; and once he had settled between them and lowered his trousers, and was clearly committed to opening his bowels, they would pounce. Animal Evans would knock him unconscious with a cosh and Holroyd would be ready to deal with any unforeseen struggling. The man would then be pushed beneath the rear canvas where I would strap him on to our stretcher. We would then set off with appropriate haste for the front of the hill, skirting well to the left to avoid the two patrolling Chinese.

My plan intrigued them: it showed in their faces. I wasn't surprised. I doubted if anything quite so unique had been suggested since Major Pat Reid and his escape committee at Colditz Castle proposed launching a glider plane out of a bedroom window.

I smiled around. Then, like an enthusiastic salesman clinching a deal, I added: "Sir! This really could put Dog Company on the map! It could become a landmark in our Korean campaign. On a par with Stanley Moss's kidnapping of a German general in Crete. And we could give it a really memorable code name. Something like, 'Operation Crap Snatch'.

There was no response, so I added: "It could make headlines in the Mirror, sir. 'Dukes Catch Chinks Crapping'. A sort of play on words."

"Contractor, do you think we're playing some kind of game?"

"Game? Good Lord, no! Sir, the Daily Telegraph would cover it more seriously. Something like, 'Dukes Strike as Chinese Evacuate'."

At this point Ralf ruined my presentation by laughing. He was so amused that he spluttered into his coffee and soaked those next to him. When he'd recovered, and his neighbours had mopped themselves down, Earl Gray said: "That's quite enough of all this nonsense. We're not here to listen to a load of utter balderdash ..."

"Balderdash, sir? No Chink going to the latrine will expect to be snatched. And even if he goes there armed, he would have to put his weapon down. And as soon as he's lowered his trousers, he's defenceless. If he tries to make a run for it, he'll only trip himself up."

"Is this your brain-child, Contractor?"

"Yes, sir."

"And who else? Not Private Sandwitch, by any chance?"

"Among others, sir."

"I thought so. So get this straight, Contractor. I don't want another word out of that bloody man Sandwitch. Whether it is spoken, written, recited, or in prose, Shakespearean blank verse, odes, sonnets, sagas, or even immortalized in endless bloody doggerel. Is that perfectly clear?"

The Earl wasted no more time. He dismissed Stan's plan with faint praise, totally ignored Ralf's, and added a further insult to mine by declaring it "piffle and poppycock" as well as balderdash. He then proceeded as he had always intended. He laid down exactly how we were going to capture a prisoner. It was to be the British Army way, the proven way, the professional way. He had overlooked nothing except--- ironically--- his own golden rule: anticipation.

The plan was very simple. The patrol would be in two sections: a snatch party and a firm base. They would proceed across the valley until just short of the Chinese warning patrols. They would wait until the Chinese had reached the extremities of their beats, then slip through the middle and proceed up the Boot to its lateral trench. There, they would select a spot between two weapon pits and cut the telephone wire. Two men would lie-up above the cut and the others would conceal themselves below it. They would wait for a Chinese wiring party to appear and then all but one would be shot dead and the survivor pounced upon by the two men concealed above the trench. Once the victim was rendered unconscious a message would be sent over the 31-set: the code word, "Bingo!" On receiving this message, the firm base at the bottom of the Boot would open fire at the Chinese warning patrols, allowing the snatch party a clear path back to our own lines.

Stan was to command the snatch party and Corporal Bridges would also accompany them as the signaller, operating the specially adapted 31-set. I was put in charge of the firm base. I would have stretcher-bearers with me and as soon as the prisoner arrived, he was to be strapped to a stretcher and rushed back to Dog Company.

On the night, there was great tension. The entire company planned to watch from the front trenches. It was our biggest test yet and everyone was confidently forecasting another triumph. Everything went smoothly right up to the moment when the snatch party cut the telephone wire and started their wait for the Chinese wiring-party. Then, with a twist of fate that so often affects these things, the Chinese decided to save time by sending out two wiring parties. Not knowing where the break might be, they set off in opposite directions around the hill.

The wiring party from the right appeared first. All of them were shot dead except for the last man. He was jumped upon and coshed. The noise this caused raised the alarm with the second Chinese wiring party, approaching from the left. They sprinted forward and were just in time to see the snatch party manhandling their prisoner out of the trench and down the hill. All that was left of the British raiders was Bridges. He was standing in the trench with his back to them, his headphones clamped over his ears, shouting into his hand-set: "Able One. Bingo! Do you read me, over? I say again, Bingo! Do you read me ..."

Stan's snatch party reached my firm base without trouble. We strapped the prisoner on a stretcher and dashed off towards Dog company lines.

There was some desultory small-arms fire from the top of the Boot, but nothing which caused any danger. Soon, we were all back in our own lines, cheered on by those watching. Everyone was euphoric at having completed a successful operation.

However, once we'd sorted ourselves out, the prisoner was found to be dead. He had been so severely coshed that he'd stood no chance. This was a disappointment, especially since the only information from his personal effects was that he was married with five children.

Earl Gray was so overwrought by this that he ordered everyone back to their bunkers, with a full de-briefing in the morning. At this gathering, we went through every aspect of the operation, but it wasn't until the Earl queried why the code word 'Bingo' had never been received by company HQ that Bridges was found to be missing. Those who shared a bunker with him said he hadn't been seen since he'd left for the Boot.

CSM Howard called for volunteers for a search party. When no one volunteered, he ordered a section of 10 Platoon to search the area. This was unsuccessful so they spent the rest of the day scanning no man's land through binoculars; but there was no sign of Bridges. He had vanished. When all hope was abandoned, it was assumed he had been killed by a stray bullet. So we ended up with a dead Chinaman in lieu of Bridges. Everyone, apart from Fletcher, considered it to be a very fair swap.*

In fact, Bridges was still alive. When the Armistice was signed, he was the first UN prisoner-of-war to be exchanged. When asked by a reporter how he was taken prisoner, he replied: "I went on a snatch patrol and got fucking snatched, didn't I?" The last I saw of Bridges was on the troopship returning to the UK. There were numerous ex-prisoners on board and those who had been brain-washed and co-operated with the Chinese were so unpopular that their 'comrades' threw them overboard as we pulled out of Hong Kong harbour. When I arrived on the scene, Bridges and the others were being rescued by sampans. The trooper sailed on. Later, an official report claimed that Bridges and his mates missed the trooper because they'd got drunk on-shore. Don't believe a word of it!

17

Murder Most Foul

After the disappointment of our snatch patrol there was a lull in the company's activities. Nothing much was seen of the Earl and it was reported back by Corporal Turnbull (the new company clerk) that he spent most of his time poring over his map and china graph overlays in the control-centre. It sounded ominous.

Eventually, it was the Chinese who took the initiative, and they did it in a very curious way. Their real enemy in Korea was America and throughout the war (with the exception of key hills such as the Hook) they concentrated on knocking hell out of the Yanks and leaving the rest of us in relative peace. They regarded the nations fighting alongside the Americans as their stooges and they often tried to exploit this by driving a wedge between us with psychological warfare. There was nothing revolutionary about that, of course, such tactics being as old as war itself as *'The Art of War'* (551-496 BC) proves beyond doubt. In the recent wars in Iraq and Afghan, this has become known as 'Winning the hearts and minds of people', but it all amounts to the same thing. Every evening the Chinese mounted loud speakers on their forward slopes and bombarded us with music, songs, and long spiels of propaganda.

To start with we were suspicious, fearing that it might be a cover for raids, or a ploy to attract us to our forward trenches so that they could shell us. When none of these things happened men settled down in their weapon pits or on their standing patrols and enjoyed this new form of entertainment. The songs were especially interesting, sort of updated versions of Tokyo Rose songs. Most of the words (although in English) were indecipherable so we amused ourselves by substituting our own lyrics. They were foul and unrepeatable, the best ones coming from Bertie Mee who had a definite talent for pornography. One of his efforts became so popular that for days most of us went around singing it. The first line went:

> *"Me--- I love your yo yo!"*

When the Chinese reverted to straight verbal propaganda they got their tonsils in a terrible twist. They used various misnomers and couldn't distinguish between the letters 'l' and 'r', making it quite common for their loudspeakers to blare out such things as:

> *"Blitish sodders! Why you orways ricking Yanky bracksides?"*

Or

"Blitish sodders! We orso velly democlatic. We orways having erections."

We got so used to this harmless entertainment that we began to feel a certain fondness towards the Chinese. "Good old Chinky!" became a commonly expressed sentiment.

Then the Chinese propaganda took a more sinister turn. They gave up broadcasting and took to planting banners in front of our positions. On the first occasion, dawn broke to reveal four banners stretching across the entire company frontage, all of them pleading with us not to be Yanky cannon-fodder. They had stuck them firmly into the ground, situated just in front of our minefields and barbed wire. No one could work out how they'd done this undetected. They put the Earl in a flat spin. He held an orders group and read us the riot act about our standing patrols being slack and in need of far greater vigilance. Then, when still more banners appeared, he went round every platoon and repeated his riot act on a more personal level. When the banners continued to appear, the Earl ordered platoon sergeants to go out on standing patrols, and platoon commanders were made to visit each patrol at least twice a night. Yet the banners kept appearing.

How the Chinese were doing this was solved by accident. Stan, Ralf, and I had occasion to visit company headquarters whilst Earl Gray and Copper Bowden were at battalion, and Corporal Turnbull suggested that we had a good look around the control-centre with all its maps and overlays. We were duly impressed and Stan happened to remark on the big gap between our frontage and the companies on our flanks. Looking into this more closely, he also realized that our standing patrols were going so far out into no man's land that the Chinese were able to go round our flanks and along a channel between the standing patrols and our barbed wire.

When the Earl returned from battalion, Corporal Turnbull mentioned this to him. He studied his map closely and then called an emergency orders group. As we assembled he was looking very pleased with himself and greeted us with announcement: "Gentleman! The problem is solved. I have discovered the Chinese Channel."

He then ordered 10 and 11 Platoons to drop everything and prepare to set-up ambushes at either end of the channel as soon as it was dark. In the dead of night, around 0300 hours, Corporal Jackman burst into my CP to report heavy small-arms fire coming from both flanks. By the time I got round to the front trench, it was all over. In the morning we learnt that the Chinese had been caught red-handed at both ends of their channel. Fifteen had been killed, for the loss of two men in 10 Platoon.

Three of their banners had been captured and the Earl sent one round to each platoon for inspection. I made full use of my Baby Brownie by taking snaps of several groups, each posing as though they had captured it.

Shortly afterwards we had what I've always regarded as our worst experience in Korea. At an orders group, Earl Gray announced a new divisional scheme to reinforce each platoon with six soldiers from the ROK 7th Division. We were immediately suspicious of the idea. I voiced our main fear: "Will these Gooks be able to speak English, sir?"

"No, I don't suppose they will."

"Then the whole thing will be a disaster."

"I agree," said Ralf. "The Gooks are only any good as porters."

"One thing you'd all better get quite clear from the start," said Earl Gray. "From now on, no one is ever again to refer to them as 'Gooks'. They are Katcoms. Anyone who calls them 'Gooks' will be punished. And I don't care who it is."

"What does Katcoms stand for?" asked Stan.

"I've no idea. And it doesn't matter a damn."

"Sounds like a typical piece of political meddling," I observed.

"No it's not! It's an attempt to help them get up to standard ..."

"Does that mean they're not properly trained, sir?"

"No it doesn't! And once the Gooks are here ..."

"Katcoms, sir," corrected CSM Howard.

"Yes, sorry ... Katcoms ... And once the Katcoms are here you must treat them like all other members of your platoons."

"But if they're not trained, and can't speak English ..."

"Contractor! Just for once, try to co-operate instead of continually making difficulties. It's going to happen whether you like it or not. And there's another thing. Next week a new Squadron of Centurion tanks will be joining the brigade. The Royal Inniskilling Dragoon Guards are going back to the UK. The fresh unit attached to us will be commanded by Lieutenant Patrick O'Hara of the Irish Hussars ... "

"Will he be able to speak English, sir?" I asked.

"If you can, Contractor, I see no reason why he shouldn't be able to."

"Touché!" exclaimed Stan and everyone had a good laugh.

As anticipated, the arrival of the Katcoms caused chaos. None of them spoke English and they'd had no proper training. They were aged around sixteen, uneducated and mainly straight from orphanages; kids who had already lost everything, just as Kim had. They wandered around the platoon in a daze. They couldn't stomach our rations and yearned for rice. Even the tomato soups made them sick and several nearly killed themselves by doing a Fletcher by forgetting to puncture the tins before lighting the fuses. Worst of all, they had very little idea of personal hygiene and Harry Wilmott's beautiful lavatory seats were fouled so often that he threatened to declare the latrines out of bounds to all Gooks. Likewise, because of the lack of any Catterick-style training, they had no conception of general tidiness. They scattered sweet papers, fag ends, and God knows what else, all over the place, and they urinated whenever and wherever it took their fancy. The rats loved it, but that didn't worry the Katcoms. Unlike us, they were indifferent to the rats.

Every morning our Katcoms reported to the CP for basic instructions in aiming and firing weapons, how to clean and maintain them, and the importance of keeping their safety catches on at all times. I also got Kim to assure them that until they were more settled, they would be exempt from patrols. However, I made it equally clear that they had to do their full share of stags in the weapon pits.

It was this last point that caused the trouble.

One of them kept falling asleep while on stag duty. For a time, Corporal Holroyd turned a blind eye to it. He merely woke him up and told him not to let it happen again. Eventually, when the Katcom showed no improvement, Holroyd got Kim to explain the seriousness of his offence. When this failed to bring any improvement, Holroyd reported the matter to Beau Brummell and myself. We likewise failed to make any impression on the lad. He became sullen and sulky and in the end I reported the matter to Earl Gray. He asked the ROK 7th Division to send round a Liaison Officer to sort things out.

After a couple of days, two Korean liaison officers appeared, both majors. They came round to 12 Platoon in the early afternoon when most of us were asleep, having been out on patrol all night. Holroyd was holding the fort and he simply called the Katcom around and left him with the liaison officers.

The first I knew of trouble was Holroyd shaking me violently. "It's the young Katcom, sir," said Holroyd. "Come quickly!"

"What's happened?"

Holroyd didn't answer. He was too upset to reply. He just caught hold of my sleeve and yanked me out of the CP, through the trenches, and down the rear slope. Suddenly, he stopped. A few yards ahead were fresh diggings. Soil was all over the place. It was an open grave. I looked down into it and there was the Katcom. He was dead: shot through the back of his head.

"Those Korean bastards!" said Holroyd.

"They shot him?"

"What the hell does it look like?"

"But why?"

"Because that's the way the bastards operate. Why we're fighting for them, I'll never know."

"Where are they now?"

"Gone! They shot him and then just buggered off. Not a word. I heard a shot and came down to find out what it was. Then I saw them pissing off down the trench. So I came straight over to tell you."

"Right. They can't get away with that."

I got straight in touch with Earl Gray on the field telephone. When I told him what had happened he wasn't inclined to believe me, suggesting that it had probably been an accident; so I challenged him to come round to see for himself. Holroyd and I waited for him and took him straight down the hill to the grave. Lying in it, pathetically twisted and blood-stained, was the Katcom, minus half his head. It was such a pointless waste of a young life that we were silent, nonplussed.

Earl Gray didn't say anything until we got back to my CP. "Get someone to take the body to battalion headquarters. I'll tell them what's happened. Then they can arrange for a proper burial. It'll be up to the Colonel to push for some kind of action."

We had no major patrols going out that night, but I was kept busy visiting the standing patrols. Around 0200 hours there was a sudden flap. Charlie Company clashed with a Chinese patrol. It wasn't really anything to do with us, but we had to monitor the development on our 88-set and be alert to the possibility of the Chinese wandering into our frontage. Two hours later Earl Gray came over the field telephone and told me to report to his CP right away. I could tell by his slurred words that he'd been drinking heavily. When I reached the control-centre he was alone, sitting at the map table with two whisky bottles in front of him. One was empty, the other heading that way.

"Sit down," he ordered.

I sat and waited. He finished off a tumbler of whisky and replenished it. "I thought I'd tell you what action has been taken against the Korean liaison officers. They've been posted to another brigade ..."

"You call that action?" He ignored me. He got up and paced about the bunker. I was determined not to let the matter pass. "Sir, I insist that you have those two men court-martialled. Charged with murder ..."

"Their punishment has got nothing to do with me."

"They committed murder in your company. In my platoon, for Christ's sake!"

"Don't tell me what to do, Contractor ..."

"But it was murder!"

"For God's sake stop calling it murder."

"But that what it was ... In my platoon ..."

"That boy was no more than a temporary secondment to your platoon. He was a Korean soldier. And every army has its own code of discipline. How the Koreans deal with their men is their business. And that is their punishment for men sleeping while on stag. It's hardly new."

"It's years out of date, as you well know. They're just barbaric."

"Nonsense! You're getting everything out of proportion, Contractor. We have done everything we can by way of protest and insisting on appropriate action ..."

"You mean there's been a whitewash."

He ignored me. He poured himself another drink, finishing off the second bottle of whisky. Then he reverted to pacing about the bunker. "You probably think I'm a callous bastard, Contractor ..."

I didn't respond, but it was exactly what I thought.

"Well I'm not. I'm just as appalled as you are by what happened. Do you think I enjoy seeing a young boy shot like that? Well do you?"

"No, sir."

"Damn right I don't. But I am not going to get all hysterical about it. In war, people die all the time. Do you know why the Russian infantry was so good during the war?"

"No idea ... And I couldn't give a damn ..."

"It was because at the rear of each battalion was a squad of enforcers. It was their job to shoot those in front if they didn't press home the attacks ... Anyone who faltered got shot. That was their discipline. And it worked. And no one has ever criticized them for it. It was their business. And at times British discipline was not far short of that. Especially in Burma..."

"I'm not concerned with what went on in World War II ...

"Sit down, Contractor ..."

"I am sitting down."

"Then keep quiet. You're just an ignorant kid who knows nothing. So just listen."

He was still pacing about, running his hands through his hair. He paused to rummage around in a cupboard for a fresh bottle of whisky. As he talked he opened it and poured another drink. "During the war I was a Chindit. And in the Chindits discipline was everything. During our third sortie we had so many casualties that I ended up doing a brigadier's job. As a captain, I was in command of a column. And what we went through is something you will never understand. No one who wasn't there ever will. One man--- a good man--- became so desperate that he deserted. Walked off into the jungle. He thought he could survive, or find a village in which the Burmese would look after him. The poor bastard was at the end of his tether. The same as many men were. It was only our training and discipline that stopped others doing the same thing.

Anyhow, about a week later he came staggering back into our lines, purely by accident. He was in an appalling state. Half starved, almost eaten alive by every ant, leach, and other filthy pest in the jungle. His head was like a bloated melon. He had no boots and his feet and legs were covered in cuts and sores. And ironically he thought he was safe at last. He thought we'd just take him back in. He couldn't believe it when I convened a field court-martial and charged him with desertion in the face of the enemy. I did it properly ... Legally ... The court-martial board was myself and the only other four officers left in the column. And we found him guilty. Unanimously. And there was only one punishment. And I carried it out. I executed him. Lawfully! I shot him through the back of the head whilst he was kneeling down. Just like that young Gook was shot."

The Earl stopped pacing about. He halted at the doorway, yanked the blanket aside, and stared out into the night. "Do you think that was easy, Contractor? Do you think I enjoyed doing that?"

"No, of course not."

"Damn right I didn't. But I did it because I had no choice. And not one man in the column questioned my action."

He came back to the table, sat down, and poured himself another whisky. The bottle rattled against his glass. He looked directly at me, searching my eyes, but I doubted if he even knew who he was talking to. He was miles away, scavenging in the past, reliving traumas that would never leave him. I began to feel sorry for him. In my ignorance I assumed that he was racked by guilt, that he spent every moment of his life regretting the moment when he'd killed one of his own men.

I was completely wrong. He smiled: a bitter, twisted smile. "I did it, Contractor, and I'd do it again. It has never worried me one iota. I've never lost a wink of sleep over it. The man deserved to die. I simply carried out our code of discipline. If I hadn't, we'd have been finished. Just a defeated rabble. But do you know what does torment me?"

"No, sir."

"When we got back to India, there was an court of enquiry. And they reprimanded me for what I'd done. They said I was callous and lacked compassion ... That in the circumstances the execution was inhuman and unjustified. Miles away, in their New Delhi arm chairs, they had the nerve to sit in judgement on me. But they took no direct action. Because they couldn't. I'd done everything legally, according to the book. So the vindictive bastards inserted snide and highly critical remarks on my army record--- my next fitness report--- knowing it would be held against me for evermore. That it would ruin my career. That I'd never get beyond being a bloody pear-shaped major. A failure ... God, those bastards! They had no idea what it was like to be a Chindit ...."

He paused, took another drink, and stumbled slightly as he resumed pacing about. "Contractor, do you realize that really I'm the most senior officer in this battalion? In fact, in the whole brigade? Or I should be. The Colonel served under me as a subaltern, for Christ's sake. And my 2 i/c with the Chindits is now a full general."

Before I could respond he slammed his glass down on the table and shouted: "BASTARDS!" He strode over to the doorway, drew back the blanket, and stared out over the hills. Then he yelled "BASTARDS!" again, as loudly as he could, a cry full of venom, as though those responsible for hounding him were out there in the hills, able to hear every word.

He was so drunk, and so consumed by anger, that he let out another cry of "BASTARDS!" When he turned back inside there was something evil and vicious about his expression. It frightened me. It was the look of a man demented by the desire for revenge. "I'll show the bastards, Contractor. By Christ, I will! By the time I've finished out here they won't be able to hold me down any longer. The bastards will have to give me my due. Filthy lies on my record will mean nothing. My chance will come, and when it does come I'm going to take it. My God, I will! I don't give a damn what I have to do .... And I don't give a damn who suffers in the process. I never spared myself, so why should others? I was expendable and I accepted that. I never bitched about it. So what was good for me, is good for others. Everyone takes their chance, just like I did. "

He rambled on, but his message never wavered. He was demonized by the injustice he had suffered. Revenge and the reinstatement of his seniority were all that mattered to him. The murder of the Katcom was the last thing on his mind. He was obsessed by self-interest. I watched with contempt as he strode about, muttering about 'the bastards!' and how he would beat them.

Eventually, and much to my relief, CSM Howard pushed his way into the bunker. I think he must have been listening outside following the first cry of "BASTARDS!" He pretended he'd come in about something else. He went into a long rigmarole about a shortage of fresh rations for the coming day and as he spoke he caught my eye and nodded towards the door.

I took the hint and slipped out, into the pitch darkness, into the face of a biting wind. I had no doubts that Dog Company faced a bleak future. Our lives were in the hands of an unbalanced fanatic.

18

Mission Command

In the following weeks the Dukes got away with four minor clashes with Chinese patrols. Other regiments weren't so lucky. They had far more frequent actions and they came off second best in most of them. Reports from Divisional Headquarters stated that the Chinese had recently reshuffled their dispositions and we were now faced by one of their crack divisions. Nor were the Chinese successes confined to no man's land. A large raiding party attacked the Princess Patricia's on Hill 355 and overran the Canadians' forward company position, and it was only after a spirited counter-attack by the Royal Fusiliers that the situation was retrieved. Then the Durham Light Infantry lost a patrol of sixteen men, the full details of which were never discovered. Most surprisingly, an Australian patrol of twenty men came off very second best against a Chinese ambush numbering around sixty.

Efforts were made to redress the situation and those of us in Dog Company had little doubt that the Earl was doing his utmost to persuade the Colonel that we should play a major part in any counter-measures.

Then a remarkable thing happened.

Divisional headquarters carried out a new appreciation of the situation and it was decided that however much activity there was in no man's land, it made no difference to the overall position; that for all the patrols going out, whether Chinese or UN, no tactical advantage was gained. They therefore concluded that our aggressive patrolling was nothing but over-zealous professional soldiers flexing their muscles in the hope of glory; that none of them could be justified when weighed against the number of casualties suffered. In six months, the Commonwealth forces had suffered 61 officers killed, wounded, or missing, and with the ORs the figure was 972, a total of 1033, mostly the result of patrol actions. Yet in the same six month period, the front line hadn't moved a single inch.

This new policy took some time to seep down to platoon level. When it did there was general rejoicing. Most of us had long held similar views and I was particularly pleased and relieved, since nothing could have been more calculated to thwart the mad-cap ambitions of Earl Gray.

Unfortunately, the new policy proved disastrous. The logic of it was irrefutable, but all three brigadiers, all nine battalion commanders, and all 28 rifle company commanders, were dead against it. They saw such a soft attitude as highly dangerous and pointed out that it went against all infantry theories and training.

The Chinese were soon in full control of no man's land. In their efforts to find out what had happened to us, they took to attacking our standing patrols in front of our barbed wire. Some standing patrols were wiped out and it wasn't long before it became standard procedure for them to report the approach of the Chinese over their 88-sets and then make hasty withdrawals. To do anything else was suicidal.

Another consequence was that the Chinese were able to leave well-camouflaged snipers in the valley throughout the day and take pot-shots at any inviting targets in our forward trenches. Fortunately they were very poor marksmen, but even so it made life hazardous. On a notorious stretch of trench between 12 Platoon and company headquarters the terrain dipped and one couldn't help exposing one's head and shoulders. I twice had narrow escapes with bullets cracking loudly a few inches from my head. Others had similar experiences.

Inevitably, the policy was reversed. All battalions were ordered to resume normal patrolling. Not surprisingly, the Chinese were waiting for us and many patrols which ventured out from our lines were severely mauled by ambushes. Hardly a night went by without no man's land resounding to the sound of small-arms fire. I often sat in the platoon OP with the Gunner's Forward Observation Officer and together we would watch the muzzle flashes and the exploding grenades of the battling patrols and speculate on what the poor devils were going through.

It was always in my mind that it would be my turn next, and although I went out into the valley several times I was always lucky. So too was the rest of the Dog Company. The nearest we ever got to a contact was when a recce patrol from 10 Platoon came across a large Chinese ambush party of around sixty men. Fortunately they were making so much noise while setting-up their trap that the 10 Platoon men were able to evade them without difficulty.

Ever since Corporal Turnbull had taken over as company clerk and signaller, the company's grapevine had improved enormously. Whereas Bridges had gloried in putting the vertical wind up men with rumours of his own invention, Turnbull stuck to repeating accurately what he picked up in the course of his duties, and since he was a good friend of Rupert's, 12 Platoon was among the first to hear of what was liable to happen. Most of Turnbull's reports concerned Earl Gray's efforts to understand how the Chinese operated in no man's land. He was convinced that, being communists, they did everything to a rigid plan. Every night he marked-up his map with predictions as to where the Chinese would place their ambushes, and in the morning, when reports of the night's contacts came in from the battalion, he would check to see how close he had been. According to Turnbull he was improving all the time. In fact, he was becoming uncannily accurate.

Turnbull also told us that Colonel Bunbury and Brigadier Kendrew often called in to the control-centre. They had long tactical discussions and because Turnbull was always on hand to serve drinks, he was able to tell us the aim and location of our next patrol before the Earl had briefed us. On one occasion the Colonel and brigadier turned up with the divisional commander, General West. He was an imposing figure who always carried a carved staff around with him, an affectation seeking early recognition rather than an aid to climbing. According to Turnbull, General West was a man of few words who liked to listen to the views of others before voicing his own opinions, only to come out with remarks that were odd rather than original or perceptive.

On his visit to the control-centre he sat through a masterly summary by Earl Gray as to what was going on in no man's land. He made no comments, no suggestions, nor any recommendations, and Turnbull had a feeling that he was envious of Earl Gray's grasp of the situation. When West got up to leave all he said was: "And what about the Chinese ambushes, Gray? Are they one-sided or two-sided?"

The Brigadier, the Colonel, and Earl Gray (and Turnbull for that matter) looked at him quizzically, wondering what difference it made.

"Well which is it, Gray?"

"I've no idea, sir."

"Well find out! Whether they are one-sided or two-sided is absolutely basic."

There was general speculation in the company as to who would get the contract. The consensus of opinion was that it was between 10 Platoon (Stan) and ourselves. We had a better track record due to our Yong Dong ambush, but Stan was rated far above me as a platoon commander, especially in Gray's judgement. It was over a week before we found out. 12 Platoon was to stand by for a patrol, probably in three nights' time. When I went to the control-centre for a briefing, I found Earl Gray in an ebullient mood. All his theories about the location of the Chinese patrols had panned out beautifully. The previous night's recce patrols had confirmed the presence of Chinese ambush patrols exactly where he had predicted. This made him more certain than ever that he could pin-point where their next one would be. He went to his map and jabbed a spot directly opposite 12 Platoon. "That is where they'll be! So now you know where they are. And you know what you've got to do."

"Not exactly, sir."

"How do you mean--- not exactly? I've already told you that General

West wants to know whether their ambushes are one-sided or two-sided."

"What difference does it make?"

"It's absolutely basic."

"In what way?"

Earl Gray put on a good act. He sighed wearily and said: "Because with a two-sided ambush they have to open fire on you much sooner. When you're still some way off. Otherwise the Chinese on the two sides will end up shooting each other as well as you. Whereas with a one-sided ambush they can wait until you're right up to their main party, their firm base ... Giving you far less time to respond."

It was a pathetically lame excuse. I stared at him with bitterness. We both knew that it didn't matter a damn whether they were one-sided or two-sided. When you were ambushed, you were ambushed, and whether the Chinese shot each other as well as you was of little consequence.

"Contractor, we can't hope to beat the Chinese unless we know how they operate. Your job is to find out."

"I see. And how do you suggest I do that? Walk straight into an ambush?"

"How you go about it is up to you."

"Me?"

"Of course ... Mission Command."

"Mission Command?"

"Don't say you weren't taught Mission Command at Eaton Hall?"

"Never heard of it."

"Well it's perfectly simple. A senior officer tells a subordinate what he has to do. His objective. And what he has at his disposal to achieve that objective. But how the man in command goes about it is up to him. It's the normal army chain of command."

"Sounds to me like passing the buck ..."

"Contractor, for heaven's sake just get on with it and carry out my orders."

"Can't you at least give me some advice?"

"Advice? Certainly I can ... Be bloody careful!"

"That's it? Be bloody careful?"

"And remember your training. Anticipate!"

I returned to 12 Platoon in the depths of despair. When I reached the CP I ignored Brummell and Rupert and threw myself down on my bunk. I said nothing and avoided eye contact with them. I could feel them watching me, anxious to know what had happened. Minutes passed but I still couldn't bring myself to tell them. How could I explain that we were on some kind of mad, suicidal mission: that there was a new British 'fair play' policy by which 16 of us were expected to walk into an ambush of sixty Chinese in order to determine whether they favoured killing us with a one-sided or a two-sided ambush.

Eventually, Brummell left the bunker, his way of showing his disapproval of my temperamental nature and all things National Service. After a while, I also went outside and attended to some routine duties, things to keep my mind off leading men into an ambush. I inspected the latrines, did a foot inspection, and then went round the bunkers and weapon pits, checking that they were in good order.

When I returned to the CP it was time for our evening meal and then Stand-to. Rupert dished up the usual food: tomato soup and chicken hash. We ate in silence but when we finished, and he had produced mugs of coffee, he said: "Saj, sooner or later you're going to have to tell us what happened."

So I told him. When I finished he smiled ruefully.

"You're taking it very calmly," I said. I managed a smile. I couldn't help admiring him. Despite his abhorrence of everything going on around him, he remained unflappable and positive. God knows what I would have done without him and Sun Tze.

"We do have several things going for us," he continued. "The essence of an ambush is surprise. And if the Earl is right, and the ambush is where he says it is, it will be us who will surprise them. Not the other way round. It makes them no more than a bunch of Chinks sitting behind bunds."

We discussed the patrol all through stand-to. We went through every possibility. My first idea was to attack them from the rear, but this had to be ruled out because they would be so near to the Boot, which meant we would be seen climbing up the lower slopes. Once we'd ruled that out, Rupert pulled out 'The Art of War' and drew up a list of patrolling essentials. These were: surprise, strike first, utilize good cover, cause confusion among the enemy, catch the enemy in enfilade fire, strike hard and leave quickly.

As a guide to successful patrolling these points could hardly have been bettered and Rupert lost no more time in drawing up a plan based on them. He also surprised me by dragging in an incident his Uncle Jasper had experienced on an Atlantic convoy. I groaned with despair at the mention of Uncle Jasper and Rupert laughed, knowing what we all thought of his uncle's letters. However, he insisted that I should listen.

His uncle had been 1st Officer on a Corvette. On one occasion, after several merchant ships had been sunk by U-boats, his Corvette developed engine trouble and they were left stranded behind the rest of the convoy. Once underway again, they went to rejoin the convoy, only to surprise a U-boat sitting on the surface at the rear of the convoy, recharging its batteries. The Corvette went straight into the attack and sank the U-boat.

It was a well-known incident in naval circles and was used to great effect in Nicholas Monsarrrat's novel, *The Cruel Sea*.

Rupert suggested that we should use the incident as a basis for our patrol. As he developed his idea, so I realized that he had come up with something which would give us at least a chance. My only remaining query was about one of the essentials Sun Tzu had listed: good cover. If the Chinese were sited behind bunds as Earl Gray predicted, we would be at a terrible disadvantage, having to approach them over an open paddy field which was as flat as a pancake with very sparse undergrowth.

Rupert smiled knowingly. "Think back to Flanders."

"Sorry... I didn't happen to be there."

"Shell craters," he said.

The following morning I went round to the OP for a long chat with the Gunner's Forward Observation Officer (FOO). As we sat on the narrow bench, we peered out of the weapon slit, or embrasure, and I explained what was afoot. Through binoculars we studied the paddy field in front of the ambush site and I asked him if it was possible to shell the area leading up to it to create a series of craters which we could use for cover.

He assured me that it would be simple, but he suggested it would be best to shell the main Chinese trenches on the top of the Boot, directly in line with the ambush, and at the same time arrange for numerous shells to fall short, accidentally on purpose. That way, he said, the Chinese wouldn't associate the shelling with any likely patrol action. He also suggested delayed fuses, which would make the craters deeper and wider than normal--- real craters, not just shallow scoops.

When I held my orders group for the patrol I was surrounded by hard and doubting expressions. They knew as well as I did that Chinese ambushes were always around 60 strong and since there were only ever sixteen of us it made the whole thing reminiscent of the Charge of the Light Brigade. So I hastened to add that instead of using the same old technique of an arrow-head formation, we would do things differently--- our way!

That didn't inspire confidence. Our way had often turned out to be disastrous. However, I persisted. I explained that we would have two point-men and close behind them a small command-group of eight. Then, well to the rear, there would be two Bren groups of three men each, one on each flank. They would be so far behind that they would be out of sight and out of hearing of those in front. In a sense they would be separate patrols, lurking so far back that when the rest of us entered the ambush area, the Chinese would be unaware of their presence.

This did at last arouse interest, so I proceeded as simply as I could. The two point-men would advance into the ambush using the cover of newly created shell craters. "But the crux of our new tactics is this," I said. "Once we are certain of the Chinese presence, the six men in the command group will close up with the point men. The Chinese are well aware that our patrols usually number sixteen, so they'll be waiting for the rest of us to enter their trap. That's when we open fire on them first. But only with grenades. Making sure they land behind the bund. We all know the advantage of that. They'll be so confused and panic-stricken that they'll open fire blindly. Not just those in front of us, but those on our flanks as well."

"And what about the Bren groups at the rear?" asked Corporal Holroyd.

"They have to act fast. As soon as the Chinese open fire, our Bren groups will see exactly where the flanking Chinese are. They'll see immediately whether it's a one-sided or two-sided ambush. They'll dash forward as quickly as they can, but instead of joining the rest of us they'll go to the end of the bunds sheltering the flanking Chinese. That way they'll get them in enfilade. In other words they'll shoot straight down both lines of them. Three or four magazines and they'll be finished. Then we all scarper and I pass back a message to bring down a stonk, cutting off the Chinese withdrawal."

Numerous questions were asked, but there were no dissenters, not even Fletcher. They sensed a good chance of success. The main concern was the danger of the two rear Bren groups wandering off and getting lost, and after we'd bandied this about Hurst suggested that men in the command group should have white patches on their backs, thereby making it easier for the Bren groups to keep in touch, even at a distance.

Later, we watched the Gunners shell the Boot. Naturally, we focused on the delayed-fused shells which fell short. The Gunners did a perfect job. When the shelling stopped there was a whole series of craters that resembled giant stepping stones leading up to the ambush site. Next, I pointed out to each member of the patrol the exact route we would take and let them use the binoculars to see the details of the craters. The final step was to hold several rehearsals in the valley at the bottom of our reverse slope. I impressed on them that once in the last paddy field it would no longer be a matter of going along in the usual crouch position; it would be flat on our stomachs, crawling and slithering from one shell crater to another, just like they did in Flanders.

We also practised throwing unprimed grenades, making sure that each man could get them thirty or forty yards in order to land them behind the Chinese. I drummed into them that the further we threw them, the further we could keep away from the Chinese. I got Animal Evans and Holroyd (in command the Bren groups) go over their manoeuvres several times, stressing the importance of identifying straight away the bunds behind which the flanking Chinese were operating and then moving like greased lightning, regardless of noise.

On the night of the patrol we assembled outside the CP and I did a thorough inspection. Faces were blackened and I issued each man with a bullet-proof vest with white patches on the back. Then we waited until midnight, leaving it fairly late so as to give the Chinese plenty of time to become tired, cold, and thoroughly browned off, an experience our own ambush patrols knew only too well.

It was an ideal night for a patrol: windy enough to mask noisy movements and with broken, scudding clouds which alternately exposed and hid bright moonlight. As Rupert reported our departure to company HQ over the 88 set, quite a crowd gathered to see us off, among them Copper Bowden, our ACC cook, Brummell, Kim, and Harry Wilmott. There were shouts of "Good luck!" as we went over the top.

"Good luck?" Fletcher called back. "We're going to fucking need it!"

"Get on with it, Fletch!" rejoined Harry. "Fucking mash 'em up like you're always saying you're going to."

We left amid nervous laughter. Someone was going to get mashed up and that was for sure.

It was very slow going. The path through our wire was icy and treacherous and once in the valley we moved cautiously, in bounds, synchronizing our movements with the cloud cover. Twenty yards, then stop: study the ground and listen. As the moonlight disappeared I would signal Hurst and Jenkins to move on again. Each time I would glance back, making sure the two Bren groups were keeping their distance, still out of sight.

We stalked along like wild animals tracking their prey, making hardly any noise. The two point men adopted a semi crouch posture as they slunk forward, ready to go to ground. They kept to the cover of bunds where possible and as we passed paddy fields I counted them off, checking our exact position. The pattern of the paddies was etched on my mind.

Eventually we came to the paddy ahead of the predicted ambush. We had no option but to go straight across it. I signalled to Hurst and Jenkins to start crawling. They inched along, hugging the ground. When they reached the first crater I went forward to join them, communicating by signs rather than whispers. We searched along the bund ahead of us but saw nothing suspicious. I checked our rear again. None of the command party were visible. Nor were the two Bren groups. I wondered just how far back they were, but I wasn't worried. I had tremendous faith in

Animal Evans and Holroyd.

Moonlight was still skipping in and out from behind the clouds. We timed our movements accordingly. Hurst and Jenkins were slithering along like snakes, slipping from crater to crater. The moment of truth soon came. We got to within thirty yards of the bund. Then Hurst and Jenkins stopped abruptly. Again, I crawled forward to them. I slid into their crater. Hurst was all excited. He kept pointing towards the bund, mouthing something I couldn't understand. Eventually he held his nose tightly and mimed with such exaggerations that I caught on: he could smell them!

I was damned if I could, but Hurst was insistent. Then Jenkins pointed towards the end of the bund. I glanced over in that direction but saw nothing. However, their certainty was good enough for me. I turned to the rear and signalled to the command group to close up. Soon, we were concentrated in three shell craters in line abreast. I mimed activating a grenade. Then, following my lead, we withdrew the pins, waited three seconds, and then hurled them as hard as we could.

I watched them soar through the air. Even though they were travelling with varying trajectories, I could see they were going to clear the bund and land among the Chinese. There were distinctive, dull thuds as they landed. Then explosions, like a vicious artillery concentration, a great cacophony of violent eruption. Vivid red, yellow, and orange flashes leapt up, and as a backdrop came yells of surprise and panic from the Chinese. Noise no longer mattered, so I shouted at the top of my voice: "Keeping throwing! Keep throwing!"

I glanced around and in each crater heads and shoulders were bobbing up and down as the lads threw more grenades. The intensity of the explosions increased, giving the impression of a force three or four times our real size. Before our second shower of grenades fell, the Chinese opened up with their Burp guns. Two distinct lines of red sparks winked and spat at us: the main force directly to our front and from behind a bund on our left--- a one-sided ambush, not two-sided!

We ducked down into cover as bullets cracked only inches over our heads. Others landed around us on the lips of the craters and sent up spouts and chips of earth.

"Keep throwing! Keep throwing!" I yelled again.

This time we hurled grenades to our flanks as well as ahead of us. I knew this was the critical point: the moment at which Animal and Holroyd would be dashing forward, to get in position, in order to fire straight down the line of the flanking Chinese.

Our grenades slackened off noticeably as we were forced to stay under cover. I had just thrown my fourth when our Bren groups burst into action. I peered over the edge of the crater. The Chinese had been taken by surprise. The sheer volume of our fire brought Chinese efforts to a halt. With the Brens tearing straight through the line of Chinese, they jumped up in confusion from behind their bund, some running, some falling, others looking around, trying to fathom what was happening.

Two men on either side of me in the control-group opened up with their Sten guns, increasing the Chinese chaos. Soon, they were in complete disarray with withering fire cutting into them from two directions. They were darting about like mesmerized rabbits, dithering all the time, with no idea of which way to run. There were shouts and screams: orders, counter orders, warnings, and the forlorn cries of men in the throes of death.

To our front, the Chinese small-arms fire had likewise tailed away. They too were shocked to a virtual stand-still. I hurled my fifth grenade, and all around me the others were doing the same, which meant that within a matter of minutes around thirty grenades had exploded among them.

It was time to pull out. I saw Jenkins half turn, getting ready to run for it, so I yelled at him to do just that. He jumped up and sprinted away. Hurst was right behind him, both doubled-up as low as they could get, heading for cover at our rear. The command-group gave them covering fire, Brens and Stens and more grenades. Then I turned to the others and ordered: "Pull out!"

It was a crucial moment. We had to turn our backs on the Chinese with no covering fire and white patches on our backs, giving them a free shoot. As we ran, we zigzagged crazily. I collided with one man and we both went sprawling; but in an instant we were back on our feet and away again. Then another man went down, right beside me. I stopped to help him. It was Bertie Mee. Another man stopped to help. I had no idea who it was. We hauled Bertie to his feet and dragged him along. Then another man went down. He kept screaming, "I'm hit! I'm hit!" Two men dashed up to him, heaved him to his feet, lifted him and ran on.

When we got to the end of the paddy field, we scrambled over the bund and into relative safety. Hurst and Jenkins were already there, trying to regain their breath. I did likewise and once recovered I peered over the bund. The Chinese were no longer firing. They were totally disorganized. Our Bren groups were still thudding away on their flank; now probably on their third or fourth magazines.

Then came a shrill bugle call, a sound usually associated with Chinese attacks; but this time they were making a hasty retreat, all discipline gone. The noise they made as they withdrew was quite incredible.

Very soon our Bren groups stopped firing and we heard them crashing through the undergrowth, heading back towards us. I shouted out to them, guiding them in. I took out my Verey pistol and fired a green flare, the signal for Rupert back in 12 Platoon to call down an artillery concentration on the base of the Boot.

Next, I went round the patrol checking casualties. Bertie Mee was not only conscious, but full of his usual foul language. He was adamant that he'd been hit several times right across his back. "But I'm not bloody bleeding," he kept saying incredulously. I detailed two men to stay with him. Our other casualty was more serious. A bandsman had been hit in the legs. Also, it seemed that most of his buttocks had been shot away. A couple of his mates were doing their best to stop the bleeding with field dressings. It was a hell of a mess, blood and shredded clothing all over the place. I told Animal Evans to hand his Bren over to someone else and carry the man back in a fireman's lift.

Finally, whilst several of the others stood by to provide covering fire, Holroyd, Hurst and I went forward to search the area of the clash. A search was never popular, especially if there were still wounded lying around; but a search was essential, our only way to prove our success. Otherwise, Earl Gray would never be convinced.

We edged cautiously along the flanking bund where the Chinese had been sheltering. There were abundant signs of the havoc we had wrought: dead bodies were sprawled about, all shot several times. In patches of remaining snow there were tracks of blood where wounded men had been dragged away. Weapons, items of clothing, and equipment lay abandoned. We approached the dead cautiously, but they were dead all right.

As evidence of our success we picked up two Burp guns and some blood-stained Chinese caps. We moved on carefully until we were looking over the main bund which had faced us. Again, there were tell-tale signs of casualties, but no bodies. They had been dragged away, leaving behind the flotsam of war. I decided we'd hung around long enough. I could still hear the Chinese withdrawing, trying to reorganize themselves around the base of the Boot, and I knew that at any moment our artillery concentration would come screaming down on them. It was time to get clear in case of shortfalls.

We had no difficulty in finding our way up our minefield path. At the top, a party of men were waiting for us, including stretcher-bearers. Only one was needed. Reynolds, the wounded bandsman, was still losing a lot of blood, far worse than we had thought. He was bundled on to a stretcher and taken at the double to the CAP.

The patrol assembled outside the CP, together with the rest of the platoon who were not on stag or standing patrols. There was excitement and relief, with Bertie Mee showing everyone the six bullets embedded in the back of his bullet-proof vest. Kim went round with a tray of steaming hot coffees heavily laced with rum. While men drank in greedy gulps, I went amongst them, thanking them and singing their praises. There was a lot of self-congratulating. Everyone agreed that we'd been bloody lucky but we didn't care if it was luck, skill, or anything else. We were still alive. That was all that mattered. To a man, we felt born again.

19

Another Blue-on-Blue

On December 12th 1952, 1st Royal Tank Regiment moved into the front line for the first time. Two brand new Centurion tanks arrived in our battalion area. As always, they were stationed on hill peaks, with no attempt at concealment due to the Chinese having no artillery powerful enough even to dent their armour. No one thought to tell the Chinese this and they never ceased to shell the hills on which the tanks were so arrogantly perched. Safe inside, it amused the crews but for everyone else it wasn't much fun.

Dog Company wasn't cursed by the presence of a tank, and the nearest to us was on Hill 163, half a mile away. Its position was unusual in that it was to our rear and diagonally to our left, giving it a clear but fairly distant view of 12 Platoon's rear slope.

Dawn broke three hours after the Royal Tank Regiment moved into their new positions and the crew on Hill 163 found themselves looking at what they assumed to be a Chinese-held hill. For a time there was no sign of activity but gradually distant figures began to shuffle about, starting their daily routine. To a raw crew, in the front line for the first time, it seemed they had been presented with a heaven-sent opportunity, and without any further ado, or any reference to their superiors, or even checking their maps, they proceeded to blow the rear bunkers of 12 Platoon to kingdom come.

I had just returned from another patrol. I was tired, frozen to the marrow, and in a thoroughly bad mood. Beau Brummell, who'd been in the comfort of the CP all night, was sitting on his bunk, eating his breakfast. He'd let the space- heater go out which meant there was no hot coffee. Worst of all, during the night he'd finished off the last of the tomato soups. I glanced at him with irritation. I noticed that he was wearing gym shoes instead of boots, which was strictly against orders. When I reprimanded him he shrugged and said: "Sorry, sir. I forgot."

I let the matter drop, but he knew what I thought and he had sufficient sense to clear off before I picked him up on something else. "I'll go and make sure everyone has stood-down, sir."

He'd only just disappeared when there was a violent explosion. It made me stagger backwards and fall on to my bunk. The saucepan of cold coffee fell off the space-heater and dust and small stones fell from the roof. A couple of rats were blown from the rafters and made a run for it out of the doorway.

The explosion was so different to any we had previously experienced that I knew instinctively that we were in dire trouble. As I dashed to investigate there was another explosion, just as violent as the first. Once again it knocked me off balance. From the way the bunker vibrated, it seemed the shells were coming straight in at us with a flat trajectory, not dropping down on us in the normal way. I grabbed my Sten and hurried outside. I had only gone a couple of steps when Beau Brummell came staggering down the trench. He had a long, deep cut across his forehead, his steel helmet was missing, and what little hair he had was dishevelled.

"It's the tank on 163," he gasped. "It's firing at us. The one you can see from the corner bunker. The bloody shell burst just a few yards away from me. My head's splitting …"

"Must be some kind of new Chinese support gun," I said.

"Don't talk wet. It's our own bloody tank. Get on the blower quick! Or it will blow-in that whole line of bunkers…"

I stared at him incredulously, still unable to believe that one of our own tanks would shell us.

"For Christ's sake pull your finger out, sir! Otherwise the blokes in the bunkers won't stand a chance."

As I continued to hesitate he pushed me aside and grabbed the field telephone. He cranked it furiously. "If you don't believe me, go and see for yourself. I'll tell Gray." Then he turned his attention back to the telephone, cranking it like mad, urging someone to answer: "Come on! Come on!"

I went to look for myself. As soon as I turned the corner in the trench I saw the long, pencil-like barrel of the Centurion 20-pounder gun pointing straight at us. As I moved along the trench to discover where the shells had landed I saw a flash from its 20-pounder gun. I flung myself to the bottom of the trench and before I could register a thought the shell landed, twenty yards to one side, above the top of the trench. The blast was so overpowering that it rendered me unconscious. My body was tossed into the air and I was enveloped in a cloud of dust. As I crashed back to the ground I regained my senses. My eyes were filled with dirt and everything was swimming about crazily.

For several seconds I lay there, too scared to move, hugging the ground for safety. Then, as I recovered myself, I recalled Beau Brummell's warning about the men in the line of bunkers. If they weren't dead already, they damn soon would be. I had to get them before it was too late.

I started to crawl towards the bunkers, keeping myself flush to the ground. Soon, I could see down the length of the trench. Outside the first bunker, cringing against the trench wall was Jessop, his face covered by a thick layer of mud-coloured shaving soap. At his feet was a bowl which a few seconds before had been full of scalding hot water as he went about his daily ablutions. He was cut about the head and the right arm of his pullover was torn and covered in blood. "What's happening?" he shouted.

"The tank on 163. Get out quickly. And tell all the others to get out. Hurry man! Hurry, for Christ's sake!"

I'd always regarded Jessop as a level-headed lad, so I was amazed when, without a thought for the others, he scrambled to his feet and sprinted down the trench. I was still lying in the bottom of it, so he literally long-jumped over me. As he went along his head must have been exposed above the top of the trench and the Centurion's machine gun opened up. Bullets began to splatter the top of the trench, chasing after him but always a fraction behind.

To my amazement, Jessop survived. As he reached the corner of the trench he literally threw himself round, into relative safety. I was just about to continue towards the bunkers, to get the other men to make a run for it, when another 20-pounder shell crashed into the position. This time it landed further away and I escaped the main blast. I hesitated, not knowing what to do, but when another shell landed among the bunkers, accompanied by more machine gun fire, I realized it would be suicidal to go any further. The best thing for me to do was try to get them to stop firing.

I yelled at the men to abandon their bunkers but I got no response. I feared the worst and in desperation I ran back down the trench, crouching low. When I burst into the CP, Brummell was still on the telephone, having a shouting match with Earl Gray.

"For God's sake what's happening, Sergeant?" I demanded.

Beau Brummell covered up the mouth piece. "The silly bastard ... He says it must be Chinese firing from either Abel or Cain."

"Tell him we've actually seen the tank firing ..."

"Do you think I haven't? You tell him."

I grabbed the receiver. "Contractor here ..."

"Where the hell have you been? And what's all this nonsense about being fired on by a tank?"

"What Brummell says is perfectly true ..."

"Don't you start. That tank on 163 isn't even facing in your direction. I've been out and looked."

"Bollocks! It's firing at us. I nearly got my head blown off."

"Now look here ..."

"No! You bloody look here ..."

We went on like that for some time, both of us getting angrier and more abusive. His rank had ceased to concern me. In my desperation I saw only dead bodies. We were still ranting at each other when another

20-pounder crunched into the position, shaking the CP, making everything fall about, as though it was caught in the middle of a storm at sea.

My tirade became even fiercer, so vicious and insistent that Earl Gray agreed to investigate my claims properly. The line then went dead. Several men had come round to the CP to find out what was happening. Before I had time to explain, another 20-pounder hit us. It was followed by yells and screams from the bunkers under fire: men I had assumed to be dead. Beau Brummell was the first to react. He grabbed the emergency stretcher at the entrance to the CP and dashed outside. I followed at his heels. We crouched low, being careful not to expose our heads. When we reached the first bunker we found two men. One had a broken leg and the other was in a corner of the wrecked bunker, whimpering. We yanked the latter upright and sent him on his way, telling him to keep on his hands and knees along the trench. The one with the broken leg we pulled out from beneath smashed timbers, ignoring his cries of pain. We put him on the stretcher and carried him back to the CP. There, we handed him on to others to take to the CAP. We grabbed another stretcher and hurried back to the other trapped men.

In the second bunker there was only one man. We didn't bother to find out how badly he was hit. We just bunged him on the stretcher and dashed back to the CP.

As we started off on our third trip, another 20-pounder smashed into the trench wall in front of the last bunker, demolishing the trench wall. In the bunker we found a Katcom on his own. He was wounded in the back and couldn't move. Ignoring his screams, we loaded him on to the stretcher, but as soon as we left the bunker we were spotted by the tank through the gap blown in the trench wall. Their machine gun opened up and another 20-pounder crashed into the bunker we'd just left. As it exploded I lost my grip on the stretcher and was blown on to my face. My head felt as though it had been sliced in two. Blood was gushing from my nose and ears and everything had gone silent.

Suddenly I was in a different world, a world that was half-missing. Yet I was still conscious and knew what was going on around me. I saw Animal Evans dashing down the trench towards me. He grabbed my end of the stretcher and with the help of Brummell completed the rescue of the Katcom. Then Rupert and a lad called Roberts came rushing to my aid. They grabbed me off the trench floor, lifted me on to a stretcher, and carried me back to safety.

The stalemate was eventually broken by Corporal Jackman. He was on duty in the OP. Although not threatened by the tank, he was well aware of what was happening. When a large chunk of shrapnel landed outside the OP he picked it up, even though it was still hot. He examined it and found that the letters WD and two arrows were engraved on it, proof beyond doubt that it had come from a British tank.

This evidence was reported back through the units and eventually the tank stopped firing. All that was left to do was evacuate the wounded. To my chagrin, I was one of them. I was no longer compos mentis and I only recall the pain of a splitting head, the frustration of deafness, and the taste of blood. When I sat up on my stretcher to get involved, and tried to issue orders, everyone ignored me. I had no idea that I was shouting at the top of my voice. Then Bertie Mee came right up to me and mouthed instructions. What he said, I'll never know, but it must have been something bloody rude. My two stretcher bearers roared with laughter as they carried me away.

As we went past the Company CP, I saw Earl Gray standing in the doorway. He looked down at me without saying a word. He didn't need to. His expression said it all. He was damn glad to be rid of me. I made it perfectly clear that the feeling was mutual.

PART THREE

JAPANESE INTERLUDE

20

A Slow Recovery

On leaving Dog Company I toured various Aid Posts. I lost track of whether I was at battalion, brigade, division, corps, or army. Not that it mattered. They all gave me the same superficial examination, yelled at me in desperation, and then gave up, concluding that (a) I was as deaf as a post and (b) it was beyond their competence to do anything about it. One doctor wrote on my notes: 'I am familiar with this condition, but forget the correct medical term for it'. The next doctor wrote: 'I know what it's called, but I can't spell it.'

This buck-passing eventually came to a halt at an American MASH unit. I was taken there strapped to a stretcher on the outside of a helicopter. It was the first time I'd ever flown and I was terrified. It was like going airborne on a Meccano set. When I got there, frozen stiff, I was told I would have to await the next visit of their roving ENT Specialist.

MASH 89 was nothing like the one later portrayed in the famous American television comedy series. There was nothing comical about MASH 89. It was working under tremendous pressure with a constant stream of wounded men being helicoptered in from fierce battles on Old Baldy, Bunker Hill, and the Hook. Consequently, a deaf (but otherwise perfectly fit) Limey was something they could well have done without, especially since the ENT specialist had gone on a refresher course to Tokyo and wasn't expected back for at least a month. In his absence it was decided to leave me well alone and rely on nature to cure me. If that didn't work, and there was still no sign of the ENT specialist, I was to be sent to the British Base Hospital in Kure, near Hiroshima.

I wasn't the only non-American at MASH 89. There was a severely wounded New Zealand Gunner there as well. They put me in a bed next to him, hoping that we might have something in common. Because of my deafness we never found out. Not that it mattered. The Kiwi had chronic verbal diarrhoea and all he wanted in the way of companionship was someone who would listen and not interrupt. I was ideally suited and it was several hours before he realized that I hadn't heard a word he'd said. Not that he minded when he did find out. In fact he was mildly amused and jumped at the chance to tell me the same things all over again, except in a much louder voice that kept the other patients awake.

When my hearing showed slight signs of returning, I discovered that he was a very tough character indeed. He had been under the knife several times on account of his left arm being blown off just below the shoulder when his 25-pounder jammed and blew up. He had also suffered cracked ribs and a broken collar bone. His name was Clancy and, like the majority of antipodeans, he swore like a Trooper (despite being a Gunner) and had a very rebellious attitude towards those in authority. If they addressed him by his rank he was happy to reciprocate, but if they didn't use his rank, he automatically addressed everyone, regardless of seniority, as 'mate'.

On regaining consciousness he found his fellow-Gunners lying dead around him, with his severed arm several yards away. He loved to describe how he got to his feet, retrieved his severed arm, tucked it under his remaining arm, and then walked a quarter of a mile to the nearest First Aid Post.

When he entered, a doctor dashed forward to help, exclaiming: "Oh, my God! You've lost your arm!"

"No I haven't, doc. I've propped it up in the doorway. Just over there. Any hope of sewing it back on?"

The wounded men who poured into the MASH unit were in a filthy state, straight out of the trenches. Most of them were lousy, which made hygiene of paramount importance. As soon as I got there I was taken to the showers and stripped. Nurses gave me a good lathering under delightfully hot water and then, for good measure, they bent and stretched me in various directions and squirted insecticides into my less accessible areas. Then they took my clothes and burnt them (a routine procedure), assuring me that I would be issued with a new uniform in due course. They also said that the rest of my kit would be forwarded from my old unit once I had passed on to a permanent hospital. All very reassuring, but it never happened.

Having de-loused me, they issued me with a surgical gown to preserve my modesty; but that was the last thing it did. The fastening tabs at the back made sure that my rear view was totally exposed. Not that it worried me, or anyone else for that matter. The nurses had already seen all there was to see, and the other patients were far too preoccupied with their own problems. Anyhow, apart from when I went to the loo, I spent my whole time in bed, enjoying the luxury of clean sheets.

For several days it was a restful existence. It was great to be away from it all--- a sheer luxury to be able to look around the place and not see any rats. Of course, I was also worried about what had happened back at Dog Company, especially our final casualty figures and what action had been taken against the crew of the Centurion tank.* Other than that, I either read magazines or pretended to listen to Clancy.

---

* *Three killed and four wounded, with no action against the tank crew.*

Then we had a visit from the new Eighth Army Commander, General Maxwell-Taylor. The American patients (almost exclusively Marines) greeted his arrival by lying to attention in their beds. They did their best to imitate corpses, except that their eyes remained open, staring blankly at the roof of the marquee. The general's retinue included the senior surgeons, the best-looking nurses, and his ADC. As he walked down the ward, Maxwell-Taylor stopped at each bed and the ADC stepped forward and said to the occupant: "Have you shed blood for your country, soldier?"

The Marines answered in their usual style. Moribund corpses were suddenly animated as they yelled: "Sir! Yes, sir!", and with each affirmation Maxwell-Taylor pinned a medal on the man's surgical gown. When they got to me, the only answer his ADC received was my usual "Pardon?", but it didn't stop Maxwell-Taylor issuing another medal.

Things were more complicated with Clancy. He'd been watching all this bullshit with great amusement, but when the ADC referred to him as 'soldier' instead of 'Gunner', his amusement soured and when asked if he'd shed blood for his country, he replied: "My bloody oath, mate! I bled like a pig. But God knows what bastards I shed it for. Whoever the bastards are, I gave them several pints. And a bloody good arm to boot."

The entourage of sycophantic officers glared at him, but he still got his medal.

(A word of explanation. These medals were Purple Hearts. Other nations scoff at them, but the Americans hold them in great esteem. Their proper name is 'Medal of Merit' and it was the first medal ever struck by the United States. Here endeth the explanation)

Soon after General Maxwell-Taylor departed, the MASH colonel marched back into the ward and confronted Clancy and me. He said he'd never seen such disgraceful behaviour and that, had we been Marines, we would have been court-martialled and sent to the stockade. However, since we were British and knew no better, and weren't even entitled to the medals, he would say no more and simply have the medals back. This brought a spirited response from Clancy. He told the CO to get stuffed. He pointed out that Maxwell-Taylor was commander of a UN Army, not an American one, so any decorations he gave out were from the UN. "So as far as me and my Pommie mate are concerned," said Clancy, "you can take a running jump, mate. We're keeping them. And if you don't like it, you can lump it."

To my amazement the CO shrugged his shoulders and walked off, leaving me--- as far as I know--- to be the only Briton ever awarded a

Purple Heart. Out of respect to Clancy, I wear it at all the military functions I attend, which infuriates the Establishment. Because they haven't got one, they consider it 'disapproved', even though they have no hesitation in wearing other foreign decorations handed out by tin-pot middle-eastern potentates.

The following morning, I was discharged. I was told my bed was needed for men with proper wounds. A blanket was wrapped around me (they refused to give me an American uniform) and I was driven by jeep to a local airstrip where a handful of British stretcher cases were awaiting evacuation. Most of them were badly burnt and were a gruesome sight. After hours of hanging around, cold, hungry, and thirsty, we were flown by Dakota to the Australian Air Base at Iwakuni, in Japan.

I arrived at the Land of the Rising Sun feeling desolate and abandoned. I was dressed in a blanket and a surgical gown, with no money, no pay book, no movement order, and not even my identity tags. The Yanks had stripped me of everything. To make matters worse I was making myself thoroughly unpopular by continually shouting at people, asking endless questions about where we were going and what would happen next. Mostly, I was ignored. Even those who took the trouble to shout back at me soon became convinced that I was stupid as well as deaf--- why else would I keep asking questions knowing I wouldn't hear the answers?

From Iwakuni we went by ferry across the Inland Sea to Kure. Then by road to The British Army Base Hospital. The hospital was part of the sprawling complex of buildings known as HQBCFK (Headquarters British Commonwealth Forces in Korea). During World War II it had been the Japanese Naval Headquarters. The facilities were first class and the hospital would have been sheer luxury had it not been for the Sister in charge of the ward I was taken to.

As soon as an orderly showed me to a bed I got in it and went to sleep. Ten minutes later I was woken by the Sister banging on my feet with her clip-board. Her normal voice turned out to be so loud and penetrating that I actually understood a few words of what she said. Even so, the ensuing conversation had the rest of the ward in fits of laughter.

"What are you doing in bed?"

"Doing instead? Instead of what?"

She consulted her clip-board which told her I was deaf. She reverted to slower, more distinctive, screaming. "WHY ARE YOU IN BED?"

"Oh, in bed! I was catching up with some sleep."

"Well you've no right to be asleep. You're walking wounded. And walking wounded go to bed at 2200 hours. Then you get up at 0630 hours. So now get out of bed and dress."

"Confess? Confess to what?"

"GET DRESSED! And to you, soldier, I am 'Ma'm'."

"Spam! Great! I haven't had spam in years."

"YOU CALL ME 'MA'M', PRIVATE!"

"Private? I'm not a private. I'm a second lieutenant."

"DON'T BE STUPID! CAN YOU SUPPORT THAT CLAIM?"

"No. All my clothes were burnt at the MASH unit. I haven't got anything."

"WHAT ABOUT YOUR PAY BOOK?"

"That's back at the Dukes."

"WHAT ABOUT TAGS? DO YOU HAVE ANY ?"

"I'm afraid not. I don't smoke."

Eventually, after a lengthy investigation, I was transferred to the officers' ward. There, the Sister in charge allowed me to go to bed and get up when I wanted to. Also--- thank God--- she gave me some pyjamas and a dressing gown. Feeling human again, I scrounged some writing material from a fellow patient and wrote to Rupert, telling him where I was and urging him to send on all my kit.

Each day was punctuated by various 'rounds': there was a drugs round, Matron's round, a medication round, a library round, a junior doctor's round, a consultant's round, and practically every other type of round bar the milkman's.

The best of these was the junior doctor's round. He was a very nice fellow. He was well aware that I was deaf but he nevertheless chatted to me for at least ten minutes each day. I had no idea of what he was talking about, but he did (inadvertently) enable me to perfect the art of conversing by pretence, the ability to keep someone prattling on ad nauseam without them realizing that they might just as well be talking to a brick wall. I became proficient at giving suitable grunts of agreement and murmurs of interest, all in response to his expressions and body language. The only real difficulty came when he confronted me with a direct question. Even then, experience taught me to assume an air of neutrality and use non-committal words or phrases such as "Well, maybe ..." and "Could be ... Really!" and "Depends ..." or "Quite possibly ..." Sometimes just a grunt.

As it happened, most of the doctor's conversations centred on the imminent arrival of an ENT specialist, and how, once he turned up, my troubles would be over. Actually, it was when he arrived that my trouble started. He turned out to be a newly commissioned National Service doctor who had been elevated to the status of 'ENT Specialist' on the grounds that he had made it known to his superiors that that was what he aspired to be.

His name was Mason and when I visited his surgery I could tell by his nervousness that I was his first-ever real patient. Outside his surgery brand new ENT equipment was piled up in its original packing and after much rummaging around, he found the funnel-shaped torch for ear-examinations. When it didn't work, I suggested that he put a battery in it, upon which it worked perfectly. His only means of testing my hearing was with tuning forks. These he found in a magnificent mahogany case which looked like an enormous, high-class canteen of cutlery. When opened, an impressive array of tuning forks was revealed. There were three rows of them, beautifully crafted in stainless steel, ranging from tiny to enormous.

"Maybe there's some kind of scale with them," he said. "You know, how many decibels they give off and how many you should be able to hear. Hang on, I'll see if I can find any instructions." He went through the packaging but drew a blank. "In that case, old boy, it's best if we start at one end of the scale and work our way through."

"Right. Can't go far wrong that way."

I was over-optimistic. I imagined that he would do the logical thing and start from the bottom and work upwards, but he chose to do the opposite. He didn't even know how to strike a tuning fork. He should have struck it against the elbow of his tunic, but instead he took out the biggest tuning fork (a real monster) and crashed it on the edge of his desk. It boomed out like Big Ben.

"Can you hear that?" he shouted above the racket.

"Of course."

"Well tell me when it fades away."

It showed no signs of fading away. It went on like an air raid siren for so long that he got bored and lit a cigarette. By the time he stubbed it out he'd become so fed up with waiting for it to diminish that he replaced the fork in its box and shut the lid on it, rather like a ventriloquist trying to silence his dummy by stuffing it in a suitcase. He didn't bother with any other tuning forks. "Medicine and duty for you, old boy. Back to some hard pounding in Korea, I dare say."

Days passed and nothing further happened. Eventually Matron, who couldn't bear to see men just sitting around doing nothing, decided I was making the place untidy and should therefore do something useful. She told me to report to Colonel McIlroy at HQBCFK each morning at 0900 hours. Colonel McIlroy was in command of Kure's fledgling Legal Department and he presided over a constant flow of minor courts-martial. I was to be one of his four Board Members, as required by Military Law.

This new, temporary, duty caused difficulties. I still had no uniform and the courts-martial would obviously require something more formal than a dressing gown, pyjamas, and bedroom slippers. Luckily, officers in the ward rallied round and fixed me up with various items. As a result I was decked out with the tunic of an Inniskilling Dragoon Guard, the cap of an Irish Guardsman, the Service Dress trousers of a major in the Royal Welch Fusiliers, the chromium-plated badges of rank of The Princess Patricia Regiment, and the size 12 boots of a captain in the Military Police. Thus adorned, and looking like the proverbial 'Dog's Dinner', I reported to Colonel McIlroy.

He eyed me curiously. "From whence have you crawled?"

"The hospital, sir."

"What is the matter with you?"

"A bit deaf, sir."

"Hardly a suitable qualification. Still, never mind. Just sit there and look impartial."

For three weeks I did just that. My opinion was never asked and I never offered one. Yet it was a fascinating experience which gave me an insight into the farcical nature of low-profile courts-martial and the danger of leaving legal matters in the hands of amateurs.

All the defendants were young National Servicemen, none of whom were in the least criminal, just naughty teenagers. They were victims of the evil thread which ran through off-duty activities in Japan, namely alcohol. Japanese beer was twice the strength of that in the UK and locally brewed sake was so potent it not only induced drunkenness, but occasional blindness. Consequently, once these youngsters had a skin full, they became convinced that because they were abroad, and in a conquered nation, they could do what the hell they liked. Mostly, they shoplifted, refused to pay girls for services rendered, beat up Japanese taxi drivers who tried to over-charge them, and up-ended pintables which failed to pay out prize money.

On the advice of their defending officer (a young subaltern from JRBD, the local Transit Camp) they pleaded guilty, not because they necessarily were, but because it was the easiest and quickest way out, and the defending officer knew that if he crossed Colonel McIlroy too often, and wasted precious time, he would lose his job and be sent to Korea as soon as he was nineteen.

Having enjoyed three weeks as a Member of the Board, I had high hopes that when I was eventually discharged from the hospital I would join the other Board Members on a permanent basis. Colonel McIlroy even hinted at this, being well pleased by the way I never said anything.

However, trouble struck when the defending officer was run over by a three-wheeler scooter-taxi on the Hondori (main street) during a Saturday evening rush-hour. On Monday morning a new defending officer appeared. He was none other than Second Lieutenant Gilbert Gilbert of the Royal Fusiliers, my old friend from Hillhead Prep Shcool and

Blundell's. We had been such good friends that he had, on occasions, stayed with me during our holidays.

He was known to everyone as Nacker, on account of his slight stature.* As soon as I saw him I knew there would be trouble. Nacker was a 'clever dick' who liked to stir things up, the type who was far too intelligent for his own good. Unlike his predecessor he knew all about court procedures, having often seen his father and uncle in action in courts. His father had been the District Commissioner in the Gilbert and Ellice Islands and had dispensed justice on a regular basis, and his uncle was a well-known QC who haunted the Old Bailey. In the coming weeks, Nacker reproduced many of their legal tricks and, added to this, he was a born winner who, on a matter of principle, did not allow his 'clients' to plead guilty. He fought every case tooth and nail, determined to upset the Military Establishment, all of whom he regarded as failed old farts, none more so than Major Johnson, the prosecuting officer, who he proceeded to stuff out of sight with monotonous regularity. Nacker was also highly contemptuous of Colonel McIlroy, and the feeling was mutual. McIlroy assumed all defendants to be guilty by definition and Nacker assumed that all prosecution witnesses to be sycophantic liars by nature. It made daily clashes inevitable.

Cross-examinations were Nacker's forte. He never asked a question without already knowing the answer and he was so adept at using his right to put leading questions, and pour scorn on the character of witnesses to test their veracity, that most of them quaked when they faced him in the witness box, frightened to death that their lurid past might be dragged up, which it invariably was.

All this added greatly to my enjoyment of the proceedings. For two weeks I sat there mesmerized by Nacker's skill. I felt proud of him. He got so many men off that the whole kilter of army justice lurched in favour of the accused. Very soon, men at JRBD who were hauled before the Colonel on 'Orders' refused to accept his punishments and instead opted for a court-martial, knowing that Nacker would get them off.

Nacker and I spotted each other as soon as he stepped into court, but we had enough sense not to exchange greetings. We waited until the day's session was over and then went to a nearby bar to catch up with each other's news. He had been commissioned a few months after me and had spent the last few weeks milling about JRBD waiting to join the Royal Fusiliers in Korea when he turned nineteen. We continued to meet

---

* Volume II of 'Memory and Imagination' relates how, near the end of our time at school, Nacker pulled several practical jokes on me that put our friendship under severe strain. Nevertheless, I was pleased to see him again.

spasmodically and before long I felt it was only right to warn him that Colonel McIlroy was getting thoroughly fed up with having to acquit defendants. He was even talking about replacing Nacker with someone who would toe the line and make sure all those facing charges pleaded guilty. However, Nacker was not the type to be intimidated and the more I mentioned Colonel McIlroy's displeasure, the more he became determined to (as he put it) uphold the course of justice.

Of course, in the long run no one beats the Military Establishment and Nacker's comeuppance soon came. What infuriated me was that in order to maintain his record of success, he used me as a scapegoat. He sacrificed my interests to satisfy his vanity--- much the same as he had on a couple of occasions at school.

The case in question was a tricky one for Nacker and when--- for the first time--- the prosecuting officer out-manoeuvred him, Nacker became so desperate that he scuttled the case with a typically cunning ploy. He turned to Colonel McIlroy on a point of order. "Could I enquire, sir, just how long Mr. Contractor has been commissioned?"

McIrroy looked across at me. "Six months, sir," I volunteered.

"Need I say more, sir?" said Nacker.

"Yes, you certainly need. What's your point?"

"Sir, the Manual of Military Law makes it abundantly clear that no officer can be a Member of the Board of a Court-Martial unless he has held the Queen's Commission for a minimum of one year ... If I might quote the Manual, Chapter Five. Terms of Reference, sub para (b) ... And here I quote verbatim ... 'No officer ...' "

"All right, all right! I take your point."

"With respect, sir, I wonder if you do? This is a copy of the Convening Order for this case. Mr. Contractor has signed it, along with the other Members of the Board, specifically stating that he is qualified to serve on a court-martial."

"Yes ... Yes ... A mistake ... He obviously didn't realize ..."

"Ignorance is no excuse, sir. And I would also point out that you also signed the Convening Order. Indeed, the Convening Order states that you, as Presiding Officer, have fully satisfied yourself regarding all requirement of the said court-martial, and that, in particular, all Members of the court are eligible to serve."

"So?"

"A false declaration, sir! And by no means an isolated case. You've done it so often that it could be construed as a deliberate attempt to pervert the course of justice. It makes dozens of cases null and void. And I need hardly add that the maximum punishment for perverting the course of justice is life imprisonment ..."

"Good God, boy! Are you threatening me with life imprisonment?"

"Oh no, sir. I'm happy to conceded that in your case there might be extenuating circumstances ..."

"Contempt! Contempt of court!"

Colonel McIlroy had had enough. He wasn't going to be trifled with. No jumped-up National Service 2ndLieutenant gave him a lecture on the niceties of Military Law. Having declared Nacker in contempt of court, he told the prosecution to proceed. He then passed a guilty verdict on the defendant and gave him twenty-eight days in the slammer for having kicked a Japanese bar owner whose dog had peed on his boot.

Nacker was dismissed as the defending officer. He was sent back to JRBD in disgrace. I also suffered. I was sent back to the hospital to await a Medical Board which would determine my future. I seethed with anger. Nacker had effectively denied me one of the cushiest jobs imaginable, just to satisfy his conceit. It meant nothing to him that once I was declared fit I would be condemned to another long spell in Korea: back to the filth and the dirt, the rats, and once again part of Earl Gray's expendable cannon-fodder.

21

A Soft Landing

My medical board consisted of four doctors who questioned me about my hearing. I was so naive and honest that it never occurred to me that deafness was one of the easiest things in the world to fake, and that if I'd kept saying, "Pardon?" or "What?" or, "Sorry, I didn't quite catch that," they would never have known the difference. Instead I answered their questions normally and was passed as A1. Three days later Major Ward, i/c Postings, told me that I was to return to normal duties. However, much to my surprise, this wasn't to 'more hard pounding in Korea' as Dr Mason had predicted. Major Ward assigned me to an office job at HQBCFK. He explained that it was customary, although by no means official policy, for those who had been wounded in Korea to stay in Japan, an acknowledgement that they'd done their bit. He added that in my case, it was only commonsense to keep me away from more loud explosions.

My new job was as Camp Adjutant. The Camp Commandant was Lt/Colonel PV Gibson, MC, DSO and Bar, of the Household Cavalry. He was a gentleman of impeccable breeding and education, with a fine war record; but after five years of sitting on a horse outside Buckingham Palace his enthusiasm for soldiering had been sapped and he was loath to exert himself any longer. As Commandant he had a well-organised and comfortable sinecure, with plenty of time to socialise in the officers' mess, luxuriate over gourmet meals at the Officers' Club, and enjoy countless gin and tonics whilst puffing away on his favourite King Edward Imperials.

When I entered his office (which we were to share), looking smart in a new uniform issued by the hospital, he rose courteously to greet me and ushered me to my desk. For a time we exchanged pleasantries and then he explained my duties. "Nothing much for you to do really, young fellow. We're just glorified house-keepers. If we do our jobs properly no one is even aware of us. Like good umpires or referees."

Colonel Gibson was able to adopt this laissez-faire attitude on account of Eddie, our Japanese Chief Clerk and Interpreter. During World War II Eddie had done the same job for the Japanese Navy and he was so familiar with running the headquarters that contributions from Colonel Gibson or myself were of a purely peripheral nature. Eddie didn't look at all Japanese. He was tall and thin, with a long, narrow face, teeth refreshingly free of precious metal, and eyes which were large and round and shaded by effeminate lashes. He dressed like an Englishman: brogue shoes, a discretely chequered sports jacket with leather patches on the elbows, and grey flannel trousers.

Once Colonel Gibson had run out of small-talk, Eddie took me on a familiarization tour of the headquarters. He talked non-stop with an Oxford accent* and was anxious to impress upon me that it would be best to leave everything to him and simply rubber-stamp whatever he put in my 'In' tray. This advice was music to my ears.

"Of course, there are plenty of things you can get involved with," he added. "Like sessions on the pistol range with the nurses. Or highland dancing and housey-housey in the Officers' Club. And you have free access to transport. In the commandant's office we believe in looking after each other. I've made sure you've got a splendid bungalow and two very fine house-girls ..."

"House-girls? I have house-girls?"

"Of course. The very best. What it amounts to is this. 'You scratch my back and I'll scratch yours'."

Such a bold and straight-forward proposition was most unlike the Japanese, and positively out of order in a military sense. However, it soon became obvious that HQBCFK was not a place where the norm prevailed. Within the headquarters, practically anything went, and the contrast with Korea was staggering. The headquarters had no financial constraints. Everyone lived as though they were politicians or top civil servants, with no regard for expense, apart from those of a private nature which were collected simply by jotting down a random figure on a memo slip and lodging it with the Pay Corps CSM. The word 'budget' was unknown. I queried this with Colonel Gibson. He replied: "Budget? What budget? The only budget I'm aware of is the one the Chancellor of the Exchequer brings out once a year. That's quite sufficient, surely?"

Eddie's view was even more basic. "The British government opted to go to war, so naturally they must pay for whatever is necessary."

Yet in Korea every regiment had two budgets, one imposed by the War Office and another by the Regimental Quartermasters, inspired by their personal meanness. For example, our one-candle-a-week quota in Korea contrasted starkly with the Officers' Club restaurant in Kure. There, in a dining room which would have done credit to a five-star hotel, every table boasted an elaborate three-candle candelabra which received the undivided attention of a Japanese girl. She ensured that no officer ever sat down to a meal without fresh candles being lit. Her weekly wage was treble that of National Servicemen in the trenches.

The only thing the headquarters and Korea had in common was

---

* He had spent a year at Oxford University in 1937.

corruption, but once again Japan was in a class of its own. Eddie made Animal Evans, Kim, and the Korean porters look like amateurs. I soon sussed out that his job carried with it a built-in employment agency whereby every time he employed local labour he pocketed their first week's wages in commission. Consequently, HQBCFK was grossly over-staffed by scores of lovely young girls in the guise of waitresses, house-girls, assistant cooks, washer-uppers, cleaners, bottle-washers, and general assistants. They were all so charming, so polite, so full of deep bows, and so enhanced the general scenery, that no one was ever going to complain.

When I first ventured into the Officers' Mess for lunch I was greeted by two such girls in national costume whose sole function was to relieve officers of their caps, swagger sticks, and web belts, and wished them either 'good morning', 'good afternoon', or 'good evening', according to the time of day. In the mess itself, no expense had been spared. The main reception room was newly decorated and boasted a long, well-stocked bar with high stools arranged along it. At the far end of the room, an archway led into a spacious lounge with occasional tables and sumptuous easy chairs.

On that first day I lunched in the mess and then walked into Kure to see what the town had to offer. I was keen to see if it would be a suitable place for me to satisfy my mounting sexual frustrations. So far in life, I'd always funked chances of sexual adventures, especially at Eaton Hall; but now, having listened to the rampant sex-lives of my men in Korea, and seen at the courts-martial how even the most insipid privates managed to organize a sex-life, I was verging on desperate. As far as I could make out (and always excepting Rupert) I was the only virgin soldier left in the entire theatre of operations, and it struck me that there was no better place than Japan for rectifying this. Their geisha system offered a civilized approach to sex. It was artistic, smooth and unhurried, with beautiful girls seducing you into bed amid highly sensual music and dancing. In short, safe sex, free of complications, with an experienced partner who came as close to guaranteeing physical satisfaction as one could reasonably expect.

Unfortunately, none of this appertained in central Kure. One glimpse of the town very nearly put me off sex for life. I was confronted by the essence of the orient: the odour of decay, the flaunting of squalor, and the presence of stark poverty. Naked children ran amok; people of all ages and both sexes urinated whenever and wherever it took their fancy; and the main street (the Hondori) was nothing but a succession of gaudy bars, brothels, souvenir shops, and pachinko parlours crowded with young men and boys mesmerized by the flashing lights of the pin tables. Even in broad daylight neon signs flashed on and off and discordant Japanese music blared out, as though retail competition was all down to noise and brightness. The traffic consisted of three-wheeler scooter trucks and taxis, all toxic fumes at one end and blaring horns at the other, with irate drivers cursing and shouting at each other. Kimono-clad women gave way to droves of young girls mincing about in tight, revealing dresses, or miniscule skirts, patterned stockings, and topped off by Lana Turner-type sweaters stretched to bursting point by jacked-up bosoms. All of them were newly painted and decorated, mincing around in doorways and posturing and preening for the benefit of passing males.

Fletcher would have jumped with joy, but frankly it was not for me. It reminded me of Rupert's comment at Catterick when we first watched the tarts from Leeds debussing outside the Naafi Centre: "The kiss of death, Saj ... The kiss of death!"

My morale was restored when Eddie showed me my accommodation. My bungalow was excellent, as he had promised. It was of traditional Japanese design, sporting wooden-framed walls and with tissue paper stretched across the lattice-work. It was situated down a long driveway between two other bungalows, standing in its own grounds behind all the others. It had a large garden featuring artistically arranged rocks, stunted conifers, and a pond traversed by an ornate wooden bridge, all very reminiscent of willow pattern. Inside, the bungalow was light and airy and spotlessly clean, even though sparsely furnished. To my relief it had a conventional double-bed, not a futon, but in the lounge I was expected to sit on cushions.

The following morning I met my two house-girls. The first I knew of their presence was when one of them woke me with a cup of tea. As I rolled over and opened my eyes, I was horrified by what I saw. The word wizened flashed through my mind. She appeared to be kneeling--- homage gone mad--- but then I realized that that was all there was of her. I rubbed the sleepiness out of my eyes but her in-focus image was worse, instead of better. She was all teeth: gold-plated tombstones which were too big for her mouth. To make matters worse she'd obviously only just Dura-Glited them and her leer was so dazzling it nearly blinded me.

As I sat up in bed and accepted the tea, I recalled Eddie's words: 'You scratch my back and I'll scratch yours.' Well, if this was the oriental bastard's idea of scratching my back, he had another think coming. I watched the old crone as she edged backwards, bowing all the time. Then, as she slid the door panel back, I saw my other house-girl loitering behind her, anxious to make sure that all went well.

I could hardly believe my eyes. She was magnificent. I had no idea a Japanese girl could be so lovely. She was taller than most Japanese girls and her working kimono was incapable of hiding her curvaceous figure. Her skin was beautifully smooth and she had high cheek bones and impeccably moulded features, as though she had been fashioned by an artist bent on perfection. She had the freshness and vitality of youth; bright, sparkling eyes, long lashes which fluttered, and lustrous black hair that hung to her shoulders in natural waves. As our eyes met she gave me a flashing smile, revealing gleaming and level teeth, not a gold one among them. She bowed deeply and then greeted me in good English, saying--- rather curiously: "Weather being very good, officer-san." Then the old woman slid the door back and the girl disappeared.

I went to the mess for breakfast in high spirits. I was convinced that with a luxurious bungalow, a gorgeous young house-girl to look after me, and such a friendly CO, I had landed on my feet.

Nacker, I thought, all is forgiven, my old mate!

This early optimism turned out to be perfectly justified. The job of Camp Adjutant was an absolute doddle, even interesting. The job had come about due to a recent review of the H.Q's establishment. In this it had been deemed that since Lt Col Gibson had recently been promoted, he was entitled to an adjutant. This demanded similar adjustments the whole way down the line with numerous minions being promoted and new duties created; and it fell to me, as the new adjutant, to use my creative flair in organizing these spurious jobs at a junior level.

There was only one source of new talent and that was the Transit Camp, JRBD. There, an ever-revolving surplus of personnel was on hand, most of them --- like Nacker---waiting to be posted to Korea when they turned nineteen. Eddie gave me every assistance in my new job and his enthusiasm for the new establishment was infectious. He explained that as the headquarters grew bigger, the more important it became, and the more important it became, the greater the chances of advancement, job security, additional recreational opportunities, and a handsome increase in perks and general expenses. Foremost in Eddie's mind, of course, was that the bigger the headquarters became so the demand for civilian labour increased, the fundamental basis of his employment agency. At one point Eddie explained to me: "What we must never do, sir, is turn men away. Look upon yourself as an empire-builder."

Early on, Eddie gave me a list of the men due to report from JRBD, together with their qualifications and how they might be best employed in the headquarters. When my interviews got underway, Colonel Gibson listened in, even though he pretended to be engrossed in paperwork. Eventually, I was confronted by a stunted Scotsman from the Gorbals whose accent was so broad I couldn't understand a word he said. So I played for time by sending him on a tea break in the men's canteen. I then turned to the Colonel. "Sir, I couldn't understand a single word that man said."

"Neither could I. And he probably didn't understand you, either. Occupational hazard, I'm afraid. The best thing with Jocks like that is to promote them to acting, unpaid, lance-corporals. No one will take any notice of what they say but it does their egos the world of good. And it stops them from becoming bolshy. Any job will do. Probably best to leave that Jock in the canteen, his natural habitat. Lance-corporal i/c the tea urn, or i/c cockroach killing ... Something like that."

At first I thought he was joking, but he wasn't. After drawing heavily on his King Edward Imperial, and blowing a perfect smoke ring, he said: "There are other possibilities, of course. Things like corporal i/c fire precautions. Or corporal i/c earthquakes or floods. Or droughts. Any natural hazard. Even i/c traffic congestion. Always a good idea to have people in charge of things. It's what civil servants call contingency planning. Rather like having more admirals than ships in the navy. It also means that if you're ever stuck for something to do, you can go and inspect them. Snooping around is very important. Keeps the men on their toes. And justifies your existence. Good exercise for you, too. I like to see my subalterns marching around the place."

I took this as a broad hint that Colonel Gibson would be quite happy for me to enjoy flexible hours and be absent for long periods. So I waited a half an hour or so, hoping not to look too obvious, and then set off to inspect the officers' bungalows. All day, on and off, I had been thinking about my young house-girl. I just couldn't get her image out of my mind. I kept wondering if she really was as beautiful as my first impression indicated. I had a horrible feeling that she'd only seemed so stupendous on account of her side-kick being so horrendous.

When I reached my bungalow there was no signs of activity, so I strolled in and looked around the living room, wondering how I would ever make myself comfortable on cushions. I was still mooching about when the old crone came shuffling in, her slippers flip-flopping on the tatami mats. My presence took her by surprise. Her eyes flashed up and down me and eventually settled on my boots. Then she let out a shriek of anger. She was so incensed that she ran straight at me. She grasped me by the shoulders, twisted me round, and propelled me out of the room to the front door, haranguing me mercilessly as she pointed at a pair of slippers. Finally, she fell to her knees and started to undo my boots and anklets.

I succumbed to it all in sheer surprise, but eventually, when she made no headway in undoing the anklets, my patience ran out. "Okay! Okay! I'll do it."

I tried to push her away, but she clung on like a bulldog. We soon reached an explosive situation, both of us shouting progressively louder in our respective languages. We were saved from violence when the young house-girl came rushing in. She pulled the old woman away and scolded her. Then, as the old woman slunk off, clucking in disgust, the girl turned to me and bowed deeply. She was so mortified that her English deserted her. She groped for words, no doubt terrified I would dismiss them on the spot. Eventually she managed to say in English: "So sorry, Officer-san. Oh, so very sorry! Prease, Officer-san! Not minding old Muma-san. She very bad in head. She been living many, many years. Oh, so many years. And orl time she being prenty crazy."

As I replaced my boots with the slippers, she continued to recite a long catalogue of the old woman's shortcomings. It appeared she was not only bad in the head, but also a poor, lonely old war-widow who had been "prenty rong time roving tatami mats too much."

When she eventually fell silent, unable to think of any more of the old crone's shortcomings, her head slumped in shame and tears jerked down her cheeks. I could hardly believe it. First of all hysteria and now tears. "Hey, come on," I coaxed. "No need to cry. No harm done." I stretched out a hand and lifted her chin. "Don't get upset. Let's see your lovely smile."

A smile came, but very slowly. Then, amid loud sniffs, she wiped away her tears on the sleeves of her kimono--- an endearing, down-to-earth gesture. I put my arm around her shoulders and led her out into the garden where the afternoon sun was pleasantly warm. I looked around for somewhere to sit. I spotted a broad slab of rock set against the rear wall of the bungalow. It had two natural dips in it, making it a comfortable and intimate seat. I sat on it and relaxed against the wall, but she remained standing. When I motioned her to join me, she was shocked by my informality. So I stretched out a hand and eased her down beside me.

"Now then! The first thing is this. Don't blame the old lady. It was my fault. I should have taken my boots off. And it's bound to take time for us to learn each other's ways. In England we don't worry too much about slippers."

"No srippers in Ingrand, Officer-san?"

"We have them. But we don't worry about them too much."

"Oooh!" she exclaimed, drawing it out in a great gasp. "Orways srippers in Japan. Japan very civirised country."

"And so is England. But we're also very different."

"Ah, so! I knowing that, Officer-san."

She smiled and I noticed how her mouth twisted to one side slightly, making her look younger than ever, possibly no more than seventeen or eighteen. "What's your name?"

"Katsumi, Officer-san."

"Katsumi! That's lovely. But I'll give you an English name. Do you mind?"

"Oh, no! Not minding. Being very big honour."

"Good. Then I'll call you Kitten. You understand Kitten?"

"Ah so! Kitten being young cat."

"And my name is Sajit. So Sajit-san from now on. And we'll give the old lady a new name as well ..."

"No needing for that, Saji-san. She being Muma-san."

"You mean she's your grandmother?"

"Oh, no! Not Obichan .... Muma-san."

"Your mother?"

"Of course!" She burst into another smile and slapped her thighs in merriment. "Saji-san, now I torking very funny Japanese joke ... Oh, so very funny! In Japan, we orl time torking that girls orways ending up rooking rike Muma-sans."

She continued to giggle, as though nothing could ever be more unlikely. I did my best to look amused, not wanting to tell her that we had the same saying, although to us it was a truism, not a joke.

When she calmed down, I added: "All the same, I'll give her an English name. How about Moggy-san? A Moggy is like a kitten, but older."

"Ah so!" she cried excitedly. "A pretty old cat, ney?"

Here, at last, was my type of girl.

I soon got used to Katsumi's picturesque and quaint English. Like most Japanese, she often substituted 'r' for 'l',* and I became accustomed to her use of 'ney' at the end of sentences, either to question something or when groping for words. The overall effect was incredibly sexy, especially when, like so many Japanese, she came out with exclamations of surprise and/or delight, such as the 'Ah so!' and often reverted to long, drawn out sighs of, 'Oooh!'

What I found most endearing was her dedication to my welfare. Right from the start she looked after me as though I was the most important person in the world. The way she welcomed me back to the bungalow each evening was typical. As I turned the bend in my drive she would be silhouetted against the paper framework of the front door. She was watching for me through a chink, thinking I couldn't see her. Then, as soon as she spotted me, she flung back the door and burst into a smile, as though to say, "Surprise! Surprise!" She would wave excitedly and run out to meet me as fast as her getas would allow, her kimono hitched up in

---

* Not to be confused with the Chinese. They get them all mixed up.

her right hand, exposing her snow-white tabi socks.

"Herro, Saji-san!" she would cry.

Then, as she drew near me she would stop abruptly, become deadly serious, and bow in deep respect. Finally she would dash forward again, happier than ever. She'd come right up to my side and fall in step with me. I always longed to grab her in my arms and give her a hug and a kiss, but all I ever managed was to place an arm about her shoulders in a brotherly fashion. She then nestled in against me, her body moulded perfectly against mine, making me feel that we had been tailor-made for each other.

On my second night in my bungalow I wrote to Rupert. I told him of my experiences and how I was now Camp Adjutant at HQBCFK and might not be returning to Korea. I paused there, wondering how he would react. I dreaded that he would consider me a deserter; someone who had turned his back on his friends, men with whom I had shared so many dangers and discomforts. I did my best to let him know I was aware of this, but I was careful not to sound hypocritical. Nor did I tell him just how cushy my new job was. Most of all, I refrained from mentioning that I had been blessed with an adorable little house-girl, upon whom I had evil designs. The whole thing seemed to be a catalogue of deceits, so I ended the letter by asking him what they'd been up to; and whether they had a new platoon commander yet? I told him I still hadn't received my kit, but the urgency had passed. I signed off by urging him to write back soon. Without actually spelling it out, I tried to convey that I missed him and still regarded 12 Platoon as *my* platoon.

The days passed swiftly. Every morning, I got up as soon as I heard my house-girls enter the bungalow, anxious to have a chat with Katsumi before going to breakfast in the mess. Likewise, later in the day, around 1640 hours, I knocked off early and conducted another inspection of the officers' bungalows, with the same aim of getting to know her better. I was soon going back at lunch time as well, so that our friendship and our familiarity developed apace. I was delighted by the way she delegated the household chores to her mother and assumed total responsibility for entertaining and caring for me.

I soon discovered that she was very au fait with the workings of the headquarters. One of my earliest duties was to help open the camp laundry. Eddie suggested that I should select the applicants for the jobs as laundry girls, and not unnaturally I picked out all the best-looking ones. When I next saw Katsumi she smiled knowingly and said: "Prenty good-rooking raundry girls today, Officer-san?"

Soon afterwards, she pointed out to me that officers could, if they so wished, have their breakfasts cooked in their bungalows, with house-girls drawing the necessary ingredients from Corporal Cane in the mess, and since she promised that she was quite familiar with cooking English breakfasts, I went along with her suggestion. It turned out to be a near-disaster. For two mornings on the trot, all she served up were six undercooked fried eggs. Not wanting to be critical, or to upset her in any way, I gulped down acres of raw gooey egg-white; but on the third morning I just couldn't face any more of it. I gave her a list of ingredients to get from the mess and told her I was going to give her a lesson on how to cook a proper English breakfast.

She didn't like it one bit. She protested vehemently and insisted that her English breakfasts were perfect, cooked according to instructions. Puffed up by indignation, she scampered off to a cupboard and produced a book on English cooking. She held it aloft triumphantly and then placed it in my lap, open at a chapter headed: 'The English Breakfast'. She traced along the print with a finger until she found the relevant passage. Then she cried: "Here being, Saji-san! Ingrish men riking big breakfasts. Oh, such very big breakfast! Six rightly fried eggies. Book saying!"

I took a closer look at the book. It was one of those foreign efforts full of ludicrous phrases which no English author could have made up even if he'd tried. Most were comical, but I was careful not to laugh and appear condescending.* "I'm sorry, Kitten," I said, "but your book is wrong. An English breakfast is nothing like that. I'll show you."

I brushed aside further protests and sent her on her way. As she hurried off down the drive she paused to wave. I laughed and shouted: "Hubba! Hubba!" She hurried off again, only to stop twice more for more bows. "Hubba! Hubba!" I shouted for a second time, pretending that my patience was wearing thin, and off she sprinted, going all the faster, her laughter clearly audible.

When she returned with the goodies I lost no time in setting up the cooking lesson. It became strictly between the two of us. Moggy-san kept well to the rear and made her usual 'clucking' noises every time Katsumi and I made physical contact, which was pretty often. The first thing I did was show her how to handle the frying pan. This entailed standing very close behind her, my arms about her, my hands over hers, and our bodies rubbing together as I demonstrated how to waggle it about in order to stop the eggs from sticking. The more I waggled, the closer our contact became. I could feel every contour of her body through her thin kimono, and likewise she must surely have been aware of my

---

* A typical example was: 'Engrish men rike to eat their potatoes with their jackets on. Some of them eat their jackets as well.'

excitement.

I emphasized the importance of pricking sausages to stop them splitting, and how, in order to get them Arab-brown and not charcoal-burnt, it was essential to cook them slowly, which meant even more jiggling of the frying pan. I also insisted that the tomatoes be skinned in very hot water and that all mushroom stalks be thrown away, only fit for peasants. The bacon had to be crisp and brittle, even a little burnt. Most of all, the white of the eggs had to be absolutely solid, with the yokes firm but a little runny, all of which was achieved by the skillful flicking up of boiling fat with the spatula: more jiggling about.

Eventually, when I came to the end of the lesson, I piled all the food on to a meat dish and declared: "Now that's a proper English breakfast. A full house. One of everything."

Then I insisted that they sat down with me to eat it all. They protested that this was way above their station, but I gave them no option and for the first time in their lives they wielded knives and forks instead of chopsticks.

When I returned to my bungalow later that afternoon, Katsumi did her usual dash down the drive to greet me. Then, amid much giggling, she said she had a surprise for me, but she wouldn't tell me what it was. She insisted that I kept to what had become my usual routine--- having a rest on my bed whilst reading a chapter or two of 'For Whom the Bell Tolls'.

Eventually, instead of Katsumi bringing me a cup of tea, Moggy-san drew my bedroom door back and beckoned me into the lounge. It was then that I noticed that both Kasumi and Moggy-san had changed into their best kimonos, Katsumi's featuring exotic birds and Moggy-san's yellow chrysanthemums. Around their waists were brightly coloured obis and they had their hair freshly arranged, piled high and supported by elaborate combs.

We exchanged bows very formally and Katsumi explained: "Now, Saji-san! Very big surprising. Oh, such big surprising! Now I showing you how civirised Japan is. Now, we having Honourable Japanese Tea Ceremony."

She half-turned and indicated the apparatus which she had arranged with great care. I was instructed to sit beside Moggy-san, on my heels, Japanese style, rather than cross-legged. Finally she adopted a stern look of concentration and started the ritual. Water in a large, wrought iron pot was heated over a charcoal burner and when it came to the boil she placed green, powdered tea in chunky ceramic bowls and poured the boiling water into them by means of a small, wooden ladle. Finally, with a split, bamboo whisk, she brought the tea to a fine froth. Being the honourable guest, I was served first. As Katsumi passed one of the bowls to me she demonstrated how it was to be held with my left hand around it and my right hand beneath it, the main design of the bowl facing me. Then she whispered out the corner of her mouth: "Saji-san! Now you torking 'osakini' to Moggy-san."

"Why do I say that?"

"You torking 'osakini' because you very sorry for drinking first." Her hiss was again very secretive, out the corner of her mouth.

"But she can go first. I don't mind."

"Never happen! Honourable guest orways going first. Japanese way. You torking 'osakini'. I saying!"

I did as I was told, realising there was more to this girl than met the eye. As we drank, she sat in a stiff, upright position, very precise in her movements, determined to demonstrate the full beauty and discipline of the Honourable Tea Ceremony. After we had had two refills, Moggy-san cleared things away. I thought that was the end of it but Katsumi retained her formal posture and said: "Now, we torking crever things, Saji-san."

"What about?"

"Oh, orl sorts of things … Just crever things … "

I found this a daunting prospect, but I needn't have worried. She had it all worked out. Her idea of clever things was a barrage of questions. She fired them at me so swiftly that all continuity soon disappeared and we darted from subject to subject with bewildering speed. She started off with questions about London and the River Thames. Then she wanted to know the height of the average English lady, and whether they wore high heels and silk stockings like American ladies. Then, was Britain as big as Japan and did I live by the sea, or maybe up a mountain?

Her questions went on for nearly an hour and whilst I was more than happy to submit to her inquisition I was eventually forced to stand up on account of excruciating pains in my legs. It was so bad that I went for a walk around the garden. When I returned she was still sitting there, but there was an impish grin across her face. In my absence she had obviously been up to something mischievous. As I settled down again she feigned great seriousness, and carried on with her questions as though nothing had happened.

"Ingrand green and preasant rand Saji-san?"

"Yes. Very."

"Rike Ingrish hymns saying?"

"Yes … What do you know about hymns? Are you a Christian?"

"Never happen! I being Nicheren Buddhist. Orso, some Shinto. Bit this. Bit that. But I knowing orl about Ingrish hymns."

She burst out laughing, so amused that she rocked backwards and forwards, slapping her thighs. She couldn't contain her secret any longer. "Now you seeing very good books. Oh, such very good books!"

She whipped out several slim books from beneath her kimono, as though doing a conjuring trick. They were companion volumes to her cookery book, battered and worn and obviously treasured possessions. She held one up triumphantly and shuffled round to my side. She opened it at the middle spread, showing a picture of the Lake District. The caption read: 'England's Green and Pleasant Land' and superimposed over the picture was the full text of 'Jerusalem'. She turned the pages, revealing pictures of famous cathedrals, with the words of more hymns.

When she finished leafing through the book she looked up at me, her eyes widening. "Ingrish books making very hard reading, Saji-san. Writing orl wrong," Then she demonstrated how, in Japanese, the text went from back to front, from right to left, and from bottom to top. "Orl time getting oh so mixed up. Orl time starting wrong prace."

As she laughed at her difficulties, I watched her closely, intrigued by one thing; wondering if I was treading on dangerous ground. "How old are you, Kitten-san?"

"Saji-san! Japanese rady not torking how many years."

"Sorry."

"Neary having birthday seventeen. Very bad in head for age, ney?"

"Far from it. You're as bright as a button. And I'll tell you what. You look after me properly and I'll help you with your English. We'll have a lesson each day and I'll soon have you speaking like an English lady."

"I being very good house-girl, Saji-san. I promising!"

We smiled at each other self-consciously, as though we had made a declaration of everlasting loyalty. I knew then that my feelings for Katsumi were a lot more than a temporary infatuation.

22

Under the Spell

A few days later there were two developments. The first was that I met Nacker again. I went into the mess for lunch and there he was, perched on a bar stool, nursing a pint of beer. We greeted each other as though we hadn't seen each other in years. He said he had a new job as Personal Assistant to Brigadier Clay, who commanded the headquarters. I told him of my posting and we sank numerous beers to celebrate our mutual good fortune. Finally, we had a very jovial lunch and by the time we parted our old friendship was back on solid ground. My resentment over the court-martial was forgotten.

The second development was the arrival of my kit from Korea. With it was a letter from Rupert. His news was bad. The casualties from the tank blue-on-blue had been three killed and four wounded, excluding me, since no one considered me to have been properly wounded, the Earl putting it around that such deafness was common, cured itself, and certainly didn't justify evacuation.

Rupert's main news was that they had a new platoon commander, a very unpleasant fellow named Denning, straight from Sandhurst. Rupert described him as a martinet, simply bursting to throw his weight around and insisting that everything be done by the book. Beau Brummell had been the first to suffer. When he committed his usual sin of letting the CP space-heater go out, Denning (who had just returned from a patrol) gave him an almighty bollocking and threatened to reduce him to the ranks. A little later, he banished him from the CP and made him share a bunker with Bertie Mee, Animal Evans, and Kim. That left Rupert alone with Denning in the CP and every time he pulled out his exercise book to work on his poems, Denning snapped: "For God's sake stop that infernal scribbling!"

Rupert related how, when Denning first saw one of his verses on the notice board, he went completely berserk. He forbade Rupert ever to do it again and made it quite clear that he was the only one with the authority to put anything on the notice board. The next thing he did was to decree that no one was ever again to refer to Major Gray as 'The Earl'. Another new rule was that no one was allowed to enter his CP unless summoned. He'd put a small square of corrugated iron outside the doorway and anyone who wanted to see him had to knock on it and wait until he had shouted 'Aventi!', an affectation he justified by telling everyone he had an Italian mother.

The Tuesday morning mail club had also been banned, although according to Rupert the lads still held clandestine meetings with Corporal Holroyd in the chair. When Denning had been confronted by the lads coming into the CP with their letters clutched in their hands, ready to exchange the latest gossip, he'd not only sent them packing but he'd rounded on Rupert and said: "Why the hell should I want to listen to their drivel?" When Rupert explained that it had all started because of the illiterates, Denning made it perfectly clear that he had no intention of becoming involved.

"So now I'm writing all their letters on my own," Rupert explained.

His most alarming piece of news was that Earl Gray had volunteered Dog Company's services as the reinforcement company on Hill 355, where the Royal Fusiliers were being stretched to the limit. On reading this, all the danger and fears of Korea came flooding back, and I was once again possessed by a feeling of guilt, that by escaping it all I had deserted my platoon. Because of this I played down my good fortune in my reply, even though I was bursting to tell him about Katsumi. I knew I would tell him eventually, but I judged it best to wait until they were back in reserve and out of danger. Even then, I intended to be pretty tactful. Good friend though Rupert was, our monastic life at Catterick, and our priggish attitude towards women, made me wonder if he would despise me for having gone the same way as Fletcher and the others.

Meanwhile, Katsumi's English lessons got under way. I kept them as simple as possible, my only rule being that she maintained a vocabulary note-book for new words or those she misused. With the latter, she had to write them out ten times as an act of discipline. This added spice to our lessons. We played a game in which I pounced on her mistakes and she did her utmost to justify them by referring to her dictionary or one of her English books. Whenever I won the day, she would write it out in her note-book, prefacing her labours with: "Oh! So very sorry, Saji-san. So bad in head!"

When she won the day--- which I sometimes contrived--- she laughed with delight. "There you are, Saji-san ... I saying!"

After her English lessons I took a bath before having dinner in the mess, and as our friendship progressed, so my baths assumed a special significance. From about the age of six, I'd always bathed behind a locked door, but this was very alien to the Japanese attitude, accustomed as they were to mixed bathing; and by dint of her personality Katsumi soon moulded my bathing habits into their ways: a time of informality and social intercourse, a shared experience rather than a solitary and secretive sojourn.

This evolved gradually and only reached fulfilment after a major row.

Each time I vacated the bathroom, Moggy-san would go in to clear up, to take the towels away for drying, and to make sure I hadn't soaked her beloved tatami mats. On the day in question I was getting dressed in my bedroom when I heard Muma-san scuttle back to the kitchen. She was going twice her normal pace and was mumbling away so loudly that I knew trouble was brewing. This was confirmed when urgent, near-hysterical cries came from the kitchen. There was a stampede back to the bathroom and finally Katsumi made a dramatic appearance in my doorway.

"What the mattering with you then, Officer-san?"

"What do you mean?"

"What you been doing in barfing water, ney?"

"Nothing! Washing!"

"Barfing water not for washing!"

"Isn't it? You could have fooled me. Then what's it for?"

Indignantly, she explained that in Japan it was unthinkable to wash in the bath. One washed under the shower and then soaked and relaxed in a steaming hot bath. The thought of me lying about in my own dirty water made her pull a face of disgust, as though I was some lower form of life.

The following day, having completed our English lesson, she made it clear that she was not prepared to tolerate any more mucky English habits, even if it meant taking full control of my bathing. She didn't regard her attitude in the least presumptuous or intrusive. She saw it as her duty to educate a foreigner who knew no better.

When I arrived at the bathroom she was kneeling on the tatami, running the water, her kimono sleeve pulled up to her elbow as she swirled the water about. She had also turned the shower on, a broad hint for me to get under it and wash. I took my time, assuming that once I'd emerged from the shower cubicle she would go away; but not a bit of it. She stayed exactly where she was, showing no signs of withdrawing. When I became just as stubborn and remained motionless, my towel wrapped around me, she was eventually forced to give way and depart, but not without the distinctive 'clucking' noises she had inherited from Moggy-san.

Having established my right to privacy, I followed her instructions and soaked in the bath and thoroughly enjoyed it. Before long the door slid open. Her small face poked round the corner and she grinned sheepishly. Then she entered tentatively, making a feeble excuse for her presence by asking if I would like a cup of tea. As she edged into the room I could see she was on tip-toe, trying to peer over the side of the bath to see if I had sullied the water with soapy scum. When satisfied that I hadn't, she smiled brightly and said: "Fetching cuppa now, Saji-san."

"Oh, good. So kind of you, Kitten-san." I waited until she was drawing the door back and added: "Would you mind passing the soap, please. ..."

"Officer-san ..." Then she saw me grin. "You teasing, Saji-san!"

This amused her so much that she went through her usual routine of doubling-up and slapping her thighs. From thereon, intimacy during my bath-time was a matter of natural progression. She popped in and out on any pretext, thinking nothing of it, my nakedness of no consequence to her. With my British middle-class upbringing I found it more difficult to adjust, but eventually I took the attitude that if she didn't mind, then who was I to object?

Soon, as a matter of routine, she was helping me in and out of the bath, as though I was an old crock, and she stayed with me while I soaked, every now and then testing the temperature of the water before topping it up with more hot water. Between these topping-ups she squatted at the side of the bath and talked of this and that with her usual enthusiasm. She told me about her relationship with the other house-girls. How, in the hiatus between lunch and tea, they met up with the waitresses in a spare room in the mess. Ostensibly it was a rest period, but in reality a forum for gossip. With great glee, and amid smiles and giggles, she told me about the other girls and their officers: how Padre Muldoon hated the Japanese so much that he never spoke to them, and how other officers grunted rather than spoke, with one house-girl reduced to a nervous wreck because her officer only ever grunted: 'Good show', 'My word', and 'Fair enough', none of which had any clear meaning.

When I asked her what they said about me, she explained that since I was about the same age as most of them, I was regarded with interest and they were curious to know if I was any different to the others, or just a younger edition; and to my alarm she explained that in order to impress them that I was indeed different, she had told them about everything we did together: how I always knocked off duty early; how we had developed a ritual for greeting each other in the drive; and her favourite story about how I had discovered pin holes she'd made in the paper walls of the bungalow in order to monitor my movements, and how, when I realized what she was up to, I'd made my own pin-holes and spied on her; and how this had developed into a game as to who could catch the other peeping, with the greatest laugh of all time coming when we found ourselves eye-ball to eye-ball, peeping through the same hole.

She said the other girls were amazed by all this, knowing that if they did the same thing with their grumpy old officers they would be dismissed on the spot. Katsumi then told me, with conspiratorial glee, that they would never have dared to lay on Honourable Tea Ceremonies for their officers, let alone help them in and out of their baths, or shampooed their hair, or washed their backs, or dry between their toes.

In more intimate moments we often experienced lingering eye-contact, during which nervous smiles passed between us, but nothing further happened. It made me wonder what had happened to my red corpuscles. Surely, any other young fellow would have made a grab for her long ago? After all, I could hardly have had greater encouragement. Whenever I put an arm around her, she always welcomed it, and during the cooking lesson there was no doubt about the pleasure she derived from our physical contacts. Furthermore, I often saw her looking at me with eyes full of devotion--- a special look for a special person.

I could only put my reticence down to something inborn, some hidden and subconscious hang-up. I was probably steeped in the fear of offending someone so vulnerable, based on the unseemly behaviour I had witnessed as a boy at Silver Coombe when the promiscuity of 'Corp' and Mary had got them into such a mess.*

Whatever the reason, and however much of a restraining influence it had, I never doubted that I had stumbled across someone very special, maybe even unique.

Letters from Rupert arrived fairly regularly. He kept me well-posted on their experiences on Hill 355. They were having a constant flow of casualties, but so far none of the old brigade. Denning came in for criticism and it seemed he couldn't do anything right. I found it hard to imagine that he was any worse than I had been when we went into the line, but then Rupert's moans and groans were not so much directed at his military incompetence, so much as his snobbery, arrogance and his love of petty discipline.

Denning had also fallen out with Earl Gray, which reflected directly on 12 Platoon; but undoubtedly Denning's biggest crime (at least in 12 platoon's eyes) was to give Kim his marching orders. He'd stripped him of his platoon wage and his uniform and beret and banished him to the Korean Porters' compound with orders to never to show his face again. However, Kim was not that easy to get rid of and Animal Evans visited him regularly, assuring everyone that if he ever found Kim being ill-treated or bullied, then he would hold Denning responsible and fill him in. He got great moral support from Fletcher who kept chipping in with: "That's right, mate. Mash the bastard up!"

I read the more palatable parts of Rupert's letters to Katsumi. She was fascinated by them and soon formed her favourites among the lads,

---

* See Volume I, 'Gran and Mr. Muckey'. 'Corp' ran the RAF barrage balloon in the field opposite Silver Coombe and Mary was our maid. 'Corp' was a sex maniac and Mary was a nymphomaniac, and the combination of the two led to dire trouble.

Animal Evans in particular. Once, after a long spell of talking about Korea, she said: "You miss your rads, Saji-san?"

I confessed that I did and I tried to explain to her that although they were just ordinary blokes, and certainly no great shakes as soldiers, they had a special place in my affections because of what we had been through together; how we'd faced up to death and how we'd come to depend on each other. I tried--- successfully, I hope---- to explain how this bonded us as nothing else ever could. "And the odd thing is," I confessed, "that although most of the experiences were awful, I wouldn't have missed them for the world."

"You being very good officer, Saji-san?"

"Me? Good Lord, no! I was hopeless."

She smiled, convinced that I was being self-depreciating. "Goto-san, he saying you being a very good officer ..."

"Who's Goto-san?"

She laughed. "Saji-san, You seeing him orl time."

"Not our clerk, Eddie?"

"Of course. He my number one cousin. One time being my nakado."

"What's that?"

"Oh, crazy-in-head thing ... No mattering any ronger."

"No, tell me."

"Rong-time gone ... Now finished ... "

"But I'd like to hear."

She blushed and tried to hide her embarrassment. "Nakado being man for finding husbands for young radies. But not working for me. "

"I can't believe that!"

"No. Not working for me."

"Oh, come on ..."

"I saying!"

I left it at that. I had ventured on to delicate ground and for the first time it dawned on me just how little I knew about her. It just amazed me that someone so efficient and well-connected as Eddie had failed to find her a husband. Surely anyone could have found her a husband? Men would surely have been queuing up to marry her? I pondered over this mystery quite a lot and eventually I guessed that a suitable young man had been selected whilst she was a schoolgirl, only for him to be killed in the war. Yet even that didn't make sense. There were clearly thousands of others who had survived and would have been delighted to have her as a wife.

23

The Green-Eyed Monster

Whilst Katsumi and I became increasingly obsessed with one another, and spent more and more time together, I still met Nacker fairly often in the officers' mess. He wasn't enjoying Kure at all, and although I sympathized with him I found his constant moaning rather irksome. He kept urging me to join him on late-night forays into town, which he saw as the only way to alleviate the boredom of his job and the staid company in the officers' mess. He just couldn't understand why I had an early dinner every night and then disappeared to the solitude of my bungalow without any explanation.

No doubt I should have told him, but I didn't. I dreaded him meeting Katsumi. I knew him well enough to realize that once he'd set eyes on her he would try to elbow his way in.

In an attempt to lure me away from my bungalow he told me of several classy bars he'd found well away from the Hondori where the lighting was dim, the décor attractive, and where slinky hostesses with good English made the blood race in anticipation. Furthermore, the bars abounded with ambitious Kure girls trying to establish friendships with officers; but since they hunted in pairs he'd never had any success, hence his desperation that I should join him.

Once or twice, and very much against my better judgement, I went out with him, but only after Katsumi had gone home. We would drift from bar to bar until the early hours, drinking watered-down beers and locally brewed sake whilst he eyed-up females duos. When he spotted some promising new talent his enthusiasm knew no bounds and as he closed in for what he termed 'the kill', he would crack the same old joke. "Here we go, Saj! Our lucky night. Don't fancy yours much, though."

Neither did I. Compared with Katsumi, they were disasters and I wouldn't have touched them with the proverbial barge pole. So all that ever happened was that we got huge bills and ended up with harsh words, Nacker accusing me of being an embarrassing drag. "What's the matter with you, for God's sake? Don't you want a good shag?"

Sunday afternoons were very different. Then, we got along fine. We concentrated on enjoying the marvellous curry lunches laid on in the mess. After two of helpings of Corporal Cane's 'Equatorial', followed by banana splits and a couple of glasses of port, we were only fit for a long siesta in my bungalow. We usually woke-up around tea time and then indulged in our old school pastime of chess.

One afternoon it was so warm that we took chairs and a table into the garden. The game took a predictable course and Nacker was just about to declare 'check-mate' when he saw someone moving about in the bungalow. He turned so suddenly that he nearly overturned the board.

"My God! Who the hell is that?"

I followed his gaze and saw Katsumi step out into the garden. She was dressed in her best kimono. As always, she looked marvellous, even though I detected a certain nervousness about her, as though she was frightened of intruding.

"Who is she?" repeated Nacker.

Again, I ignored him. I hurried towards her, smiling broadly, my arms stretched out in welcome. Nacker followed close behind. "Who is she?" he demanded more urgently.

"Kitten!" I exclaimed. "What a marvellous surprise! I didn't expect to see you today. And you look stunning. Absolutely stunning. Meet my good friend, Nacker Gilbert."

She bowed to him and Nacker bowed back. His eyes never left her face. Katsumi was so embarrassed by his admiration that she blushed and glanced downwards demurely. Then she turned to me and said: "Saji-san! So very sorry disturbing you on rest-on-bed day ..."

"Nonsense. You're welcome any time. Take a seat and I'll go and make a pot of tea."

"Never happen! Officer-san not making tea. I doing that. I saying!"

I knew it was futile to argue with her once she'd declared 'I saying!' so I shrugged and said: "Okay. If it makes you happy. But bring a cup out for yourself."

As she hurried off, I chuckled. "She's a lovely kid. I call her Kitten. A little joke between ourselves."

"You crafty bugger! Who is she? An actress?"

"My house-girl."

"Good God! How come you've got one like that? Mine's an old bag."

"Luck of the draw, I suppose."

"Bollocks! No one gets a house-girl like that without a good reason."

When Katsumi returned with the tea tray, we crossed over to the rock-seat, intending that she should join us, but she considered that far too informal and squatted on the ground in front of us. She took great care over pouring the tea and when Nacker received his, he complimented her on it.

"Kitten is an expert on making tea," I said proudly. "She knows all about warming the pot. And cooking my English breakfast."

"She cooks your breakfast? No wonder I never see you in the mess."

"Yes, well... There are house-girls and house-girls, old boy."

"So it seems!"

When Katsumi finished her tea she shifted about nervously, adopting a stern attitude. She was clearly about to make an announcement. "Saji-san! This afternoon I coming to bungarow very serious. Oh, so very serious! Not minding serious torking, ney?"

"Not at all."

"Saji-san, I torking very big number-one thanking you ... From orl the young radies you giving jobs to in raundry. They orl knowing you taking on prenty girls too many. Raundry not needing forty young radies."

"Really? I'm afraid I wasn't counting. I left that to Eddie."

"Everyone saying you very kind man, Saji-san. Oh, so very kind. Very good the way you keeping orl those young radies from jig-a-jigging."

The sudden introduction of army vernacular, especially coming from such an innocent-looking young girl, took us by surprise. Nacker was so taken aback that the tea he was drinking went down the wrong way and burst back out of his nose in an unsightly mess. Katsumi watched him with great concern as he coughed and spluttered. When he'd recovered himself, and was mopping up his embarrassment with his handkerchief, she asked: "I torking wrong thing, Saji-san?"

"No, no. Don't take any notice of old Nacker. Any mention of sex and he always does that. And anyhow, how exactly have I saved these girls? And perhaps they like jig-a-jigging."

She was shocked. She sat bolt upright, bristling indignantly. "Saji-san! I not torking about nice jig-a-jigging. Not jig-a-jigging in rove. I torking about number ten dirty jig-a-jigging on the Hondori."

"Oh, I see! That's different."

"So sorry! I torking wrong thing. I knowing."

"Not at all. You just caught us on the hop, that's all."

"You thinking I being young girl not knowing things, ney?"

"Of course not. It's just that we call it love-making. But tell me how I've saved these laundry girls?"

She explained that if I hadn't given the girls jobs, they would have ended up working in bars along the Hondori. The bar owners and pimps were so excited by the number of British troops flooding into Kure that they were signing up girls as fast as they could in order to cater for the extra demand for sex.

"I know jig-a-jigging going on orl time, Saji-san. My cousin, next hill-over, she being New Geisha in Wirrows Hotel. She orl time jig-a-jigging profession-wise. But jig-a-jigging on Hondori not nice, ney?"

"Awful," I agreed. "In England we call them whores."

"In Japan, pan-pan girls. Getting vocab book. Must be remembering 'rove-making', ney?"

She hurried indoors to up-date her vocab book.

"Is she always like this?" asked Nacker.

"Always! Wonderful, isn't she?"

"Out of this world! And you're no doubt shagging the arse off her?"

Thankfully, I was saved from having to answer by the speed with which Katsumi returned. We rose to our feet as she reappeared, as though she was the lady of the house rather than my house-girl.

Shortly afterwards, we went for a stroll around the garden. Katsumi walked between us, her arms linked through ours, creating a delightful intimacy. She was explaining the intricacies of Japanese rock gardens when I had another visitor. It was Lance-corporal Baker, one of the men from JRBD who--- in an inspired moment--- I had appointed i/c goldfish and ornamental ponds. As he came from around the side of the bungalow Katsumi stopped abruptly, withdrew her arms from ours, and moved towards him in welcome.

He was a bizarre but captivating sight. He wore dark blue football shorts, knee-length Wellington's, and a brown pullover that was so baggy it could only have been knitted with utility wool. In one hand he had a shrimping net, as though he was looking for the Inland sea, and in the other a string-handled jam jar full of murky liquid, as though he was about to deliver a sample to the hospital. Despite all this, he was an incredibly handsome young man, a potential male model if ever I saw one. By the way he and Katsumi kept exchanging bows it was obvious that they were old friends. "What's going on here, Baker?" I demanded. "What are you doing?"

"Stock-taking, sir. Miss Katsumi said you would be in."

"How come you know each other?"

"Baker-san, he coming every day for fooding the fish."

I didn't like the sound of that at all, but I made a conscious effort not to get stroppy. I ushered Baker over to the ornamental pond and said: "Well now you're here, you may as well carry on. Do whatever it is that you have to do."

We watched as he went about his self-invented duties. He knelt beside the pond, sprinkled flaky bit of food over the water, and made soft cooing noises. As the fish surfaced, he caught them in his shrimping net and then studied them minutely, as though sexing them. Then, very lovingly, he returned them to the water, saying: "Wee ... Off you go, Tiddler!" Finally, he recorded his finding (whatever they were) in a note book.

It struck me that he was taking his duties a little too seriously, so once he'd finished I rejoined him. "Corporal, has it ever occurred to you that the War Office might resent paying you a quid a week to feed goldfish?"

"Yes, sir. It has, actually."

"Good. Then keep it under your tin hat. And never visit officers' bungalows again. Just keep to the headquarters buildings."

When I rejoined Katsumi and Nacker, they were deep in conversation. She was doing all the talking, divulging something which amused her and intrigued Nacker. She had a hand on his knee and was sitting close to him, speaking very confidentially. He was leaning towards her in exaggerated interest. They were behaving as though they'd known each other for years. I edged in between them.

"Saji-san, I been torking about Baker-san. He the most rovery boy I ever been seeing. Orl us house-girls, we orl roving him. Oh, so crazy about him."

Divulging this mass passion for Baker sent her into giggles. Nacker looked at me and smirked, as though delighted that Baker was the apple of her eye and not me. Once Katsumi had stopped giggling she added with conspiratorial glee: "Now I must be terring you number one big time secret! Oh, such very big secret! Baker-san, he being wrong-way-round boy." Nacker and I looked at her in amazement even though her meaning was quite clear. "We not minding. We orl roving him just the same."

Nacker and I tried our best to persuade her to stay on, to share an evening meal with us, but around five o'clock she excused herself and said she had to return home. I offered to call a taxi for her, but she wouldn't hear of it. Once she'd gone, the bungalow was horribly empty. Nacker kept asking questions about her. I wasn't surprised. He, just like every other young bloke who ever met her, had fallen in love with her at first sight.

Eventually, we went to the Officers' Club for dinner. It was the first time Nacker had visited the club, so we didn't stint ourselves. We started with prawn cocktails, went on to steaks with fried onions, and finished off with Peach Melbas. As we ate, Nacker either talked about Katsumi or moaned about his house-girl.

"And just look at this place," he said, indicating the two delightful waitresses who had been serving us, and who giggled like mad every time he gave them the eye. "The place is crawling with crumpet, all of them crying out for it. Yet all I've got is a boring job and an old bag as a house-girl. What I need is a job like you've given that bloke Baker. What a job! Free access to wander around the bungalows shagging all this gorgeous crumpet."

"He's a poofter, for God's sake. You heard what Katsumi said."

"Bollocks! With a girl like Katsumi there's no such thing as a poofter. I'd watch him like a hawk if I was you."

"Nacker, you're pathetic! She's not like that …"

"Oh, no? You'll be telling me next you aren't shagging her."

"That's none of your damn business."

"Come off it, Saj! We've been friends since we were kids."

I blushed deeply, but didn't reply. He stared at me and then sighed, despairing of me. "Well all I can say is that if you aren't, then you're a bloody idiot. Girls like that don't grow on trees. And if you don't ..."

"You will ..."

"Don't put words into my mouth, Saj! All I was going to say is that if you don't you'll regret it for the rest of your life."

Lying bastard, I thought.

24

I Take The Plunge

Despite Kasumi's assurance that Baker was a homosexual, I was glad I'd banned him from the officers' quarters. I only wished that I could have banned Nacker too. I knew he'd have no compunction in casting aside our friendship in order to land a prize like Katsumi. He would justify it with a whole lot of garbage about there being no rules in love or war; and that anyhow the choice was hers, not mine.

It did at least make me face up to reality. It forced me to admit that neither Nacker nor Baker were my problem. My problem was myself. I was so bloody pathetic. I began to hate myself for my feebleness and I realized that unless I got on with things, I would only have myself to blame if someone else stepped in where I feared to tread. So I resolved to act. I would definitely take the plunge. Definitely!

How I was going to go about it was another matter. I just didn't have it within me to make a crude lunge at her and end up grappling with her like a frustrated teenager, even though that's exactly what I was. Mercifully, the perfect chance soon came. We were halfway through one of her English lessons and had come to the end of one of her books. She hurried off to get another and came back with one entitled: 'The United Kingdom: Four Different Countries'.

"Very good book this, Saji-san! First chapter, being orl about Ingrish men. And Ingrish men, they being oh, so very funny. Book saying Ingrish men …."

"Don't tell me! Englishmen need time."

She looked up enquiringly, wondering what I meant.

In answer, I burst into an old army song, one of our favourites during our forays into Yorkshire pubs with Sergeant Evans.

> *"An Englishman, even when in his prime,*
> *Has to adapt, and that takes him time.*
> *While Frenchmen will do it at the drop of a hat,*
> *And Eyeties surprise girls on the Welcome mat,*
> *An Englishman …An Englishman, he needs time."*

She burst out laughing, discarding her book and clinging to my arm. "Why you singing funny song, Saji-san?"

"Oh, I don't know. It just seemed appropriate. Sort of sums up our situation."

"Not understanding …."

"Well, look at it this way. Has it ever occurred to you that you come here early every morning. You stay all day. You help me in and out the bath. And then you have an English lesson. And then you wait for me to come back from dinner at the mess. And by the time we've finished talking about this, that, and the other, it's pretty late. Often very late."

"I not minding. I rike staying rate."

"Maybe. But since you come so early, and go so late, you might as well stay here all the time. All night."

She blushed and swallowed hard, almost gulped. For several second we looked straight into each other's eyes. I'd made my move, but it was hardly romantic, hardly something to bowl a girl over and make her swoon with delight; a far cry from the amorous seductions I had so often fantasized about. Frankly, it was such a stark proposition that it made me feel like a Victorian prig, or a pompous hero out of Jane Austen. As we continued to look at each other in silence, I even wondered if she understood. "You know what I mean, Kitten?"

"Oh, I knowing … You wanting all-night jig-a-jigging!"

"Not only that. I want you here all the time. So will you stay?"

"Of course. Big honour staying … Oh, so very …"

"Kitten! Never mind all this …'Oh, so very' business … Do you want to?"

"Saji-san! That Japanese way of saying 'Yes prease!' Not right for Japanese rady jumping up and down yerring 'Yippee!' rike Mickey Mouse. Very important Japanese rady being porite …"

(A word of explanation. I am about to tread on delicate ground. Many will consider the details of how Katsumi and I consummated our relationship to be a personal matter. However, you will recall that at the outset of this memoir, I took the stance that an author has to be completely open and honest if his reminiscences are to have any true value, so I will stick to that; but for those who consider such openness to be in bad taste I suggest you skip the next couple of pages and rejoin the story at the paragraph starting, 'Katsumi was soon in control of our domestic life'. Here endeth the explanation.)

Our first night together was a triumph over inexperience and mutual anxiety. She was plagued by the fear of not pleasing me and I dreaded being ham-fisted, over excited, and ending up with an anti-climax, or even--- horror of horrors--- a premature ejaculation. It was, after all, a relationship which had never been tried or tested. There had been no unequivocal declarations of love, no kisses to smooth the way, no foreplay to establish compatibility.

We started shyly, exchanging tender kisses, between which we divulged to each other our innermost thoughts and desires: how she'd trembled with excitement during her cooking lesson; how I'd always wanted to dash down the drive to greet her, as she did me; and how I'd been too cowardly to invite her into the bath for fear of offending her; and how she'd always been naked beneath her kimono, awaiting the invitation, ready to jump straight in, yet never daring to give any hint of willingness, fearing rejection and humiliation, frightened that an English officer would never sully himself with a Japanese servant.

We laughed over our lost opportunities. We totted them up until they were legion, but we didn't mind in the least. We knew they weren't lost at all, only deferred, reserved for an uninhibited affair in which we could turn back the clock and do whatever we had previously desired.

Such intimate declarations, and the prospect of the delights that lay ahead, clearly made Katsumi's pulse race with excitement. The more I talked of what I intended to do to her, and how I was going to unleash passion upon her, and how I was going to savour every inch of her glorious body, and keep on loving her and loving her until we collapsed in exhaustion, the more sexually charged she became. Eventually, she could stand it no longer. She jumped up, flung off her kimono, and skipped off for the bathroom. I watched her bare bottom bob up and down as she went and when she reached the bathroom she called out: "Saji-san! Now I making water. Then I jumping straight in it."

I chuckled with delight. She was quite incorrigible: a girl in a billion. In the bathroom I found her kneeling beside the bath, swilling the water around in her usual way. I went to the taps and turned them off. I eased her to her feet so that she stood before me, naked. I held her at arms-length and let my eyes feast on her body.

It was the first time I'd been able to luxuriate over the sight of a naked girl and I knew I would never see anything more perfect. She was a golden girl, the hue of her skin deep and mellow, a uniqueness which could never be challenged or duplicated. My hands went to her, as though drawn by magnets, revelling in the feel of her silkiness. I caressed her face and chubby cheeks and then slipped my hands down her body to encircled her tiny waist. Then I played with the plumpness of her bottom and finally, with the back of my right hand, felt the flatness and warmth of her tummy, above which her breasts were erect and firm, like buds bursting into life, unencumbered by gravity.

I took her into the shower and we lathered each other with volumes of suds, our hands slithering up and down, over and under, our bodies slipping and sliding against each other as the water tamped down on us. Then we soaked in the bath and she reclined against me so that I could nuzzle the nape of her neck and cup her breasts in my hands.

Finally, I carried her to my bed and laid her down. Then I joined her and we became as one.

Katsumi was soon in control of our domestic life. She took over quietly and discreetly. The bungalow became her domain. Without her doing anything dictatorial or disruptive, an officer's rented accommodation became a Japanese home. Moggy-san was gently pensioned off. She remained on the headquarters payroll and continued to attend the house-girls' social meetings, but the only times I saw her was when she led an odd little man in an old army uniform down the drive, pushing a hand cart piled high with items of furniture and personal odds and ends of Katsumi's.

The biggest item he brought round was her prize possession, her altar, or butsudan. It was a magnificent piece of furniture, handed down from her great grandfather. It stood some five feet tall and was finished in mahogany veneers. On the top half, carved double doors opened up to reveal a small altar on which she kept freshly-cut flowers. Below, jutting forward a little, was a shelf bearing rows of candles and joss sticks, and once she had it all set up in our spare bedroom she pinned a large sheet of paper above it covered in Japanese script. When I asked her what it said, she replied: "It saying, 'Roof not reary there. Onry crouds and sky between us and heaven'."

She had regular prayer sessions each day and the fragrance of joss sticks and candles often lingered when I returned from duty; but it was some time before I realized just how addicted she was to her worship. She often knelt before her butsudan for hours on end, her soft voice wavered in an endless chant, only interrupted by the lighting of fresh candles and joss sticks.

Religion was the foundation of her life. She'd already told me that it was a curious mixture of Nicheren Buddhism and Shintoism but now she explained to me in detail its philosophical demands. The guiding principle was never to seek anything for herself, total unselfishness; that mankind's sufferings were universal and caused by the evil of craving and lusting after creature comforts and material benefits; and that the only way to overcome the dire consequences of these vices was to devote oneself to the happiness of one's partner: unwavering and unrestrained love and total subordination. She believed that if she achieved this, then Buddha would at all times guide and safeguard her.

Her sprint down the drive to greet me was still the thing about our relationship which thrilled me most. It was a demonstration of how the familiarity between us never dampened her enthusiasm or lowered her respect. When she stopped just short of me, her bows were just as deep and formal as ever. Yet once indoors all that went by the board and we ripped off each other's clothes, headed for the bedroom, and made love. Then we would lie still for maybe an hour, physically spent, mentally calm, contentment that needed no expression. To have spoken would have banished the perfect tranquillity between us after such physical delights, all so adequately expressed by the simplicity of holding hands.

Eventually, I would ask: "Whose turn to make tea?"

"Saji-san, you never making tea!" and off she'd go, revealing her glorious rear view as she slipped into her kimono.

In all our time together we kept to a regular routine: the honourable tea ceremony, bath-time, and her English lessons. We also discovered some pretty childish amusements. In her book cupboard I unearthed a pack of cards and various board games, such as Ludo, Snakes and Ladders, and even Monopoly. She also taught me several Japanese games, her speciality being "Paper, Rock and Scissors", a game of bluff at which she always won easily. Our favourite card game was 'Snap!' This was new to her but she managed to win more often than not. Her cry of "SNAP!" would always be fractionally ahead of mine and she would squeal with laughter as she grabbed the cards up before I could dispute her claim on them.

She also had some curious ways. Often, after making love, she would nip out of bed, strip the blankets back, tuck the top sheet in all round, and then, having rejoined me, pulled it over our heads so that we were in a secret world all of our own--- what she called our wigwam, although cocoon would have been a better word. In it, we were insulated from the world, lying nose to nose and toes to toes, our lips brushing lightly as we whispered to each other. We discussed the most intimate things. We had no boundaries, no secrets. Nothing was too embarrassing to recount, no shame too deep to own up to, and no hopes and ambitions too bizarre to mention.

Childhood memories predominated. With both of us, our early years had been dominated by the world war. I told her how we had been bombed out by Hitler's first hit-and-run raid on London. How I'd been thrown out of bed by an enormous explosion to find the floor covered in broken glass, and how, when I looked out of what had been the window, I saw that the house opposite had been reduced to a rubble, smoke, and great clouds of dust, a shambles in which all four residents had died. Then I related how, a month or two later, my father had taken me up to his factory in London to fire-watch during the Blitz. Once the bombing was over and everyone was out in the streets, fighting fires and dodging collapsing buildings, he made me responsible for distributing mugs of tea. I told her how the firemen, egged on by my father, gave me the nick-name 'Din' after Rudyard Kipling's famous Indian character, the water-carrier, Gunga Din. I recounted with pride how they loved to tease me, chiding me for being slow, and greeting my belated appearance with more mugs of tea with the chorus:

"Din! Din! Din!
Where the bloody hell yer bin?"

She laughed and laughed at that until she cried, but what she enjoyed most were stories of my evacuation to Cornwall with my dog, Lucky. How Lucky had been stolen off me by the village policeman, and how, when I saw him riding his bike through the village with Lucky tied to his handlebars by a long piece of string, I had let out my usual whistle with the result that Lucky stopped dead, then dashed towards me, causing the policeman to take a terrible crash off his bike.

That brought more tears of laughter and she insisted that I told her the story over and over again. She also loved to hear of the pranks I got up to at Silver Coombe with my brothers, James and Brother Nothing; and the tragic love affair between my Indian grandmother and our ancient gardener, Mr. Muckey, which ended when they died together in the cabbage patch due to the explosion of a doodlebug.* At that, she went from laughter to tears but not just tears of sadness. She was convinced that their deaths had an Elysian connection and that they would find happiness in heaven. "They onry roving each other in different prace, Saji-san."

Her stories were more harrowing. They started with the invincibility of the Japanese in the early days of the war. Patriotism ruled and each new triumph was hailed with jubilation. School children were forever singing the Victory Song and Katsumi described how, when things started to go wrong, and Mr. B (B29 bombers) droned across their skies, they prepared to die for the Emperor. Small defence units consisting of six families were formed. Her father commanded their unit and ludicrous things were expected of them, from impaling American parachutists on sharpened bamboo poles to strapping explosives to their bodies and throwing themselves in front of tanks. She told me of the night Kure was razed to the ground by fire. Late one evening, instead of passing over Kure, Mr. B circled them twice and then dropped tens of thousands of incendiary bombs which set the town ablaze. Her family fled from their well-appointed house and took shelter in slit trenches on the outskirts of town, from where they watched Kure turn to ashes.

Finally, she told me how, on a fine August morning, her school had

---

* *See Gran and Mr. Muckey, Volume I of Memory and Imagination.*

been sent to clear fire-breaks just outside Hiroshima. As they marched down a long incline a few miles out the town, they had a perfect view of Mr. B dropping the first atom bomb. As the mushroom cloud went up, they fled in terror, convinced that it was the devil himself bursting forth from hell to aid the Americans. However fast they ran they couldn't evade the Black Rain that fell from a previously clear sky. At the time, they had no idea of its significance, but within a year or two most of the girls had died of radiation poisoning.

Her most traumatic story concerned her father's reaction when he heard the Emperor's surrender broadcast. She knew that for him it was the end of the world. She knew what he would do, and he duly did it. Together with other elderly male members of the family, he lined up in front of the Naval Headquarters main gates and committed suicide.

After she related that, there was a long silence. When her tears were exhausted we fell into a deep sleep, still linked in love. When I awoke I could only ponder over the thought that here we were, two youngsters with only a handful of years between us, yet we had witnessed two of the most monumental events in modern history, one the Battle of Britain and the Blitz, the free world's most vital battle; and the other the world's most brutal act, a bomb that altered human behaviour forever, and--- unbeknown to me then--- would blight our lives forever.

I also told her of my experiences in Korea. I kept it as light-hearted as possible, including Rupert's love of poetry and the comic verses he pinned on our notice boards. Then the incident when Fletcher jumped off the stretcher and made a run for it, and the mysterious disappearance of Bridges, and how Animal Evans had befriended Kim. She was intrigued and bombarded me with questions, and her interest in my men soon became an obsession with her. When I ran out of stories about my men in Korea, she wanted to know all about the men in the Kure headquarters: how did they spend their off-duty hours, and were they happy in Japan? When my ignorance of these things made me look indifferent, she begged me to change my attitude. She couldn't bear to think that I regarded them merely as supernumeraries serving out their time in a strange country. She saw them as lonely young lads in need of love and friendship; lads who were in my care rather than under my command; and lads who had been sent to Kure by the grace of Buddha in order to befriend Kure's huge surplus of lovely girls. She told me how the other house-girls and waitresses were longing to meet them. Indeed, she got so carried away by it all that she conjured up visions of idyllic romances between them, with the headquarters becoming one big, happy family, a sort of military Butlin's on the Inland Sea.

Once, she asked: "Saji-san, how you knowing your rads not rove-making with pan-pan girls?"

When I admitted that I didn't know, and that in all probability most of them were, she begged me to integrate them into the more desirable aspect of Japanese life. While I admitted that this was a fine aspiration, I told her that the chances of them taking any notice of a junior officer like me were practically nil.

Her greatest concern was Nacker, Why hadn't he found himself a nice Japanese girl yet? And why didn't he come to see us more often?

The answer to this was simple, although I didn't like to tell her. Nacker was still so smitten by her that he found it unbearable to spend evenings with us, knowing that when he disappeared to the loneliness of his bungalow, I would be in bed with her, making love.

Gradually, things did change. Every time Nacker scored a success with a girl from one of his bars, his envy eased sufficiently for him to bring her round to meet us; but none of them lasted more than a week or so. Katsumi never enthused over them and she kept telling me that she knew other girls in the headquarters who would be much more suitable. Eventually, she arranged for him to have a date with Akiko, one of the receptionists in the officers' mess and then at last things settled down and Nacker's visit became more regular.

Just how swiftly Nacker progressed with Akiko was impossible to tell. To me, in private, he claimed that success was instantaneous, that she had been unable to resist him; but knowing Nacker as I did I realized he would never claim anything else. However, he must have done pretty well because only a week or so after their first date, he came to me with a proposition. He'd discovered that one of the better officers' bungalows had become vacant and he suggested that I, as camp adjutant, should transfer him into it, and whilst about it wangle things so that Akiko became his house-girl.

With typical craftiness, he made the suggestion in Katsumi's presence, knowing she would be highly enthusiastic, a first step towards closer friendships among house-girls and the HQ lads. Consequently, I had a word with Eddie and he put everything into motion, his only proviso being that Akiko had to be willing. There wasn't much doubt about that and within a couple of days the whole thing was a fait accompli. A week later Akiko moved in with him on a permanent basis.

25

Pure Joy

What followed was the most enjoyable period of my life.

It was a time of liberty and impulsive behaviour with full adult privileges freely available for the first time. There were precious few constraints imposed by the army and all four of us were deliriously in love. It was a foursome in which the closeness between us sealed our fun, laughter, and happiness. God truly smiled down on us. Compared to modern-day life-styles our activities were tame and naïve, but we were simple kids, content with simple things, classic endorsement of the old adage 'the best things in life are free'. I doubt very much if any National Servicemen ever enjoyed a better time than we did.

The closeness that blossomed between Katsumi and Akiko was a joy to see and we were forever in and out of each other's bungalows. Nacker and I used the officers' mess much less often and in the evenings we often went to quality restaurants with the girls, giving them a chance to dress up in the new kimonos we'd bought them. In our bungalows we invented our own amusements. We played Monopoly until the small hours, or had impromptu and unaccompanied sing-songs in which Nacker and I were taught traditional Japanese songs, and the girls did their best to sing English airs such as *Any Old Iron,* and *Knees Up Mother Brown.*

Due to the laxity of our duties in the headquarters we were able to get out and about, away from Kure. One of our greatest pleasures was to walk along the shores of the Inland Sea, to paddle in water that was still cold despite sunny days. Nacker and I often returned to our bungalows at lunch-time and got Katsumi and Akiko to rustle up picnics. I would then draw a jeep from the MT Section and we motored down the long, twisting road that hugged the coast line of the Inland Sea, visiting small villages and exploring remote beaches between rocky headlands. After eating our picnic we split into pairs and scrambled across outcrops of rocks and along the golden beaches, exploring in opposite directions. When we met-up again, perhaps an hour or so later, Nacker and I would compare notes about the shell-fish we'd seen, or the hidden caves we'd found, and whilst we delved into these matters in minute detail, Katsumi and Akiko stood to one side and giggled, not too shy to admit to each other that all that happened was another session of jig-a-jigging.

Then we became more adventurous and took out two Royal Enfield motor cycles. We told the girls to dress in their warmest denims and we plonked them on the pillion seats with orders to hang on for dear life.

Then we roared off with Katsumi and Akiko screaming with excitement, heading along the rough dirt tracks into the mountains that overlooked the azure water of the Inland Sea. We always returned by late afternoon so that Nacker could check if any crisis had occurred during the Brigadier's absence in Korea. I likewise made a point of putting in a late appearance in the Commandant's Office, even though Colonel Gibson was rarely there.

Katsumi never lost sight of her ambitions for an integrated headquarters and things eventually moved in that direction far quicker than I ever anticipated. It came about due to the visit by the British Minister of Health. He was a pompous, publicity-seeking old windbag who spent his time either looking for trouble or seeking reflected glory by being photographed with the wounded in the Base Hospital. When he heard of the VD rate among the troops, he insisted on a night-tour of Kure. Colonel Gibson, the Provost Marshal, and I accompanied him in a staff car and when he saw what a hot-bed of vice it was, he was appalled. He kept pointing at sordid bars surrounded by posturing pan-pan girls and demanding: "Why isn't that place out of bounds?"

The answer was easy enough: Eddie was receiving back-handers from the bar owners who he allowed (through me!) to remain 'In Bounds'. I was the only one aware of this and I certainly wasn't going to let on. It would have been a stark betrayal of our 'back-scratching' arrangements, of which Katsumi had been an integral part.

As a result of our tour, the Health Minister sent a letter of complaint to Brigadier Clay demanding that greater attention should be paid to the social and medical welfare of the men. This 'buck' was duly passed down the line and when Colonel Gibson handed it on to me, he said: "I think sport would be a good idea, don't you? How about some Rugby? Wonderful game for letting off steam with controlled fisticuffs. Think you can arrange that?"

"Yes, sir. I don't see why not."

It was clear from the start that regular games of rugby would take some time to set up. First of all I had to find a suitable playing field. Then I had to get a local carpenter to make goal posts and there was also the matter of kit--- boots, jerseys, balls etc. This meant having to indent to the Commonwealth's main stores in Tokyo.

While all this was going on, I formed an ORs Social Committee in order to organize other activities, not in an effort to please the Minister of Health, but to implement Katsumi's original idea of a military Butlin's on the Inland Sea. Getting the Social Committee to decide on anything wasn't easy. They were a very conservative lot and highly suspicious of any ideas, suspecting that they were a ploy to curtail their existing freedom. However, I persisted and eventually it was agreed that--- quite contrary to the non-fraternizing policy--- we should invite the house-girls and waitresses to a bun-fight in the canteen after one of the men's afternoon drill parades.

This was such a resounding success, with many new friendships formed, that I was inundated with requests to make it a weekly affair, which had always been my intention. Soon, so many ORs and house-girls or waitresses had become 'items' that the next logical step was to organize a weekly dance. I wondered if I was being too ambitious, but Katsumi, Akiko, and Nacker were full of enthusiasm. When Katsumi floated the idea at the house-girls' daily get-together, they were thrilled. They shrieked and laughed with joy and discussed what they would wear to sweep the Tommy-sans off their feet.*

I dreaded that the lads would turn up in their Best Battle Dresses (which had the texture of sandpaper), and their Best Boots (with their statutory 26 hob-nails), but I needn't have worried. To a man, they were Teddy Boys and they arrived at the canteen in Edwardian suits which had cost hundreds and which more than matched the glamour of the new kimonos and obis. As Katsumi and I stood in the doorway of the ORs canteen, welcoming the couples, she couldn't understand why her 'This England' books hadn't prepared her for such splendour: jackets that reached down to the men's knees, velvet collars, natty boot-lace ties, pocket flaps with black braid surrounds, blue suede shoes with thick crepe soles, and trousers that hugged their legs and exaggerated every contour.

"I not seeing anything rike this in orl my rife," exclaimed Katsumi.

"Yes. Marvellous. They'd be arrested on sight in England."

The Japanese band Eddie hired was good and the floor of the canteen bounced merrily. What I found especially cute was the way the girls discarded their getas and danced in their snow-white tabi socks, with separate compartments for their big toes. We always had a lengthy interval during which some of the Tommy-sans put on party pieces while others took the chance to do some serious drinking at the bar. I joined the drinkers, keen to get to know them better. A good spirit developed and I soon concluded that there wasn't much difference between them and the lads in 12 platoon, to whom I was so attached.

Not surprisingly, Katsumi was in great demand on the dance floor and when Corporal Swain, the pay clerk in the orderly room, brought her back to me after a foxtrot he drew me to one side and said: "I gather this young

---

* The men in the headquarters became known as 'Tommies' or 'Tommy-sans',and the girls all became 'Geishas'.

bird is your house-girl, sir?"

"That's right."

"Blimey! No wonder you're always skiving off early."

Rugby--- which was to have kick-started our social programme--- was the last thing to get under way. Having organized a playing field, and acquired the necessary kit from Tokyo, I touted around for interest among the Tommies. The response was very poor. Since they were now fixed up with Geishas, they saw little point in wasting good courting time on a game devoted to knocking the daylights out of each other. Consequently, most of them insisted they were soccer players.

In a way it was a blessing since fixtures proved impossible. I tried a local New Zealand unit, but they were so small they had no hope of raising a side. An Australian stores depot had enough men, but they were from Melbourne and only played Australian Rules. The best possibility was JRBD, but when I approached them I got a very negative response. Captain Starkey, the adjutant, made it quite clear that he had no intention of getting involved in something that wasn't essential. "Rugby?" he echoed. "Why the hell should we want to play rugby?"

"So that the men can let off a bit of steam," I suggested.

"If men need to let off steam, I'll send them to the Hara Mura Battle School."

So I forgot rugby and organized other social events. The most popular was a weekly cinema show in the men's canteen. I arranged this with 'Curly' the Australian corporal in charge of the Cinematograph Unit, and for the first performance he showed 'Where's That Fire?', starring Will Hay. The canteen was packed and although I had fears that most of the Geishas would find it hard to understand, they loved it anyhow. I had never seen people laugh as much as they did.

From thereon, by popular demand, we had a different Will Hay film every week and they were so popular that soon half Kure seemed to be turning up. The best performance came when Curly accidentally put a film on upside down and backwards. This truly brought the house down and from there on all performances became double-features, first the film as it was intended and then upside down and backwards.

A more sedate attraction was a Library. When I heard that thousands of ex-Boots library books were due in on the Devonshire, I had a room in the headquarters fitted out with shelves and Eddie lost no time in hiring four girls to run the place, adding handsomely to his agency fees. It was also a good opportunity for Katsumi to further her grasp of English. She visited the library most days and took out basic classics such as Treasure Island and Alice in Wonderland.

For several weeks the dances remained the main feature of our social programme and it wasn't long before a number of us felt the need to extend our socializing further into the night. Rather than go to one of the local bars, we took to visiting the homes of various Geishas. I placed a standing order with the MT Section for a couple of 15cwt trucks and we would squash into these and drive off into the buraku (slum) areas of Kure.

To start with, I could hardly believe the squalor that was revealed in the headlights. We twisted and turned along interminable alleyways, squeezing between an assortment of wooden and corrugated iron shacks. Scores of children scampered about with barking dogs at their heels, and ancient street-vendors wandered about like lost souls, ringing hand bells or playing repetitive tunes on their flutes as they sold noodles.

The most popular of the homes was that of a diminutive girl called Richi-san. Her family boasted a wooden bath tub in one of the rooms and there were several hilarious evenings when some couples went through the Japanese custom of communal bathing, with the rest of us cheering them on. Eventually, there was a party at Katsumi's home. I'd never been there, but I wasn't surprised that it was the poorest of them all, hidden at the top of such a steep hill that we had to abandon the trucks and walk the last fifty yards.

Her house consisted of two rooms, a living room which doubled as a bedroom, and a kitchen. The toilet was two wooden buckets beneath a makeshift lean-to in a tiny backyard. Despite the conditions, it was one of our best parties. I stayed overnight but I hardly slept. Noises never ceased. If it wasn't the neighbours shouting, it was dogs barking or the flutes of street vendors; and deep in the night, when humans were at last hushed, came the scampering of mice and rats.

At the hint of dawn I dressed and went outside. I wandered about, watching the neighbourhood stirring, all the noise and bustle returning, the never-ending circle revolving once more, with workers emerging from their homes and padding down the hill in their curious, split-toe boots, heading for the smudge of Kure, determined to improve Japan's GNP.

As I turned back, I saw Katsumi struggling along the alley with a yoke across her shoulders, no more than a bamboo pole with buckets suspended by ropes on each end. I hurried forward to help her, but she stopped dead. "No, no, Saji-san! Not coming near, I saying! My officer-san not carrying honey buckets. Very big ross of face for me."

I watched as she hurried past, occasionally struggling to stop herself slipping over. Several other women were already standing at an alleyway junction further down the hill. Katsumi waited with them for the honey cart to arrive. It was a great, wooden wagon drawn by an ox and when it came to a halt the women took it in turns to toss the contents of their buckets into it, jumping back smartly to avoid being splashed. As Katsumi came back up the hill she was smiling broadly, her cheerfulness declaring it a job well done. By the time she reached me, breathless but smiling, her empty buckets swinging freely, I felt a depth of compassion and devotion I'd never experienced before.

One morning Colonel Gibson asked me how I was getting on with organizing the rugby. I explained that I'd got everything set up but we had no one to play against, with my main hope--- JRBD --- being vetoed by Captain Starkey.

"Then why not go to Tokyo?" suggested Gibson. "The Ebisu Leave Centre is crying out for sporting fixtures."

"Bit distant isn't it, sir?"

"Not if you fly. There are flights going up there every day from the Aussie Air Base at Iwakuni. Get in touch with my old friend Squadron Leader Frith. He'll fix you up no trouble at all."

I took a trip over to Iwakuni and when I met Squadron Leader Frith he couldn't have been more helpful. He not only agreed to give us lifts backwards and forwards to Tokyo--- leaving every Saturday morning and returning late on Sunday night--- but he was happy to take as many as we liked.

"Only one proviso," he said. "If you're going to take supporters, any Japanese must be employees of the Commonwealth Forces. Otherwise they don't qualify for insurance and we could land up in a real mess if there's an accident."

"Right," I said, hardly able to believe my luck. "I'll guarantee they're all bona fide employees. Any restrictions on numbers?"

"None at all. The Dakota goes up and back more or less empty. Just mail and papers. But it'll be cold. So tell them to dress up."

When I renewed my call for volunteers and mentioned that all fixtures would be in Tokyo and that Geishas could go as well, with the Leave Centre providing accommodation and meals, I was inundated by volunteers. Those who had previously claimed to be soccer players suddenly swore black and blue that they were experienced rugby players as well. "Played it since I was a kid, sir," said one. "Put me down as centre-half."

The British Forces in Korea had several leave centres but the Ebisu stood alone. Tokyo had a special buzz, with all the modern requirements for making whoopee. It was a city of a thousand delights where men, after months of living in trenches like animals, could at last avail themselves of the debauchery they craved. Nothing had been seen like it before or since, and so much money was changing hands that the re-floating of a defeated and bankrupt nation was under way, all based on man's insatiable desire for alcohol, bright lights, shady bars, female nudity, and sexual intercourse.

Going to Tokyo to play rugby every week-end made us unique. The staff of the Ebisu Leave Centre called us the Newcastle Coal Carriers, reflecting their astonishment when we turned up with our Cotton Oxfords strung around our necks, oval pills beneath our arms, and every man with his own girl in tow. The staff treated us like royalty and after each game players and spectators sat down to a huge tea, with mountainous heaps of freshly cut sandwiches, scones, cream cakes, and lashings of toast oozing with butter.

Katsumi and the Geishas loved those teas. They squashed in among the Tommies and delighted in all the shouting and banter that went on, marvelling at how men who only minutes before had been knocking hell out of each other had suddenly became life-long friends. They watched incredulously as the piles of food were demolished and how the Tommies then thumped the tables and demanded more.

After the teas, we broke into small groups and went our own ways. No questions were asked and in all our visits there was never any trouble, with no one missing the Sunday evening Dakota back to Kure.

Katsumi, Akiko, Nacker and I always stayed in a hotel well away from the Leave Centre. It was the most exclusive in town, an ancient building which had somehow survived the 1923 earthquake and wartime fire-bombing. Really, it was out of our social league, but Nacker and I refused to let that deter us. We both had a tidy sum in savings and we judged that this was the time to blow it, regardless. So every week our taxi fought its way between the Rolls Royces, Cadillacs, and Buicks that thronged the driveway, and once inside we rubbed shoulders with admirals, generals, and show-biz stars, among them Kay Starr and Bob Hope.

There were plenty of things to do in Tokyo, but we soon learnt to steer well clear of the shrines and temples, otherwise Katsumi and Akiko became embroiled in prayer sessions, lighting candles and calling up various ancestors. We went to a fascinating variety of restaurants and timed our meals to catch the final performances at either the Ernie Pyle Theatre or Tokyo Casino. The shows were gaudy and spectacular, teeming with long-legged girls in flimsy costumes. Yet to Nacker and me, these beauties were incidental. Our pleasure came from watching the reactions of Katsumi and Akiko. They could never get over the plush fittings, being jostled about by crowds of huge Americans, and the thrill of the orchestra's opening notes as the curtain rose on a new production.

Our most memorable Tokyo visit coincided with the match in which I nearly threw away our unbeaten record with some appalling place-kicking, including a missed conversion straight in front of the posts. At tea this brought accusations of a lack of concentration, with Katsumi among my severest critics. "Very big ross of face for me, Officer Sajit-san! Oh, such rousy kicking! Orl time you thinking about a bit of the other."*

This brought roars of laughter from the lads and they encouraged her to scold me even further. However, having taken just so much, I soon silenced her. "Any more cheek out of you, Miss Katsumi, and there will be no big surprise for you."

Since she loved surprises more than anything, she abandoned her mock indignation and burst into one of her most fetching smiles which the Tommies--- all of whom doted on her--- lapped up.

The surprise I had in mind was to buy her western clothes, her first. On this occasion, Nacker and Akiko opted out which only increased the mystery for Katsumi. When we arrived at the classiest dress shop in town she stopped in front of the windows and stared in wonder. The displays created visions of haughty high society ladies dressed to seduce millionaires and she was so in awe of such luxury that she was reluctant to go in. She just stood there saying: "Never happen!"

"Now don't start all that old rubbish, Kitten. Shops like this are made for girls like you."

"Not possible! You not understanding ..."

"Yes I do. You're frightened they'll see you in your old-fashioned bloomers. But it doesn't matter. These people have seen it all before. And I won't let you walk out of here in high heels and tabi socks. You'll come out looking like a million dollars."

Thanks to the expertise of the sales staff, that's exactly what happened. When she finally emerged from the fitting room I couldn't believe that anyone could look so beautiful. She was dressed in a pale blue suit that hugged her figure and complemented her golden skin and black hair perfectly. Her waist was so tiny it almost disappeared and the cut of the skirt was downright provocative, accentuating her thoroughbred flanks. I stared in wonder, never in my life so proud of someone. I hurried forward and ran my hands over her, which sent the sales girls into peals of laughter.

When we left the shop we met Nacker and Akiko again and there were more 'Ohs!' and 'Ahs!' about how good she looked. She shrugged it off modestly but kept saying how strange it all felt, especially the high heels.

The Geishas weren't slow to pick up army expressions, although they weren't always aware of their crudity.

"Don't worry," I assured her. "You'll soon get used to them. You'll have to. These are your going away clothes."

"Going away, Saji-san? Where to?"

"Back to England of course."

She laughed with embarrassment, treating it as a joke.

Nacker didn't see it that way. As we walked on, he drew me back a few paces and said: "For God's sake, Saj! Buy her all the presents you like, but don't start saying things like that."

26

An Ominous Warning

Nacker's rebuke stung deeply. I had no answer to it. It made me realize just how abstruse my position was. It was a great life--- I'd never been so happy--- but where was it heading? To a multitude of complications, that was for sure. Whichever way I looked at it, and however many avenues I explored, they all came to a dead end. I even asked myself if this really was love, or was I just infatuated by my first taste of female beauty?

When I dismissed that thought with contempt I was still left with the question as to what I could do. Marry her? Unless I had that in mind, the affair was bound to fizzle out when I returned to the UK, and if I married her (always assuming she was willing) I'd need the army's permission, and that was out of the question. So how would I get her back to England? Anyhow, how could I possibly marry at the age of nineteen with no financial means--- not even a job waiting for me in England? Then there was the attitude of others. Dad would love her, but Mum would go berserk. Marrying someone named anything but Blodwyn or Megan, would probably send her round the bend. Also, with Japanese wartime atrocities still so fresh in peoples' thoughts, Katsumi would be ostracized as soon as she set foot in England. The situation called for major procrastination.

What did happen was another letter from Rupert. In it, he acknowledged the head-and-shoulders photograph I had sent him of Katsumi. His response was: "Well, she certainly didn't get off one of the Saturday night coaches from Leeds! I've shown it around, and the lads can't understand why such a raving beauty would want to waste her time on you. I even showed it to Denning, but he wasn't in the least impressed. He claimed that head-and-shoulder photos of Japanese women meant nothing because they're all bandy, like Fletcher. In fact he made his one and only joke so far and said Fletcher and Japanese girls were made for each other and if they ever got round to making love they would look like a reef knot. Then he got serious again and said it was a damned disgrace that an officer in the Dukes should consort with a coloured person. I took great delight in telling him that didn't matter because you're coloured as well. He couldn't believe it. He even checked with Copper Bowden and when it was confirmed, he said: 'No wonder the platoon was such a shambles'."

Katsumi read the letter, as she always did, and the accusation of bandy legs really worried her. I kept reassuring her it wasn't true, but for days afterwards she kept standing in front of the full-length mirror in the bathroom, her kimono hitched up, examining herself.

In the end, I couldn't resist teasing her. As I caught her doing it yet again, she said: "Saji-san, I not bandy, am I?" I professed great concern and told her to hitch up her kimono a bit higher, then a bit higher still, and then even higher. Eventually, she realized she was exposing her mini bloomers and cried out: "Saji-san! You just having rude rooking!"

Denning's accusation that she was coloured puzzled Katsumi. It had never occurred to her that she was anything other than perfectly normal. "In England, everybody thinks the Japanese are yellow," I explained. "It's all part of what we call discrimination."

"Ah so! I know that wording."

"And have you ever experienced it?"

"Oh yes, Saji-san. Orl time ... But never because of corour."

"In what way then?"

"Because of being caught in the Brack Rain. People thinking that Brack Rain people passing on sickness. We are known as The Exposed, Saji-san. You once asking me about Goto-san being my nakado and not getting me husband. That being reason. No Japanese man taking on Exposed girl. Being frightened of what might happen."

"That's ridiculous."

"Ah so! I orways saying."

The comments about bandy legs and Denning's colour prejudice were merely incidental. Two other things in Rupert's letter were far more worrying. To my surprise, he'd enclosed one of his poems. Although I knew he had written dozens during quiet spells in the front line, whilst awaiting messages over his 88-set, this was the first he had ever shown me. It needed no interpretation, but I saw it as yet another omen, a premonition just like I'd had as a boy when I foresaw the death of Charlie Smith (one of Dad's workers) in the Blitz. The poem read:

BEWARE

We Tommies at the front suffer, sir,
We Tommies in our trenches die,
And all in the name of freedom, sir,
Though few of us understand why.
Yet officers like you abound, sir,
Fornicating and skiving at the rear.
Forever wine, women and song, sir,
With nowt but wedding bells to fear.
But your cushy job is an illusion, sir,
In the end the war always wins.
Notice the cross-bones of death, sir,
And the skull above it that grins.

The real sting in his letter came in a post script. He wrote: "We've now left 355 and rejoined the Dukes. A month in reserve! The officers are about to enjoy R and R and Earl Gray is going to take his in Kure. He wants to see the Battle School at Hara Mura. He's told Turnbull that he's also going to see what you're up to. So if I was you I'd keep your girlfriend under wraps. You know what he thinks of the Japanese!"

Earl Gray arrived in Japan on a Sunday. He spent his first night at JRBD, the CO having been a subordinate of his in the Chindits. On Monday morning he turned up bright and early at the Commandant's Office and asked to see me. Colonel Gibson made a big fuss of him (as he did with everyone) and then excused my absence by explaining that I was usually a little late on duty on Mondays on account of having spent the week-end playing rugby in Tokyo.

Earl Gray couldn't hide his amazement. "He goes there every week-end?"

"That's right ..."

"And has every Monday morning off?"

"Well, not off, exactly ... Just calls in later. They're doing very well. Unbeaten so far."

The Earl wasn't impressed and he became more determined than ever to wait for me. Time dragged by and when I still hadn't appeared at lunch time Gibson forsook social niceties and rang through to the MT Section for a jeep. He told the driver to take the Earl to Hara Mura. After lunch, when I at last put in an appearance, Gibson told me what had happened and added: "With any luck he'll be so impressed by the Battle School that he'll stay there for the rest of his leave."

The Earl came back three days later. This time I was present, so I did my best to make him feel welcome. It wasn't difficult because he'd had a wonderful time at Hara Mura. He rated it the finest Battle School he had ever seen and for over half an hour he told us all about their schemes and innovations and how the rugged countryside made a perfect training ground. We eventually got rid of him when a Humber staff car came round to replace his jeep so that he could visit the famous shrine at Miya Jima and then the A-Bomb site in Hiroshima.

On the Earl's last night, Colonel Gibson and I invited him to dinner at the Officers' Club. I wasn't keen on the idea but Gibson insisted that it was a matter of common courtesy. The only good I could see in it was that it would give Katsumi a chance to see what the Earl was like. Having heard so much about him, she couldn't wait to see him in the flesh. She had no automatic entrée into the officers' club so I had a word with the security men and told her to masquerade as a waitress, putting her wise to the old army trick of pretending she was going about official duties by carrying a pile of plates around the restaurant.

The dinner didn't go too well. The Earl took one look at the opulence of the Club and made it clear that it was not his idea of soldiering. When the young Japanese girl showed us to the best table and lit the candles on our silver candelabra, I made things worse by saying: "No shortage of candles here, sir."

Small-talk between the Earl and Gibson ran out over prawn cocktails and silences became embarrassingly long. Since I was the link between these two senior officers I felt obliged to keep the ball rolling. The wine waitress, always a generous girl, kept refilling our glasses and although I had no more than they did, they could hold their liquor and I couldn't. Consequently, I was soon pretty merry; indeed I was well and truly pickled.

Earl Gray was no stranger to drunkenness, of course, but he didn't approve of it in a junior subaltern. On the other hand Gibson became increasingly amused by my condition and encouraged the waitress to keep topping up my glass. To this day, I can't remember exactly what I said, but my general theme was the contrast between the luxury of Japan and the hell of Korea. For the Earl's benefit I waxed lyrical about our rugby trips to Tokyo and for Gibson's amusement I related stories about Dog Company: our first night of action when three patrols tried to wipe each other out, the mysterious disappearance of Bridges, and our fun and games with Big Dolloper! Colonel Gibson was highly amused but the Earl wasn't.

The biggest disaster came when we were on biscuits and cheese and digging into a truckle of stilton. Katsumi suddenly appeared out of the kitchen swing doors carrying a pile of plates. It was so tall she could hardly see over it. She circled the dining room twice, looking for our table. When she spotted us she slowed right down and kept going to and fro, taking a close look at the Earl. Eventually our eyes met and we couldn't resist exchanging smiles. Typically, she even tried to bow, which meant that she nearly lost control of her plates. That sent us both into giggles and when she hurried off her plates rattled so loudly that officers at other tables turned and stared, wondering what on earth was going on.

"You know that girl?" asked Earl Gray.

"Katsumi? Yes. That is, I've seen her around … I know most of them by sight … All during the course of duty, naturally."

Gibson turned to the Earl. "One of Sajit's main jobs is to look after the house-girls and waitresses in the headquarters."

The Earl didn't reply, just gave me one of his looks. This time, disgust rather than contempt.

Three days later I returned to the commandant's office after lunch to find Colonel Gibson waiting for me. As I went to my desk, he said: "Orders have just come through for you, Sajit. You've been posted back to Korea. To rejoin the Dukes."

"Really, sir?"

"Afraid so. Pity! Especially now you've settled in so well. Do you want to go?"

"No, sir..." It was the greatest understatement of my life.

"Oh dear! But I'm afraid I can't do anything about it. Your regiment always has first call on you. And it seems they're keen to have you back. You go in three days' time."

"Three days! Was it requested by Major Gray, sir?"

"I've no idea. Posting orders don't specify things like that. Do you think it was?"

"I'm sure of it, sir. If Colonel Bunbury had wanted me back he would have sent for me ages ago."

"I suppose so. Bit mean of Gray in that case. But if you've never got on with him, why should he want you back?"

I didn't reply. It was pointless to explain how the Earl's mind worked: that it was beyond him ever to forgive me for having escaped his clutches with a 'non-wound'. Also, my wallowing around in luxury, and looking after Japanese girls, was hardly in line with his vow to make sure I saw the Korean campaign through to the bitter end; and if I told Colonel Gibson that the Earl had a really evil streak in him, it would reflected badly on me rather than the Earl.

"Captain Starkey will be taking over from you," said Gibson. "He's up at JRBD at the moment."

"Yes, sir. I know him. He's the one who refused to organize rugby at JRBD."

"Oh dear! Never mind. No time for a proper handover, I'm afraid."

"That won't worry Starkey. He does everything his way, anyhow."

"Yes, I rather gathered that when I spoke to him. Anyhow, as I said, you leave in three days. The ferry to Pusan." Then he added, "And be sure to tie up all your loose ends. Captain Starkey will inherit your bungalow so we don't want any incriminating clues left lying about."

So he'd known all along!

Tying up loose ends--- in other words moving Katsumi back home with Moggy-san--- meant that I had no option but to tell her right away. I had hoped for an appropriate moment of my own choosing, but it didn't work out that way. As she ran down the drive to greet me, there must have been something about my expression that told her something was amiss, or perhaps she had already been tipped off by Eddie, who was obviously aware of what had happened. Whatever it was, there was an immediate frisson of dread between us and it left me no option but to spell out the details.

She took it remarkably calmly, but deep hurt and sadness showed in her eyes. She was convinced it was caused by our ridiculous pantomime in the Officers' Club, but I assured her that it would have happened anyhow. Once we'd settled down for the evening she became more philosophical about it. She convinced herself that it was Buddha's will, something we had no right to oppose. She was equally sure that Buddha would watch over me and make sure I returned unharmed.

Until then I'd been so concerned about being parted from her that the possibility of being killed or seriously wounded had never occurred to me. Seeing my anxiety she tried to reassure me. "Saji-san, maybe good thing. Helping you become important officer. You needing medals ..."

"Like hell I do."

"And you being happy to see all your rads again."

"That's true. But that's nothing compared to missing you."

"But I still be waiting for you."

I looked down on her and smiled, then gave her a big hug.

"I will, Saji-san. Honestry!"

"I know that, Kitten. You don't need to tell me that. And I'll come back to you safe and sound."

It was a stupid thing to say, a cliché that just slipped out. Far too many men, particularly Americans and Australians, had left girls behind them and never returned. There were hundreds of girls in Kure, left in limbo, often with a baby to cope with.

Quite a crowd gathered at the Kure docks to see me off. I'd been issued with new battle kit and as I lingered among my friends, waiting for the last moment before embarking, I must have looked like the proverbial Christmas tree. When time ran out, I gave Katsumi a final farewell kiss, wiped the tears off her cheeks, and made the same banal remark about being back soon, safe and sound. Then, as I walked off towards the gangway, Nacker hurried forward for a quick word.

"Keep in touch, Saj. I'll write regularly. You'll be okay. And don't worry about Kitten. I'll make sure she's looked after."

The ferry lost no time in slipping away from the quayside. We were soon out at sea, heading for the Land of the Morning Calm, the greatest misnomer ever attributed to a country.

PART FOUR

THE BLOODY HOOK

27

Back to 12 Platoon

The Empire Longford was such an old 'bucket', and rolled so violently, that everyone on board was sick; but the stench this caused was nothing compared with the odour that drifted off the oily water of Pusan harbour. To make matters worse, the two-day train journey back to the combat zone was a repeat of our first journey north, especially the frequent stops when shaven-headed boys ran down to the train, arms outstretched, begging for anything to be thrown down to them. Throughout the first day an obnoxious sergeant in the Military Police took great delight in sticking his head out of the window to shout: "Oi! You! Get your hair cut!"

He raised a good laugh the first time, but from then on he got on everyone's nerves. I became so sick of it that I pulled rank on him and told him to shut up. He gave me a sour look and replied: "Very good, sir. But never forget that with military policemen like myself, occasions arise when we're in charge, regardless of rank."

Quite unnecessarily, I'd made an enemy for life, as we shall see.

My hopes of an enthusiastic reception at the Dukes were soon dashed. Captain Hawthorn was still adjutant and his attitude hadn't changed. This time he pretended he didn't remember me. When I said curtly: "Contractor!", he answered: "Ah yes. So what brings you back?"

"Orders! Nothing else, I can assure you."

I was no longer in awe of him. I'd seen far more action than he had, and that counted for a lot in the front line.

"Well, since we're in reserve, I've no idea what we're supposed to do with you, Contractor."

"You can always send me back from whence I came."

"What a splendid idea! But not within my authority, I'm afraid. You'd better report to Major Gray. That's from whence you came originally, I believe."

Before reporting to Gray, I sought out 12 Platoon. I found them in a narrow re-entrant at the rear of battalion lines, a collection of pup tents drawn up in perfectly straight lines, with taut top-sheets, a sure sign of bullshit. At the base of the re-entrant was the cookhouse. It was lunch time and the lads were sitting around the area, eating out of their mess tins. For a time I watched from a distance. They weren't at their best. Harry Wilmott and Fletcher were arguing, the latter mouthing off in his usual way, and Bertie Mee was disputing the quality of the food the cook had just slopped into his mess tin. Eventually, Corporal Holroyd and Animal Evans spotted me and waved enthusiastically. Soon, there were cries of "Aye up!" and "Well I'll be buggered!" and I was surrounded with men laughing and joking and demanding to know what the hell had possessed me to return. Animal punched me playfully on the shoulder and nearly sent me spinning. Then Rupert emerged from a pup tent and hurried over.

"Hail! Here the prodigal skiver comes,
Back again to the same old bums!"

It wasn't one of his best, but that didn't matter. Everyone laughed. Beau Brummell appeared and gave me a smart salute. There was more back-slapping until everyone suddenly drew back and stood to attention. I looked up and saw Denning striding towards us. He was tall and slim and very smart. His beret sat perfectly on his head, the leather band two inches above his eyebrows and his cap badge dead over his left eye, his sandy-coloured hair close-cropped.

"Who are you?" he asked.

"Sajit Contractor ... You must be Denning?"

"Yes. James Denning. Can I help you?"

"Just come to see the lads ... My old platoon."

"I see. My platoon now. Have you reported to Major Gray?"

"Not yet ...."

"Well it would be courteous if you did, don't you think?"

"Yes, of course."

I looked around. They were still standing to attention, staring straight ahead. "I'll see you blokes later," I said and when there was no response I realized just how much things had changed.

Earl Gray was the last person from whom I was expecting an enthusiastic welcome, and I was right. He showed no surprise at seeing me, yet had the gall to imply that he had no knowledge of my posting. "I heard a rumour you were returning," he said. "Get bored with Japan? Hawthorn sent you to me, I suppose?"

"Yes, sir."

"Well, I've no real need for you. Better report to Corporal Turnbull. He'll sort out a tent for you. Only a pup tent. No more officers' tents available."

For the next week the battalion spent most of its time training in the surrounding hills. I was never included. I was shuffled off to battalion HQ to help Hawthorn with clerical tasks, either checking stocks of ammunition or adding up columns of figures, the relevance of which escaped me. It was much the same in off-duty hours. The Earl had organized a comfortable company officers' mess but he and Copper Bowden were rarely there, always out playing bridge with the Colonel and Hawthorn, and although I got along well enough with Stan and Ralf, Denning went out of his way to make me feel an intruder.

Being a spare officer in the company was such an embarrassment that it came as a relief when I was assigned to a series of gash jobs. First I became a Liaison Officer with the neighbouring Turkish Brigade. My task was to write a report for Colonel Bunbury assessing their reliability as a flanking unit. For several days I had no idea of what was going on or what anyone was saying, but I eventually established a common link with them through marksmanship. They simply loved to blaze away with their weapons and each day we spent our time shooting at empty Pepsi Cola bottles. This, together with every last one of them looking like a cut-throat, enabled me to report back to Colonel Bunbury that there was no fear of the Turks letting anyone down. My next job was as assistant coordinator of patrols, under Major Bunny Austin. He was the only field officer in the Dukes ever to venture into no man's land.* Since we were in reserve, the scope of this job was limited but I derived a certain amount of pleasure from knowing how furious the Earl would be if I ever had any influence on the patrolling activities of the battalion. That never came about, however. Instead, I was summoned before Hawthorn once more. Eyeing me with supercilious amusement he said: "I've got a very suitable job has for you, Contractor. Assistant adjutant at the Seoul Detention Barracks. We've heard a lot about your activities as assistant adjutant among the Geisha girls, so now we can see how you get on among a bunch of hard cases. Should make an interesting contrast."

It was the first time I'd had a close look at Seoul. It was worse than Pusan. It had changed hands a record four times in two years and each time both armies had done their best to level it, making it look like Dresden after the allied bombing. The Detention Barracks, despite a multitude of shrapnel scars and bullet holes, was one of the few buildings left standing. For years it had been a notorious civilian prison, so activities within it were fairly traditional, except that political prisoners were now executed further down the road, as the shots we heard every dawn confirmed.

The prison 'screws' were a mixture of nationalities with British Red

---

For this 'offence' Major Austin received a note from his fellow field officers telling him that his 'Union Card' had been withdrawn for letting them all down by setting a dangerous precedent.

Caps predominant. Unlike the previous civilian jailers, they weren't murderers. They were certainly sadists and torturers, but they had an uncanny ability to stop a fraction short of murder.

The place horrified me. It gave me bad dreams. It was all keys and locks and crashing metal doors, with row upon row of cells stinking of disinfectant. Yelling and screaming went on all day and night as the punishments handed out drove men to the point of physical collapse and/or suicide. The main form of discipline was the 'Hill'*--- a huge, triangular mound of sand, up and down which men had to run in full battle order until they dropped. Then there were futile things, like digging holes and then filling them in again; and the ever-present threat of solitary confinement in 'The box'. It was sadism honed to a fine art. Another thing I discovered was that Sergeant Cuthbertson (the Red Cap I'd crossed swords with on the train from Pusan) was on the staff. I didn't have any direct dealings with him but I saw enough of him to realize that he was in his element, already one of the most loathed screws.

My new job of Assistant Adjutant was simple and straightforward. Thankfully it had nothing to do with the punishment side of the barracks. That is, until I became orderly officer. I had never been an orderly officer before and I had no idea of what it involved. I had hoped that my orderly sergeant would guide me through the day, but it turned out to be Sergeant Cuthbertson and he watched with glee as I made mistake after mistake. The worst came when I inspected the prisoners in their cells. Most of them ignored me as I passed by and when we got to the end of them, I said to the CSM in charge: "It all looks very satisfactory, Sergeant-Major."

"Yes, sir. I'm sure it is. The only trouble is that you have to ask each prisoner if he has any complaints."

So we had to go through the whole procedure again.

Real trouble struck when the alarm siren suddenly sounded. It wailed continuously for a minute or so but since I was having lunch I ignored it. When it stopped I imagined that the crisis--- whatever it was--- had passed or been sorted out, but no such luck. An announcement boomed out over the Tannoy system.

"Orderly officer! Orderly officer! Report to the square immediately. Urgent! Orderly officer to the parade ground."

I rushed off and when I drew near the parade ground I heard shouting, cat-calls, and derisive whistling. When I reached what was normally a wide-open space I was confronted by what looked like the crowd at a

---

There was a film called 'The Hill' which depicted exactly the same kind of punishment. Whether or not it was based on Seoul, I don't know.

small football stadium. The entire body of prisoners surrounded the square, several deep in places, all of them baying for blood. I pushed my way through them until I was at the front.

In the middle of the square was a lone figure. He was a huge man, a great hunk of Australian muscle with tattoos and a bush hat. In his right hand was a Gurkha's kukri, the curved, razor-sharp, knife with which the little men loved to behead their enemies.

I had only just absorbed all this when Sergeant Cuthbertson appeared at my side. "Here at last! Better late than never."

"Never mind your sarcasm, Sergeant. What's happening?"

"That bastard Bainbridge. He's in for a double murder. Mutilated both his officer and platoon sergeant on 355. His court-martial is due tomorrow. So he's gone berserk. Threatening to kill anyone who goes near him."

It was a very succinct summary of the situation, but there was no hint as to what business it was of mine or what anyone intended to do about it. Before I had a chance to enquire, Sergeant Cuthbertson added: "You'll have to go and disarm him."

"Me? Why me?"

"Because you're orderly officer."

"That's ridiculous. What can I do about it?"

"It's the orderly officer's job to read him his rights and inform him of the action we can take if he becomes violent."

"If? It's bloody obvious he's going to be violent."

"We don't go on the obvious ... Only the actual."

"Can't we just overpower him?"

"How?"

"I don't know ... Shoot him ..."

"You can't go around the place shooting people before they've done anything. If we show aggression towards him before he does to us--- or in this case you--- he'll be legally entitled to claim self-defence... That we used undue force." Then Cuthbertson added in the sing-song voice NCOs always adopt when quoting from Queen's Regulations or the Manual of Military Law: "'No physical action of an incapacitating nature shall be taken against a prisoner until such time, or occasion, that he has first committed an offence, or used unwarranted, or unnatural physical violence.' Section Twenty Two, Paragraph B (ii) Rules of Disarmament, by Act of Parliament."

"You mean we can't do anything until he's hacked someone with that knife?"

"Until he's tried to. Like the Act says ..."

"Then what happens."

"Then we shoot the bastard. I've called out the Guard and there are two marksmen standing by."

"So I have to go out there …"

"Afraid so. Don't blame me. It's all part of Manny Shinwell's Act of Parliament.* If I was you, I'd tell Bainbridge that he is surrounded and can't possibly get away."

"I imagine he's well aware of that already."

I decided the whole thing was utterly ridiculous. None of the screws ever took any notice of any rules, regulations, or acts of parliament. Only now, when they were scared stiff and too cowardly to risk their skins. I decided to be decisive; to issue firm orders; to take control. "Right, Sergeant! This is what you are going to do. First, you will get in touch with the CO and get him down here pronto! And I mean pronto!"

"He's already been. Not his responsibility. He's the one who ordered them to call for you over the Tannoy … The Act plainly states … and he again broke into his sing-song voice, quoting the regulation.

"All right! All right!"

"It's not as bad as all that," he said. All you have to do is inform Bainbridge of his rights and then stand well back …"

"You mean scarper quick…"

"Certainly not! He has to be disarmed."

"But how?"

"That's up to you. Mission Command! Good luck."

With that he put a hand on my shoulder and shoved me forward.

I marched across the tarmac, my swagger stick tucked under my arm. I felt like a midget in the middle of a nightmare. My only consolation was that I was unknown to Bainbridge. I had never been among those to torment him or heap sadistic punishments on him. If any of the screws had confronted him, his reaction would have been a foregone conclusion, straight decapitation, but he had no vendetta against me. He had never even seen me before. Now, he watched warily as I approached him. His squint became quizzical, as though thinking: 'My bloody oath! What the fuck is this?'

The nearer I got to him the more frightening his physical presence became. He was so massive, and so solid that I reckoned that unless the marksmen shot him straight between the eyes he would survive God knows how many bullets pumped into him and still be able to chop me

---

* *Shinwell was Labour's Secretary of State for War 1947 and Minister of Defence, 1950-51. His military experience is not listed in reference books. They deal mainly with his period as Minister of Fuel and Power, during which time the country ran clean out of both. Once, he was imprisoned for inciting a riot, but he was careful not to take part in it.*

up. By the time I got up to him, all Manny Shinwell's Rules of Engagement were forgotten. In fact, I had no idea of what they were, anyhow. As things turned out, that was probably just as well. Quoting rules and regulations at Bainbridge would only have riled him further. I decided to reason with him. To strike a friendly note. I halted directly in front of him, close up, within kukri distance. I stood at ease. I recalled Clancy and his antipodean insistence of being addressed by his rank. So I said: "Good day, Private Bainbridge. Would you please hand over that knife."

He glared at me. His face screwed up in a tight knot, all belligerence and loathing.

"If you don't mind, Private," I added. "Be a sport."

To my astonishment his expression changed. He strained forward, as though he hadn't heard me properly. "Be a sport?"

There was a pause. It wasn't a natural pause. It was a pregnant pause. The yells and cat-calls of the prisoners had stopped. There was silence. Tenseness became increasingly tangible by the second. Bainbridge's expression changed again. The tight knot on his brow unfolded. His facial muscles relaxed. He stared at me incredulously. Everyone was waiting for him to raise his right arm to slice me open.

"Yes, there's a good fellow, Private. Hand it over, please!"

A suggestion of a smile flickered across his face. Then it became a real smile. From the distance it no doubt looked like a gloating smile, the smile of a maniac anticipating spurting blood and a dismembered officer; but close up to him I could see that Bainbridge was genuinely amused. He even chuckled softly.

"Be a sport?" he repeated. "A good fellow ... Please!"

"Yes, come on. There's a good chap."

"A good chap!"

He stared at me long and hard, as though I was a freak, a relic from the past; a pathetic little Pommy half-caste toff who was being made to do the dirty work of the screws who hadn't got the guts to confront him. His expression indicated that there were limits to what even he was prepared to do, and this certainly wasn't 'fair dinkum'. He stepped forward. One stride and he was right up to me. Those watching gasped, convinced that this was it, that the blood was about to flow; but all he did was turn the kukri around and offer it to me, handle first. I took it and said: "Thank you very much, Private Bainbridge."

I didn't wait around. I did a smart about-turn and marched back towards Sergeant Cuthbertson. I fought back the urge to run. Bainbridge shouted after me: "Don't mention it, old chap!" and then he roared with laughter.

I could still hear him laughing when I drew level with Sergeant

Cuthbertson. I was trembling all over. Even so, I managed to hand the kukri to him with apparent calmness. Then I said: "Carry on, Sergeant!" and walked off.

That wasn't the end of it. When Cuthbertson and two other Red Caps went out to apprehend the unarmed Bainbridge, with every intention of doing the business on him the moment they got him back in his cell, he became extremely violent. Before further reinforcements were able to help them (and no one exactly rushed forward) he beat hell out of them with his fists.

The following day I visited Cuthbertson in the Prison Hospital. He had two lovely black eyes and some broken ribs. One of the other screws was still unconscious. The third was in intensive care.

28

Rain, Rain Go Away

My success with Bainbridge didn't go unnoticed, even though no one in the Detention Barracks said anything. They pretended I'd done no more than was expected of an orderly officer and no more than they would have done themselves. Nevertheless, a full report went back to Colonel Bunbury and he was sufficiently impressed to want me back for a reorganization he was doing among his officers prior to returning to the front line. His aim was to enhance the future efficiency of the battalion by redeploying regular subalterns in specialist roles such as the Signals, the Machine Gun Platoon, the Mortar Platoon, the Intelligence Section, the Assault Pioneers, and Motor Transport, leaving National Service officers in command of the rifle platoons. Consequently, Denning was transferred to the Assault Pioneers and I replaced him as 12 Platoon commander.

For the first time in months, Rupert pinned a verse on the platoon notice board.

> *"So, dear old Denning's gone, and gone for good!*
> *My God, what a relief after all we've withstood.*
> *Contractor's in charge again; back to where we started,*
> *Like the bloke who paid a penny, then only farted."*

It caused great amusement. Surreptitiously, I watched men as they read it and it was good to see them laughing and smiling again. Yet I couldn't help thinking that 12 Platoon was starting to get the better of Rupert. Crudity was creeping in.

I soon discovered that the others had changed as well. Quite apart from all the new faces--- youngsters from Hara Mura--- the old hands were sullen. Their chirpy spirit was missing. They were careworn and morose. Among the bandsmen only Jenkins (now a corporal) retained any élan and I was astonished to find that Harry Wilmott was now a Bren gunner and hating every second of it. Bertie Mee, who I had often cursed for his effervescence, no longer went around the place singing rock'n roll songs. Nor was his mouth organ seen or heard. As for Fletcher, he was more bitter and twisted than ever. He kept staring at me for seconds on end, convinced that I was nothing but a skiver who had been leading a life of debauchery, shagging away like a two-stroke.

Fair comment really, I suppose.

I put this deterioration in the platoon down to Denning's officiousness, and no doubt that was part of it, but I soon discovered it was a direct result of Hill 355. I questioned Rupert about it and he admitted he had played things down in his letters, seeing no point in alarming me. Their greatest trauma came with hand-to-hand fighting. Thrice they'd counter-attacked after the Chinese had captured company positions, and each encounter had been murderous; hunting down human prey and then systematically disposing of them with cold steel. They had to ferret the Chinese out of a network of narrow trenches, dark, unfamiliar bunkers, weapon pits, and tunnels. They plunged in after them not knowing what to expect and face-to-face confrontations became the norm, with a fifty/fifty chance of being stuck like a pig. At such close quarters they could smell their adversary's fear and see the terror in their eyes. Reflex reactions and naked ferocity won the day; a moment's hesitation and they came off second best to physically inferior Chinese, a humiliating way to die.

Eight men in Dog Company died by the bayonet.*

The British 29th Brigade was due back into the line in approximately a week, but no one knew the disposition of the three battalions. So far the Black Watch had monopolized responsibility for the Hook, but that couldn't go on indefinitely. Either ourselves or the King's Regiment would have to take a turn. Yet when orders came through it was again the Black Watch who were on the Hook. The Earl was furious, but he needn't have worried. Our turn came soon enough.

In the meantime we were under canvas three miles from the Hook. Our re-entrant was a quiet spot, well away from the MSR, so overhead cover was not necessary. The noise of battle on the Hook never stopped. There were the usual Chinese milk rounds, one before evening stand-to and the other at dawn; and during the rest of the day intermittent shelling and mortaring was like background music, always there but hardly noticed.

Divisional intelligence reports warned that this was the calm before the storm. Auster spotter planes reported a build-up of fresh troops behind the Chinese lines and it was confidently predicted that if the peace talks in Panmunjom broke down, the war would take off again in earnest, with

---

* Dog Company's most unlikely death was that of CSM Howard. After a successful counter-attack he was found in a tiny OP, standing bolt upright, face to face with a weedy Chinaman. They appeared to be embracing each other, but in fact they'd bayoneted each other simultaneously, with no room to fall in the confined space.

the Chinese launching a major attack against the Hook, seeking a breakthrough to Seoul, and the Americans changing their tactics with regard to bombing across the Yalu.

No one reckoned on the weather. Late spring was said to be the best time of year in Korea. When Animal Evans heard this, he said: "Aye, I wouldn't be too sure about that. The winters are unbearably cold, the autumns unbearably foggy, and the summers are unbearably hot. So spring is bound to be unbearably something else."

He was right. Korean springs were unbearably wet. In 1952 it was the wettest Spring ever known, just as the winter of 1952/3 had been the coldest ever known, and the summer of 1953 turned out to be the hottest ever known. Korea was a great country for climatic records.

Spring started well enough. The showers were gentle and the warm sunshine made plants sprout with miraculous speed. Wild flowers and unknown weeds blossomed to provide a splurge of dazzling colours on the hills and in the valleys. Birds chirped away, the sun warmed our backs, and men's fancies turned more than ever to their five days R and R in Tokyo.

Yet there were nasties as well. Long brown snakes came out of hibernation and slithered around the place, all evil eyes and flicking tongues, heading for the rats which were encamped with us in their usual numbers. The reptiles caused far greater panic than the rodents ever did, and we often watched--- at a very safe distance--- as the former swallowed the latter in one gulp, snakes versus rats being a very one-sided contest. Wild cats and mangy dogs also came out for an airing and the mosquitoes, which had been with us all the time, became more blood-thirsty than ever, swooping and diving around like squadrons of migrating swallows, searching out men who'd smothered themselves in insect repellent, which they regarded as a sort of salad dressing.

Then it rained. It really rained. My God, how it rained!

There are no words to describe the late spring rain in Korea. In normal places, when it rains really hard, one talks in terms of 'sheets' or 'cats and dogs' or 'hammering down' or 'stair rods' or 'buckets', and it is quite common to blame God for 'throwing it down'; but Korean rain is all those things combined. Only those who have suffered it can ever believe it. Even Burmese veterans like the Earl were stunned.

Within seconds we were wallowing in deep mud. Vehicles bogged down, bunkers collapsed, and trenches caved in. Those of us who thought we were pretty safe under canvas had the ignominy of seeing our tents slip their moorings and float down the hillside like motorized cow pats. Men dashed about, frantically retrieving weapons, kitbags, and personal belongings, grabbing anything as their tents slithered off, bound for the Yellow Sea. Rivers overflowed, carrying away houses, vehicles and anything else in their path. Whole villages were swept away. The terraced hills became a series of waterfalls as paddy fields overflowed into the ones below, and the human excrement the locals spread on them floated to the surface, vast patches of stinking scum which made it look like a bad day in the English Channel.

Most disastrous of all, the Imjin broke its banks and demolished all the bridges along its length. Supplies from the rear dried up and not infrequently men drowned trying to contest the power of nature.

"It's all this shelling," explained Animal. "It was the same in the Great War. Pissed down all the time in Flanders. Isn't that so, Rupert?"

"Absolutely," agreed Rupert.

"There you are then!" said Animal, as though Rupert had disputed the point. "You're not the only bugger who knows about these things."

Rupert laughed. "Only one difference, Animal. In Flanders it was flat. So everything just floated. It didn't disappear like our tents have. What I'd like to know is where the hell do we sleep tonight?"

It was a good question. When we put it to Earl Gray he said he'd get some TCVs sent up from battalion HQ so that we could sleep in the back of them, everyone in a sitting position. Unfortunately the TCVs were up to their differentials in mud and the roads had become rivers, so they never made it. It left us with no option but to sleep on the open hillside, the bottom of the re-entrant having been reduced to a raging torrent. Some, who had managed to save their ponchos, used them as ground sheets. Others preferred to sit in the mud with their ponchos over their heads, keeping off the rain that continued to cascade down. Fletcher had the best idea. He climbed the only local tree and made himself comfortable where the trunk forked. There was room for others but when they tried to join him, he told them to bugger off.

"Go and find your own bloody tree!"

Rupert was sitting beside me with a wet arse, having opted to use his ponchos as overhead cover. After listening to Fletcher offering the same advice to several men, he observed: "Good old Fletch! He'd never have got on with 'Old Bill' in Flanders."

29

A Taste of Things to Come

When the rain stopped a scorching sun sent everything mouldy with a musty smell that was enough to make one puke. Once the bridges across the Imjin had been repaired supplies got back to normal and we were issued with new tents. This time I got a decent size one in which I could stand up, together with a low-slung officers' camp bed.

In the front line both armies became more active, making up for lost time. Chinese shelling returned to normal levels and on the Hook the Black Watch concentrated on getting trenches back into shape and rebuilding CPs and weapon pits which had collapsed or been severely weakened. Units of the Royal Engineers went up there to help every day, as did Denning and his Assault Pioneers.

Further complications came when Syngman Rhee ordered all North Korean prisoners of war to be released--- a deliberate attempt to scupper the peace talks and prolong the war. It made an attack on the Hook all the more certain, with the prediction that it would coincide with the Chinese New Year. On May 6th, Earl Gray called an orders group. It was the first he'd held for some time and there were several new faces. In the Colonel's reorganization, Stan Bennett had gone back to the UK for the Coronation parade and Ralf Waugh had been transferred to battalion HQ. 10 Platoon was now under the command of Phillip Barrow and 11 Platoon was in the hands of Frank Tremlett. CSM Howard had been replaced by CSM Jessop. I knew Barrow and Tremlett from Eaton Hall. Tremlett had been junior to me and had left no lasting impression, but Phillip Barrow was a good friend and a fine all round sportsman, tipped as a future rugby star.

The Earl started the orders group by saying: "In three days' time, on May 9th, we take over the Hook from the Black Watch. Dog Company will be on the Hook itself. The Turkish Brigade will be on our left and Baker company on our right, occupying the feature known as 'Sausage'. Being given the Hook is a great compliment to us and a direct result of the way we performed on 355. So well done. Just make sure that you keep it up."

He went through a host of details. A vital part of the Hook's defences were the standing patrols. There were three, known as Ronson, Warsaw, and Green Finger. They stood on the three main avenues of attack used by the Chinese, coming up from man-made caves beneath the hills opposite the Hook. The Earl went on to explain that on the night of May

8th, the evening before Dog Company moved on to the Hook, platoon commanders would do a thorough recce of their new positions, with especial reference to the standing patrols. We were to go up just before last light and stay up there until thoroughly briefed by our opposite numbers. "Listen carefully to everything they say," instructed the Earl. "And welcome any advice they give you. Captain Bowden will also be going up to familiarize himself with company headquarters. Any questions?"

Our recce coincided with a Chinese attack.

To this day, the Black Watch always refer to the night of May 8th as the 3rd Battle of the Hook, even though officially it was later classified as a major probing attack. Having been on the Hook at the time, I accept the Black Watch version.

We were picked up at company headquarters by two jeeps from the Black Watch. The corporal in charge explained the procedure. Transport going to the Hook's jeep-head was always spotted a quarter of a mile or so before the Hook due to the dust they threw up. Consequently, arrivals at the jeep-head were always greeted by shelling. "So everything has to be done at top speed," explained the corporal. "We dash in, screech to a halt, and whilst we throw the jeeps into reverse and do a quick about turn, you all jump out and make a dash for the Company Aid Post, which is the nearest safe cover."

It was just as he said. The speed at which they approached the Hook and the manner of their 3-point turns could have been straight out of a Hollywood gangster film. In his haste, Tremlett left his Sten behind, but he had no chance of retrieving it. Shells were already landing as we dashed into the morgue. We piled into the deep, spacious bunker, laughing with relief at our narrow escape. We stopped laughing when we saw wounded men lying on bunks ranged against the walls, each with various pieces of medical equipment in evidence, mainly drips. Standing by the doorway was a pile of blood-stained stretchers. A corporal in the RAMC approached us. "On the way up?"

"Yes," replied Copper.

"Then I'd wait a good ten minutes if I was you, sir. It'll give Chinky time to calm down."

As suggested we waited until the shelling had stopped and then made our way up the hill. We reached the company CP unscathed. The Black Watch platoon commanders were waiting for us. My opposite number was David Milne. He was another I remembered from Eaton Hall. He had inherited Lord Hatchleigh's ex-girlfriend in Chester on the strength of going to Oxford to qualify as a barrister, wearing Wolsey socks, and expecting a sizable inheritance. They'd ended up engaged to be married.

I was due to take-over the right-hand platoon position. Phillip Barrow had drawn the short straw with the forward platoon, and Tremlett was on the left, perhaps the least dangerous of the three, although if the Chinese overran the position it didn't make any damn difference where you were. Perhaps Phillip Barrow and 10 Platoon had the advantage with their tunnels, but who the hell wanted to die buried alive?

One of the main features of the Hook was the lack of any 'living' bunkers. Men were expected to stay on the forward slope the whole time and they slept, fought, and ate in their weapon pits. They only left them to go on patrol or visit the latrines--- the worst in Korea. It went back to the days of the Americans and their foxholes and although weapon pits had since been well-developed, living for a month in a space roughly ten foot square was a pretty debilitating experience, especially since they looked out on a barren, crater-pitted slope on which bodies and human remains from previous attacks still dangled on the belts of barbed wire.

The three standing patrols were accessed through the forward platoon, Ronson on the left, Green Finger straight ahead, and Warsaw to the right. Milne showed me all three and explained the tactics they employed. Each patrol position had rudimentary slit trenches and from these the enemy were engaged. If they became too heavily outnumbered the standing patrols retired as quickly as possible before calling down stonks on the Chinese. Clashes on all three patrols happened nightly, sometimes twice nightly like theatrical performances.

By the time Milne had shown me the exit points for the patrols, darkness was closing in and he was anxious to get back to his platoon CP. He kept looking at his watch, saying "Milk round coming up any second."

We made his CP just in time. The first shells poured down like the spring rain. A thousand or more of them. Men had no option but to cower in their weapon pits. They were all built to withstand shelling, but eventually, given enough direct hits, they were bound to crack up and collapse. Probably the worst thing about the milk round was the noise. As it went on, so it tore into men's nerves until they felt they could stand no more. Everyone knew it was suicidal to make a run for it, yet most men were tempted. Occasionally, a man would slip over the edge, pull himself free of his restraining comrades, and run screaming down the trench. None of them ever survived.

When the milk round stopped there was an immediate stand-to: a routine procedure. Standing patrols were despatched post haste and everyone strained for the sound of Chinese bugles, wondering if tonight was the night.

As already mentioned, it was the night.

I was sitting with Milne in his CP when reports came over his 88-set that all three standing patrols had heard movement in dead ground in front of them. Two-inch mortar flares were hoisted and the searchlights of neighbouring tanks were switched on to scan the forward slopes. Then artillery star flares soared into the sky. It was as though daylight had returned.

Chinese bugle calls soon followed. I trailed after Milne as he went to check the readiness of his platoon, and then we went round to the Ronson entrance to meet his patrol as they returned. They soon came sprinting in. One man was wounded and being dragged along by others. When the patrol commander reached us, he panted: "Bloody hundreds of them. Far more than usual. No chance of holding them back ... Honest!"

Soon, all the patrol were back. Two stretcher bearers appeared. They slapped shell dressings on the wounded man and carried him away. Milne and I stayed in the trench long enough to see the Gunner's lay down a heavy concentration along the company front. "If they come on through that lot they'll mean business," Milne explained. "But they might just clear off. They do sometimes."

This wasn't one of those occasions. The Chinese came straight on, sprinting through the shelling towards the barbed wire. It was the first time I'd witnessed a mass frontal assault and the first time I'd felt the desperation of having to mow men down before being overwhelmed by sheer numbers. In the forward platoon automatics were cutting into the enemy as they tried to force their way through our wire. Even those who found gaps and wriggled through were slowed down by the steepness of the slope. Just as I thought they were bound to be repulsed, another wave of them appeared. They far outnumbered the first lot.

"Oh, God!" swore Milne. "Back to the platoon. They'll be coming at us as well."

We ran back along the trench and when we got to his platoon his men were already firing flat out. All the automatics were on rapid, with empty magazines being tossed aside. There was no question of having to aim or select a target. They just held their finger on their triggers and sprayed bullets back and forth. Then the Black Watch's mortars came into play, laying down their defensive fields of fire just in front of the barbed wire. All around us activity and noise increased dramatically. Another Battery of 25-pounders joined in, shelling Chinese forming up areas, and the entire forward slopes of the Hook were criss-crossed by a crazy pattern of tracer bullets as machine guns opened up, some from the Turks on our left and the British Vickers on our right from the distant Yong Dong. Then the machine guns of the Centurions came into play, picking off targets exposed by their spotlights. Soon, every conceivable weapon had joined in.

Chinese Burp guns sounded for the first time as the Chinese closed in on the forward trenches; and all the time human voices punctuated the battle noises: cries of anguish and warning, screams of fear and elation, and the banshee yells from the Chinese as they continued to struggle up the slopes amid more bugle calls.

Milne led the way into his CP. He checked with his batman for messages over the 88-set and then grabbed my arm and said: "Come on! We'll go to our new bunker up by the Gunners OP. We'll call it the Look Out. It's the most dangerous spot in Korea. But it has a marvellous field of fire."

We branched off into a trench with a short but steep incline. It brought us to a bunker at the peak of the Hook, looking straight down over the front platoon. In it, two men were firing a Browning, the barrel swinging from side to side, the bunker heavy with the smell of overheating metal. As we went in I looked through the weapon slit or embrasure. All I could see was a desolate group of Chinese standing in the open, overlooking the trenches of the forward platoon. They were dithering about as though lost, with no idea of what to do next. It cost them dearly. They were going down steadily under the automatic fire until soon there were hardly any of them left.

I was convinced that their attack had foundered, but then another wave of them flooded over the crest of the hill, leaping across the trenches of the forward platoon. This time they were being led. Several figures at the front kept turning to urge them on and they followed without hesitation, surging straight towards us, sprinting over open ground, regardless of the fire being directed at them. For a moment I was paralyzed by fear. Then my training and sense of discipline clicked back in. I helped Milne lift a second Browning on to the firing ledge, adjusting the tripod so that we could bring more fire to bear on the Chinese. They were firing at us from the hip and bullets bit into the ground just ahead of us, sending up spouts of earth. Others cracked loudly as they passed a few inches over the Look Out.

We were holding them back and so many of them were falling, littering the ground, that they were impeding those behind them. I saw several of them trip and fall, only to rise again and carry on towards us. Casualties meant nothing to them. They ran into a curtain of certain death. They were like zombies, drugged to the eyeballs.

We soon came to the end of a belt of bullets. Milne looked around, searching for a fresh ammunition box, but there wasn't one. He cursed and shouted to me: "Go back to the CP and get more ammo. McIntyre knows where."

He reverted to using his Sten and I ran off down the trench. When I got to the CP I told McIntyre what had happened. He pointed to the reserve ammunition boxes and then took his head phones off. "The Gunners are going to bring down VT.* The forward platoon has been ordered into their tunnels. Better warn Mr. Milne. They'll be exposed as hell up there. Hurry! The VT will arrive any second."

I dashed off. When I got to the bunker, the ammunition box cradled in my arms, I realized straight away that something was wrong. There was no noise. No firing. Not even Milne's Sten. When I entered the bunker I stopped abruptly. All three were dead, riddled by bullets entering through the embrasure. Each had been hit several times, head, neck, or shoulder wounds. Blood was splattered about with a large pool on the firing ledge where the head of one of them was resting. I glanced through the embrasure and saw the Chinese still coming forward, now virtually unopposed, apparently unstoppable.

Then, without any warning--- without even the usual split-second scream of incoming shells--- VT burst over the hill ahead of me. Great balls of fire erupted some twenty feet above the ground. I had never seen anything like it. Multi-coloured flashes burst like an extravagant fireworks display. The sky became full of rainbow shades, jagging out in all directions. The effect was dramatic, instant, and horrific. Shrapnel scythed through the Chinese, felling them in hundreds. No living thing in the open stood a chance.

A chunk of wood was taken out of the embrasure directly in front of me. Instinctively I ducked, then fled back to the platoon CP. Thanks to the deepness of the trenches I made it safely. I collapsed on to a bunk. McIntrye was watching me closely. He had his Sten at the ready and he'd obviously been on the point of shooting me when I dashed in. I told him what had happened, breaking off only when a message crackled over his 88-set. He listened for a few seconds and then said: "Roger and out." He took his headphone off and added: "VT for another ten minutes. Everyone under cover. All we can do now is sit tight and watch out for Chinks survivors coming in through the doorway."

We took up positions on each side of the curtained entrance. "If they lob in a grenade, be ready to grab it and toss it back out again," added McIntyre.

We waited in silence, safety catches off, our fingers resting lightly on our triggers, concentrating on the first sound of someone approaching. We heard nothing, but suddenly there was some slight movement on the blanket hanging over the doorway. It moved again. The bottom of it swayed forward. We braced ourselves for the inevitable. Then a huge rat pushed its way in. We watched it as it scuttled into a corner and started to

---

VT shells are also known as 'Air burst'. They explode shortly before landing giving very little chance of survival for anyone still in the open.

climb the sandbag wall.

"Jesus, I never thought I'd been so glad to see one of those bastards," said McIntyre.

An hour later everything was quiet: nothing, apart from an occasional burst of small-arms fire from the forward platoon as they picked off Chinese survivors entangled in the barbed wire. Eventually, I went to the doorway and peered down the trench, both ways. I yelled towards the entrance of a weapon pit I could see. "You blokes all right?"

A head appeared. "Aye! Right as rain. We've sorted them out okay."

The next thing was that I heard my name being called out. It was Copper Bowden. When I replied, he stuck his head into the bunker and said: "Excitement over, Din. We've been ordered back to the Dukes."

30

The Sharp End

The following day we marched to the Hook in silence. Our orders were no singing or bugles and to throw up as little dust as possible. I spent my time thinking about Katsumi. There was hardly a moment when I didn't think about her. Now, having just received her first letter, she was in my thoughts more than ever. I'd already read her letter a dozen times or more and I had it handy in my map pocket, ready to read again. It was in reply to letters I'd sent her and it delighted me. Writing letters in English obviously wasn't easy for her but somehow or other she had retained all her quaintness and spontaneity. I had dreaded that she would enlist the help of Eddie and end up sending me several pages of beautiful prose, all as dull as ditch water, like his memos.

Instead, every line was pure Katsumi. Each one made me smile or chuckle. She called Captain Starkey 'Mister Starchy' and described him as a toy soldier. "Oh, he so very ticky-tocky." She said he spent so much time in the mess and the Officers' Club that they hardly saw him. Even when they crossed paths he seemed unaware of her presence. He regarded Moggy-san as senior house-girl and dealt exclusively through her. He summoned her by calling out, "Boy!" and if he wanted Katsumi to do something, he would say: "Boy! Tell Number Two ...", not even gracing her with a name, just a number. He hadn't even twigged that it was Katsumi who spoke English, not Moggy-san.

"Of course," wrote Katsumi, "being Ingrish, he orways washing in barfing water behind a rocked door. But I not terring him off, rike I terring you off, Saji-san! If I do, he putting me straight in sack."

She wrote that Nacker and Akiko were still desperately in love, as were the Tommy-sans and their Geishas, but things had changed a lot in the headquarters. It was back to the dreary old days and poor Baker-san had been sent to Korea.* "No one fooding the fish now, Saji-san. But they keep froating around okay."

Mostly, she wrote about how much she missed me and looked forward to my return. She'd already worked out to the day when that was likely

---

* Baker was sent to the Hook as a reinforcement and was killed serving with Charlie Company on Sausage.

to be. What she thought would happen then, she didn't say and she obviously had no more idea than I did. All that really mattered to her was that I returned safe and sound.

In the same post I had a letter from Nacker. He was more down to earth. He mentioned that Akiko and he were keeping in touch with Katsumi and often invited her back to his bungalow; but that it wasn't too easy with all the changes that were taking place. Colonel Gibson was due to return to England in three months (which I already knew) and it was assumed--- mainly because of the way he was throwing his weight around--- that Captain Starkey would be promoted to Major and take over as commandant. Nacker said that Eddie was worried sick and that he (Nacker) was being damned careful to cover his tracks so that no one caught him cohabiting with Akiko. He went on to explain that Brigadier Clay had completed all his required visits to Korea to qualify for extra medals, which meant that Nacker now had to keep regular office hours like everyone else. When he turned up late one Monday morning after a rugby trip to Tokyo, Clay was so furious he cancelled all future fixtures.

The good days had gone forever.

As we marched along, I wondered how the platoon would react if I ever read out Katsumi's letter to them as I would have done in the good old days. How, for example, would they react to: "Saji-san! Now I terring you very big secret. Oh, such rovery secret. Orl time on bedding, I thinking about you. Orl those times we making rove … Oh, so many times …"

Fletch would go mad with jealousy!

Then I thought of the laughter it would bring if I read out another bit: "Prease, Saji-san, orl time keeping head deep down. Very important! And prease, orways be wearing burret proof vest and broomers. I not knowing your rads out there, rike I knowing your rads back here, but if your rads out there are as rovery as your rads back here, prease give them my rove."

Love! It was all she ever thought of, bless her.

Eventually, I was unable to resist taking her letter out to read again as I marched along. "Give it a rest, Saj," Rupert called out from behind me.

I laughed but otherwise ignored him. He knew just how many times I'd already read it and he alone in the platoon realized just how crazy I was about her, and how my feelings towards her went much deeper than infatuation. When I'd first returned to Korea I had been wary of his reaction. I was afraid he might take the mickey, especially because of my change of heart since our days of celibacy at Catterick. However, he'd made no adverse comments and had been more than patient at the way I kept talking about her. He was sensible enough to accept that everyone got bitten by the bug in the end.

When we reached the Hook I put Katsumi's letter back in my map pocket in order to concentrate on the job in hand. Whenever real danger threatened, I tried not to think of her. I had a job to do and couldn't allow personal feelings to get the upper hand. Right now, I was trying to convince myself that the action on the Hook the night before was the exception rather than the rule, that even on the Hook such attacks were rare. It was only the third major attack in six months so with any luck we would avoid another all-out attack. On top of that, statistics indicated that even in a major attack most of us would survive. I'd been ramming these comforting thoughts down the throats of the lads for days, trying to convince them that the Hook was just another front line position.

At the Hook jeep-head all was quiet and we took a ten-minute break. As we rested in the monsoon ditches, two stretcher cases came down the hill. The stretcher bearers were sweating profusely and going as fast as they could. We heard them mouthing the same old assurances: telling the victims that they were okay, that they had Blighty touches. We also saw a dozen or so blood-stained stretchers at the entrance of the morgue, a reminder of just how much blood had been shed the previous night. Further evidence of the battle came when we reached company HQ. On an open stretch of ground thirty or forty corpses were laid out on stretchers. A corporal was bustling about, making arrangements for them to be removed and buried. Fletcher called out to him: "What you got there, Corp?"

"Chinks! Ones they couldn't cart off themselves." Then he laughed and added: "Still plenty more up there, though. Mostly bits and pieces. You'll see."

We did indeed! Throughout our time on the Hook body parts, broken weapons, and scraps of clothing, were always cropping up, and not only Chinese, but very often American, Canadian, Turkish or Scottish. Rats were often seen carrying body parts about in their mouths, or rummaging about it the dust and debris hunting for more. Worst all of all, the lads had to get used to looking through the embrasures of their weapon pits and seeing the dead Chinese hanging on the barbed wire, all at grotesque angles, some badly decomposed, the more recent ones swollen like balloons, letting off foul noises as gases escaped from them.

As I anticipated, the most unsettling thing of all was the size of the rats. When I'd described them to the lads they hadn't believed me. They thought rats were rats and that was the end of it, but when they saw several obese specimens waddling along the top of a trench wall on our way up the hill, they revised their ideas. Even Animal Evans steered clear of them. They were like size fifteen army boots marching along independently, their incisors protruding and reminiscent of miniature trenching spades. At one point, as we were going along a trench in single file, those at the front stopped abruptly, confronted by a column of rats heading along the bottom of the trench towards us.

"Make way for a rat patrol," shouted Hurst from the front, and we all stood to one side and watched them pass by. Fletcher took a kick at one but only succeeded in kicking it on to someone else's leg, making the man yell out in disgust. As we marched on, Hurst called out: "They're heading south. Think they know something we don't?"

Then Bertie sang out to the tune of 'The Quarter-Master's Stores',

> *"There are rats, rats,*
> *As big as bloody cats,*
> *On the Hook, on the Hook.*
> *There are rats, rats*
> *And even more bloody rats*
> *Where 'ere you ruddy look ..."*

I had a sketch of the platoon layout so was able to direct the section commanders to their weapon pits. I then left them to it, knowing that the Jocks they were relieving would give them all the necessary dope. I went to the platoon CP with Rupert and formally took over from the Black Watch platoon sergeant. He was a quiet, efficient fellow, not interested in small talk, and he watched in amazement as Rupert sorted out his shelf of books. "We'll bug out as quickly as we can, if that's all right with you, sir. I'm keen to break a record ..."

"What's that?"

"Ever since the Yanks were up here, no platoon commander or platoon sergeant has ever survived in this position. So I aim to be the first. Any problems, have a word with Corporal Salmon. He's staying on to show your lads the ropes on the standing patrols."

With that he left. He made it safely to the jeep-head, breaking the all-comers speed record in the process. I was certainly glad to hear that. It set a precedent for survival.

Rupert and I had barely settled in, and had only just reported our take-over completed to company headquarters, when we had our first casualty. A message came through over the 88-set from Corporal Jackman of One Section. I hurried through falling shells to see what had happened. I found several men outside a weapon pit about to load a man onto a stretcher. I pushed my way through. It was a bandsmen named Weldon. He'd been shot through the head, the back of which had virtually disappeared. On the trench floor was a large pool of blood and what I imagined to be most of his brains. "What happened?"

"Sniper, sir," replied Jackman. "He peered over the top to see what the Chinese hills looked like."

Corporal Salmon of the Black Watch was among those man-handling Weldon on to a stretcher. He looked at me, aggrieved. "I told them all, sir! I bloody well told them. You just can't take any bloody chances up here. Stick your head up and you're a goner. And don't bloody stand around here gawping. If the Chinks make a hit, next thing is they mortar the area. The bastards read our minds. They know bloody well we'll all be milling around, trying to help ... So for God's sake get the poor bastard away and take cover before someone else gets it."

The mortar bombs came over even as we dispersed. Then we heard them switch their fire towards the jeep-head, knowing the direction the stretcher bearers would take.

An hour later we were subjected to even heavier shelling. In the CP I heard more yells for stretcher bearers, so when the shelling slackened off I once went again to investigate. Part of the trench in Two Section had caved in and when the dust and smoke cleared away we saw that a man had been partly buried. Only his head and shoulders were visible but he was alive. His eyes were wide open, staring around, startled and terrified. A stretcher was laid out beside him and when the two bearers took him by the shoulders to pull him clear of the rubble, so the man died. When we saw the state of him we weren't surprised. He had been chopped in two. From his groin downwards there was nothing. The rest of him was still buried in the rubble. I very nearly fainted and another man turned away and was sick.

"What the hell was he doing out here?" demanded Corporal Salmon.

"Just went out to stretch his legs," someone replied.

"Christ! You bastards won't last five minutes up here," said Corporal Salmon. "You must keep under cover."

It was not a good introduction to the Hook, but fairly normal. Two deaths a day was something we would soon be happy to settle for. I was more affected by the nature of our second casualty. It left me badly shaken and I grasped for the first time exactly what we were in for.

In the month that followed we had numerous deaths and God knows how many men wounded. Naturally enough, when men I knew well became casualties I was especially saddened but as platoon commander I had to remain detached: a stiff upper lip had never been so vital. Mostly, I was successful but there were two cases I have never been able to eradicate from my mind. To this day, sixty years on, they still haunt me. One was the needless death of a lovable rogue. Another was the disintegration of a fine young fellow who had everything going for him.

Hurst's death was as ironic as it was tragic.

As I watched his body being taken to the morgue, I recalled the first time I'd met him, the occasion when he told the Earl in no uncertain terms that he was after some action. Well, he got his action, but he should never have died--- not then, anyhow. He had always been MM material, but his bravery only earned him the ignominious death of a blue-on-blue.

He was on Corporal Jackman's Ronson patrol when they were attacked by forty-odd Chinese. They stood firm and for ten minutes there was a fierce small-arms exchange. Eventually, when the Chinese were about to overrun them, Jackman ordered them back. Hurst still had two full Bren magazines left and he was damned if he was going to pull back until he'd used them. He ignored Jackman's order. He stayed put and emptied his magazines into the Chinese. Only then did he dash back up the hill, some seventy-five yards behind the others; in terms of time, only a matter of seconds, but long enough for 10 Platoon to assume that the whole patrol was back in. Stragglers were invariably wounded, limping along slowly, being helped by others, but a lone figure dashing full pelt towards them could only be the first of the attacking Chinese.

The section commander yelled: "Here they come!" and he and his men opened fire. Because they were all using Stens, it was impossible to tell which one of them killed Hurst. It was only one of them because Hurst died from a single bullet wound to his throat.

The 10 Platoon men were devastated by what had happened and I have often wondered how they've coped with it over the years, none of them knowing who had fired the fatal bullet.

The second incident occurred as a result of Earl Gray trying to improve the standing patrols to prevent further accidents. He ordered that in future they would be commanded by either a sergeant or an officer. To spread the strain, CSM Jessup and Copper Bowden were included. It was hardly within their normal duties, but to their credit they didn't complain. The only objection came from Phillip Barrow, my cricket team-mate at Eaton Hall.

At one of the Earl's orders groups, Barrow didn't turn up. We waited for some time, but when he still didn't appear Copper Bowden sent a runner to 10 platoon to see what had happened. He soon came back, but alone. "Where is he, then?" demanded the Earl.

"His bunker has been blown in, sir. He's been buried alive."

"Well are they digging him out?"

"They already have, sir. But he's resting."

The Earl uttered an oath and rested his head in his hands. He had no time for faint-hearts, but he controlled his anger and said to the runner: "My complements to Mr. Barrow. But tell him that much as we all sympathize, he must come round here immediately."

Again, we waited. After ten minutes Barrow appeared in the doorway. He was dishevelled, covered in dust and dirt, his combat trousers torn. His face was pale and, despite his size, he suddenly looked thin and feeble: washed out. Everyone watched as he remained in the doorway. He stared back at us, looking at each of us in turn, as if counting us. "I've just been buried alive," he announced.

"So we heard," replied the Earl. "But you're all right, aren't you?"

"I was buried alive ... It was completely dark ..."

"Well it would be, wouldn't it ... Anyhow, take a seat and listen in. We've wasted enough time as it is."

He sat next to me. He was still shivering. The Earl started on the details of the new arrangements for the standing patrols, but Barrow ignored him. He turned to me and said: "I was buried, Din. They only saved me in the nick of time."

"This new system," continued the Earl, ignoring Barrow, "will come into operation as from tonight. Mr. Tremlett, you and your sergeant will look after the Green Finger patrol. Mr. Barrow, you will do the first Warsaw ... Relieved by Contractor."

"Me?" said Barrow. "But I've just been buried alive."

"So you keep telling us. Tonight you will ..."

"But officers don't do standing patrols. They never have."

"Mr. Barrow, I'm perfectly aware of that. But these are hardly normal standing patrols. It's why I've decided to change the system."

"But I won't be able to control my platoon properly if I'm on patrol. Surely, it's quite sufficient for a NCO to ..."

"Mr. Barrow, I've made a decision, and that's it. And you're going to do your share whether you like it or not. And if a withdrawal is ordered, everyone must obey. We don't want any more blue-on-blue incidents. Is that perfectly clear? Right, that's all. Except that tomorrow the Colonel and the Brigadier are coming up here. So make sure everything is ship-shape. I don't want the Brigadier to find the trenches littered with fag ends and sweet papers."

"Is that what he'll be looking for?" I asked.

The Earl ignored me and the orders group broke up. I returned to 12 Platoon and passed on the new orders to my section commanders. When I told them about the Brigadier's visit they all groaned. It was well known that whenever he visited the sharp end he had a nasty habit of calling down a stonk on the Chinese, just for the hell of it. "Must make my little contribution," he'd say and then bugger off quickly before they retaliated, leaving others to dodge the flying shrapnel.

No one anticipated any difficulties with the new patrolling system. I was in command of the second Ronson patrol and I made a point of taking my six men around to the exit in good time, knowing that after five hours out there, Phillip Barrow and his men would be keen to get back. It was whilst we were there, preparing to go out, that I saw a lone figure standing right at the end of the front trench. He was watching us, but when he saw me eyeing him, he stepped back into the shadows. I was certain it was Barrow because of his height, but since we were supposed to be relieving his patrol I couldn't make out what he was doing there. For a moment I wondered if he had been killed and I was seeing a ghost. I went down the trench to investigate. It was him all right. Before I had a chance to say anything, he blurted out: "I didn't go, Din! I couldn't. I just couldn't."

We went back to his CP. There was no one there, as there should have been. The head-phones of the 88-set were lying on the table, emitting static. The field telephone was off the hook, abandoned, and there were a couple of mugs of unfinished coffee; all the signs of a rapid evacuation. He sat down, pulled out the platoon carboy of rum from under a bunk, and helped himself to an enormous tot. Then, for a minute or two, he just sat there looking thoroughly miserable. Eventually, in no more than a whisper, he said: "I couldn't do it. I just couldn't go over the top. I just seized up. I just knelt in the trench. Stuck there as though in prayer. And I was trembling, shaking like a leaf. My blokes tried to help me. They pleaded with me to get up. They even tried to force me up. But they couldn't. I hit out at them and they couldn't budge me. I think the whole platoon must have come round and seen. In the end they went out without me. I don't know how long I stayed there like that. Maybe a half an hour or so. Eventually, I came back here to the CP, but as soon as I stepped inside my batman and the platoon runner just got up and left. Refused to stay. Now, I don't know what to do. God knows how I'm ever going to face my men again. How will I ever face anyone again?"

He refilled his mug with rum. He was about to take a swig when his chin puckered up and he started to sob. It reminded me of Oglethorpe back in the winter, but there was a vital difference. This was no act. Barrow was gripped by deep shame. Oglethorpe never was. I was so embarrassed I didn't know what to do. Among other things, I was already late for taking my patrol out. So I telephoned Copper Bowden and asked him to sort things out. He came round immediately and looked to me for an explanation. "I've got to go," I said. "My patrol is waiting. I'm late already. He'll tell you what happened."

I got a very curt reception from my patrol. "Where the hell have you been, sir?" demanded Corporal Jenkins. Then he was passed a message to the standing patrol over the 88-set, telling them we were on our way. Whoever replied disregarded all RT procedure. "About bloody time too, you buggers. Over and out!"

It turned out to be an eventful patrol. Twice, we saw Chinese groups milling about on the slopes below us. We engaged them and inflicted enough casualties to chase them off. The next time we spotted them it was a bigger party and I was just about to order a withdrawal, convinced that so many would overrun us, when they suddenly broke off. It was strange because usually they liked to have the last word and force us back into our fortress. Just before dawn we passed the code word over the 88 set and returned. It was only then that I remembered about Phillip Barrow. Being attacked on a Ronson was enough to expunge all else from one's thoughts.

We filed back to 12 Platoon and men dropped off at their weapon pit, hoping to catch some sleep before stand-to. I went to the company CP. Everything there was perfectly normal. A couple of runners were standing by in readiness, the company signaller was talking over the 31-set, the Earl was studying his maps, and Copper was lying on his bunk, smoking his pipe. As he saw me he jumped up and ushered me back into the trench. It was still dark so we could hardly see each other.

"Barrow's gone," he said. "Gone back. We won't see him again. But don't say a word. Pretend it never happened. You know, morale ..."

"Sure," I said. "Poor fellow. I'm amazed it has happened to Phillip. He's always been such a big, tough fellow."*

"Size has got nothing to do with it, Din. It's what's here--- in a man's heart--- that counts." Then he patted me on the shoulder added: "Come in and have a drink. I'm told that you got a few?"

We laughed. Already 'getting a few' was the stock answer for when one had little or no idea of what had been achieved.

"A few few?" persisted Copper. "Or a lot of a few?"

The Hook was always in a state of flux. Personnel changed so frequently that for many each day was their first. Also, apart from the two milk rounds, there was never any pattern or rhyme or reason to the Chinese shelling, so one could never relax or take anything for granted. We were forever on tenterhooks. When we tried to sleep we were continually woken by the cry, "stretcher bearers!" At first, men were so concerned

---

Two years later, Phillip Barrow attended a TA summer camp near Scarborough. There was a very drunken mess night during our final evening. An officer who had served in Korea let slip what had happened to Phillip. It was an innocuous remark ('Like you on the Ronson patrol') and it passed off virtually unnoticed. Phillip said nothing but when he returned to his tent he took out his Webley revolver and blew his brains out. The officer who made the remark was of a mind to do the same thing, but he never did. Thus the legacy of the Hook lingers on.

that it might be one of their friends that they would forsake sleep to find out; but that soon stopped. Abject tiredness meant that we just rolled over and tried to blot out the noise. We let the stretcher bearers get on with their duties, knowing they preferred it that way. The essence was speed, to get men evacuated as quickly as possible. Who it was, and what had happened, and how they would fare, became academic.

Reinforcement arrived daily, young National Servicemen straight from the Hara Mura Battle School, or more Katcoms, all of them just as young and untrained as their predecessors. Beau Brummell and the other platoon sergeants went to the jeep-head every afternoon to share them out. He'd bring ours back to the CP so that I could have a chat with them. I'd try to memorize their names and pass on tips for survival. On one occasion they were a man short.

"Where's the other one?" I asked Brummell.

"Oh, him! As soon as he got out of the TCV a mortar landed and took off most of his hand. He went straight into the morgue, got bandaged up, and then went back with the TCV."

Nothing more was said, but I often think about that man, even though I never met him. Now, I imagine him as a pensioner, possibly a member of the British Legion or the Korean Veterans Association, a victim of the Hook who never actually set foot on the hill.

Most nights there were patrol clashes with the Chinese. They knew exactly where our standing patrols were, so they crept up to them and exchanged fire for several minutes. Then they cleared off, taking their dead and wounded with them. There appeared to be no logic to their tactics and they never achieved anything worthwhile. I suppose it was a matter of harassment, of inflicting casualties on us and keeping us guessing as to what they were up to. Playing on our nerves. They paid heavily for it, especially when we brought stonks down as they retired along known escape routes. Yet still they persisted. They seemed to regard that as a good night's work. It merely convinced us that, man for man, we had the measure of them and that back in Peking the commissars didn't give a damn how many of them perished.

A constant task on the Hook was repairing and strengthening the trenches and weapon pits. My chief ally in this was Harry Wilmott. I took him off the Bren gun he loathed and gave him the title of 'Timber Man'. This pleased him enormously and he never stopped telling me that he was "reet proud" of such a responsibility and how his dad would be 'chuffed t' bollocks!' since that's what he was down one of the Yorkshire pits. Harry was pretty good at it too, although he had a tendency to waste time by chatting excessively with those he was helping, explaining to them that,

"Without good timber work, the whole lot will collapse and we'll all be buried alive."

Dog Company also had help from a troop of Royal Engineers who came up to the Hook every day. They were hard workers but their NCO, Corporal Underwood, although a first class engineer, considered Harry a total, bungling amateur and never stopped criticizing his work and telling him where he was going wrong. Harry ignored his advice and grew increasingly indignant. He even lodged an official complaint with me, during which he claimed, "The bloody fellow is nothing but a fooking poofter from Surrey! And he's telling a Yorkshire lad about timber work. Bloody roll on!" *

Each afternoon I got a few hours' sleep, like the rest of the platoon. They usually got more than I did since my sleep was often interrupted by Earl Gray. He either woke me with urgent messages or questions, or went one better and summoned order groups to warn us that battalion had issued a prediction that tonight might well be the night. As if we didn't know!

After these visits to the company CP I often went down to the jeep-head to look in at the morgue. There was always someone there from the platoon who had been wounded and was awaiting clearance to the RAP, or the nearest MASH unit. It was good for their morale if someone showed an interest in them and saw them on their way. I was always amazed by their good spirits. I suppose it was thankfulness at having escaped a close brush with death.

Every evening I carried out a few essential tasks. I checked weapons and made sure ammunition levels were up to scratch. I also held foot inspections and as I poked around between men's toes they invariably had a good old moan, but this didn't worry me. I knew by now that the time to be concerned was when they stopped grousing. One of the points of contention was Harry and his timber work. They claimed he was looking after everyone's weapon pits except theirs; and it was also a sore point that Harry and Rupert never did patrols. I lost count of the number of times I explained the reasons for this, and I would retaliate by telling them they were damned lucky they didn't have to do a Ronson every night, like poor old Beau Brummell and I did. That in turn sparked off grumbles about Earl Gray--- always an easy target--- and that kept us all happy.

The Ronson patrol became our sole responsibility. We sent out two

---

* *The grudge between them started when Harry completed a restoration job and then stood back to admire his work (Shades of Lem Putt) and said: "Aye ... Fooking perr---fect!" Corporal Underwood was watching nearby. He laughed and commented: "Perfect? It's a load of crap."*

patrols every night. Brummell did the first, until 0100 hours, and my patrol then took over for the rest of the night, roughly five hours each. It was far too long, especially for poor old Brummell. Every night I went down to the Ronson exit with him to see and his patrol off. As I watched them disappear into the darkness I wished them luck. Sometimes their luck was in, but more often than not it wasn't. During our month on the Hook our Ronson casualties were seven killed, fifteen wounded, and three taken prisoner.

Having seen Brummell's patrol on its way, I usually called in on Jim Lazenby* and Frank Tremlett, mainly for a chat, but also to compare notes on anything that might be of mutual concern. Finally, I would report to the company CP. Every night the Assault Pioneers came up to the Hook to repair the barbed wire and put out more belts. I had to know where they would be working in order to warn everyone. I felt sorry for the Pioneers. They had a thankless task and they weren't at all popular on account of the noise they made. As soon as they started driving their metal stakes in to the ground, up went Chinese flares and--- a couple of minutes later--- down came their shells. Most of them fell well short of the weapon pits, smack among the pioneers, but it wasn't unknown for some Dog company lads to get hit. Denning was in command of the pioneers and at odd times, driven in by the shelling, he would call in at my CP. We got to know each other pretty well and he certainly improved with time. He handled men very differently to me, but there was no denying his bravery, or that of his platoon.

One afternoon a curious thing happened. An Auster spotter plane, which for weeks had been stooging about above the Chinese lines, was shot down. I was about to start my afternoon sleep when a lad from 2 Section dashed into the CP.

"Sir! Come quickly. You should see this."

He was so excited that Rupert and I went out into the trench. Half the platoon was already there, watching. High above, over the Chinese lines, the Auster was coming under fire. Little puffs of smoke kept bursting all around it. It reminded me of the Battle of Britain, when I as a boy I watched dog-fights between Spitfires and Messerschmitts, hoping and praying that our man would win.

Now, I was expecting to see the Auster survive. The Chinese fire was inaccurate and the Auster had every chance to climb away out of range. Yet for some reason it didn't and the accuracy of the Chinese shelling suddenly improved. The Auster was forced to bank steeply but as it did

---

* Phillip Barrow's replacement. Another from Eaton Hall. No end to the flow of keen subalterns, just as Dad had told me!

so it went straight into the midst of shell bursts. It shook violently, the engine spluttered, and it began to lose height. Then one of its long, fragile wings was badly torn and it became obvious it was going to crash. Very slowly it went into a spin. We watched in silence. Then the side door of the Auster burst open and two men jumped out. They plunged earthwards for a second or two before their parachutes opened and they drifted down. Their plane continued on its spiral descent and when it crashed into the top of a Chinese hill it exploded and burnt merrily. We continued to watch until the parachutes finally disappeared out of sight because of the height of our trench wall. No one attempted to look over the top for fear of another death. At least we had learnt that lesson.

That night Rupert and I dined together, as we always did. That makes it sound very grand but in reality it consisted of sitting on the edge of our bunks with our mess tins on our knees, being watched by a bevy of rats crawling around on the overhead beams. Our menu was still the same: tomato soup, chicken hash, and a tin of Kim's illicit fruit salad. Not bad, but by God it was monotonous.

The Auster incident was very much in our thoughts and Rupert asked: "So what did you make of it? The Chinese shooting it down like that?"

I shrugged. "They got fed up with it, I suppose."

"Oh, come off it, Saj. No one ever shoots down a spotter plane. And the Chinese have ignored it for weeks. Then all of a sudden they decide to shoot it down."

"So what's your theory?"

"Sun Tzu says that if the enemy acts strangely, always examine his motives."

"And you have?"

"Of course. They shot it down because they're up to something which they knew they couldn't conceal and what we need to know, like heavy transport moving up, or fresh gun emplacements, or masses of troops moving up."

Inspired by these thoughts I asked Earl Gray at the next orders group if the Auster had spotted anything of significance before being shot down. Naturally enough, he didn't know and hadn't bothered to ask. He shut me up in his usual brusque manner, but I sensed his embarrassment and the next time we met he told us that the Auster had been shot down before they'd had a chance to send messages and divulge what they'd seen.

"So what's going to happen is this," said the Earl. "Two special patrols will be sent out. One will be from the Dukes, seeking up-to-date information about the Chinese caves at the rear of their hills directly ahead of us. And the other a much more ambitious operation by the King's Regiment which will probe far deeper behind the Chinese lines.

They'll be looking for sites of newly installed artillery pieces and forming-up caves. They'll be supported by demolition specialists from the Engineers in order to blow up any new installations."

The first of the patrols went out the following night, commanded by Simon Berry from battalion HQ. They evaded the Chinese on our front and got well behind their lines. They located several newly dug caves. They went into each and in two of them encountered Chinese. They engaged them with grenades, hoping that they might explode stocks of ammunition, but nothing came of it and they withdrew, claiming to have killed 'a few'.

The patrol sent out by the King's was less successful. They found plenty of evidence of a build-up of Chinese troops, and they heard the constant rumbling of heavy transport on the move. They also noted several unknown forming-up caves and blew-in two of them. Then came trouble. They walked into an unknown and unmarked minefield and suffered numerous casualties. Trying to extract the wounded proved well night impossible. In the process more men were blown up and killed. Then, to round off their misfortunes, they were heavily shelled. Less than half the patrols made it back to safety.

At our level, we were not privy to these details. Our information came in dribs and drabs, either rumours from Kim and Animal Evans via the porters or snippets Corporal Turnbull picked up. However, when Earl Gray held his next orders group he had a map showing all the Chinese forming-up caves. Every one of them faced due north which, according to Earl Gray, made them impervious to shelling and in most cases out of range of the mortars.

More messages went up the chain of command from 12 Platoon's master tactician suggesting that if the caves faced due north it made them very vulnerable to air strikes sweeping down from the north, heading south. It was pointed out that the bombs, rockets, and napalm would be able to enter and penetrate the caves by virtue of their forward thrust. The word came back agreeing to air strikes but warning that the strikes would be risky and that the nearest targets to us would not be attacked in case the jets over-shot and caused friendly-fire casualties.

We had three days to prepare ourselves for the air strikes. The first thing we did was double the number of air identification panels on the top of the hill. Then we filled sandbags, ready to pack them into the embrasures of the weapon pits as a precaution against an over-shoot. Not much protection, but better than nothing, or so we hoped.

Despite the risks, everyone in 12 Platoon watched the strikes. We reasoned that if we were hit it would make damn-all difference what we were doing, or what precautions we'd taken. One napalm on the Hook and we would all be burnt to a crisp. When zero hour approached we spotted the jets way out to the east, little specs catching and reflecting sunshine and leaving thin vapour trails. We watched them grow larger and then saw them zoom north before peeling off a few at a time to double back south. In the distance they were silent and apparently innocuous, so small and fragile that I was impossible to comprehend their destructive power. They approached the target area at a good height and then dived steeply, flattened out, and dropped their bombs before pulling skywards to reform in their squadron formation.

The first two strikes were so distant they made little impression on us, but as the strikes drew nearer, so the explosions became more vivid and we began to feel their blast, especially the searing heat of the napalm. Also, we experienced the frightening manner in which the jets flashed over us as they pulled out of their attacks. They were so low they seemed almost within touching distance. We saw their silver underbellies and we ducked instinctively as we heard the deafening shriek and roar of their engines

The strikes soon drew so close they made the Hook shudder and clouds of dust and high-flying earth billowed up before us. The napalm caused sheets of smoke-capped flame to surge up from the Chinese hills, leaving us with the feeling of omnipotence, realizing that we had it within our power to call in several million pounds-worth of advanced technology to scatter our enemies.

On the second day of the strikes we knew our greatest danger was now at hand. In fact, the jets did overshoot their targets and they ended up knocking hell out of the caves nearest us, the ones they had declined to attack for fear of hitting us. It was during these latter strikes that the Chinese fought back. Those who had shot down the Auster spotter plane wheeled out their antiquated anti-aircraft guns and had the audacity to take on the jets as they flashed over them. There was no evidence of any hits, but one had to admire their courage. When the jets completed their strikes, one of them, instead of rejoining his squadron, circled high in the sky, headed north again, and then turned its attention on the Chinese gunners.

Realizing what was happening, some of the Chinese wheeled their guns back under over, but others stood their ground and battled it out, defiant and ridiculously optimistic. The jet swooped on them like an eagle after prey, so swift that the Chinese had no chance of escape. Now, too late, their nerve cracked; they abandoned their guns and scattered. They were still running when the napalm fell. It exploded on impact on top of the hill, a solid ball of yellow flame. The gel cascaded down all sides of the hill, burning everything in its path, a tidal wave of instant death.

We watched as the Chinese tried to escape, but they had no chance of outrunning the flames and those at the rear disappeared like men swallowed up by an avalanche. Those ahead of them, still hopeful of outpacing the flames, were overtaken one by one and devoured. They became human torches. Then they shrivelled into twisted sticks, as grey as charcoal as they lay smouldering on the hillside. No protest were heard, or any cries of terror. Nothing but the smooth roar of the jet as it sped over us into the safety of the blue sky. All that was left was the sight of cremated men.

Even Fletcher refrained from cheering.

About this time we had trouble with mines. In the past, the Chinese had never bothered with them. Their technique was to wage war en masse, with no interest in trivialities. Their positions had no minefields so it came to a shock to us when they copied our style of gruesome warfare; but whereas we stuck to conventional minefields properly marked, they specialized in single, anti-personnel mines. They had a great talent for placing them where least expected, which had a devastating impact on our morale. Somehow, they planted them within our lines, often as far back as battalion headquarters. It could only have been the work of North Koreans infiltrators masquerading as porters.

Their mines were particularly fiendish. Unlike most mines, they did not explode when weight was put upon them. At that point their mines gave out a loud 'clonk' as wooden plungers were forced down. They only exploded when the weight was removed. It left men in a hiatus of terror. As soon as they heard that dreaded 'clonk' they knew they were doomed. They had no possible escape. The instinctive reaction was to freeze, even though men realized that as soon as they shifted their weight the mines would explode and literally blow them away--- vaporize them. One second they would be standing there, perfectly healthy, and the next second they would be gone forever, leaving no trace other than tiny red specs blown far and wide. Steel helmets and the occasional boots were usually the only evidence of their previous existence.

When men heard the dreaded 'clonk' they were often known to remain stationery on the mine for minutes on end, pleading for help from those who watched in dread, realizing that there was nothing they could do, that if they went anywhere near they too would die.

12 Platoon only suffered one such death. It was Beau Brummell. He was leading a small party of men back to battalion headquarters for a special treat, hot showers and fumigation, a rare chance to get away from the shelling for a time. They were in single file, going along the MSR. They pulled into the side to allow trucks to pass and then came the dreaded 'clonk'. They all knew what it was. They all knew who had

stepped on it.

"Stand back! Stand back!" Brummell yelled. "Get well back ..."

They did as he ordered, staring in horror. He was facing them. They saw perspiration trickling down his face. They had no idea what to do or say. They edged further away. Brummell stayed perfectly still for at least a minute. He just stared down at his feet as though devising some new form of escape. Eventually, he went into a crouching position. Then he looked up at them and shouted: "Watch this, lads! Just watch. You are now going to see the world record for a standing jump. I'm going to be off this thing so quick ..."

As soon as he straightened his knees the mine detonated. The men flinched and turned away from the blast. When they looked back there was nothing there. Just smoke and a hole in the ground. As Rupert later said, with great sadness, "Poor old Brummell never died ... He was simply blown away."

We also lost Harry Wilmott. Harry had been in his element as our timber man but during his constant moving around the platoon he had formed a theory about the shelling. He reckoned that shells, like lightning, never struck in the same place, not in quick succession, anyhow. It was absolutely rubbish but he believed it so implicitly that he gave up sheltering in weapon pits and instead sprinted about the trenches, going to the site of the last explosion.

Corporal Holroyd saw what he was up to and told him not to be so damn silly, to take cover in the nearest weapon pit. Ten minutes later the weapon pit he chose took two direct hits. It collapsed and Harry and one of the Katcoms were buried. Digging them out proved a hard task. The Katcom survived but by the time they got to Harry he had suffocated. No one in the platoon was more missed than Harry. The letter I had to write to his parents was bad enough, but the one I sent to his girlfriend--- the devoted striptease artist--- was the most difficult I ever had to do.

31

Bad News All Round

Earl Gray called an orders group to clarify our final tactics for the battle we all knew was coming shortly. He included the platoon sergeant as a precaution, in case any of the platoon commanders became casualties in the meantime, as was quite likely. Nothing new or revolutionary was divulged. We were to repeat the well-tried methods of the Black Watch. We were to fight off the Chinese with small-arms as they came through the minefields and barbed wire and then, if we were overrun, VT would be called down. The signal for its arrival was to be two green Verey light and once the Verey lights went up men were to fortify their weapon pits as best they could, including stuffing sandbags into their embrasures and entrances. Those who took cover in the tunnels were to fighting the Chinese off, preventing them from entering, and thereby retaining possession of the Hook

A new idea was introduced by Colonel Bunbury. Each day a two-man patrol was to lie-up, heavily camouflaged, deep in no man's land in order to give early warning of the Chinese emerging from their forming up areas. Once news came through that the Chinese were on the move, all standing patrols would be withdrawn and weapon pits fully manned so as to give the enemy a bloody nose.

Another precaution was that two platoons were to standby in reserve at the jeep-head, ready to counter-attack as soon as the VT shelling stopped. Having swept the hill clear of Chinese they were to stay on the hill in case of any further assaults. Meanwhile, two more platoons would replace them at the jeep-head, ready for a repeat performance ... And so on.

When the Earl finished explaining all this, there were no questions, so he merely reminded us of a host of details, such as having fresh batteries for the wirelesses, ear-marking additional men as runners in case of communication failures, and making sure ammunition levels were adequate before the battle started. When I relayed all this to my section commanders in my CP, only Rupert raised a query.

"To me, the whole thing is flawed," he said.

The section commanders and I exchanged glances. Everything was always flawed to Rupert.

"We are underestimating the amount of shelling we will be subjected to," he continued. "The milk rounds will be mild compared to the final concentration. And what with the Chinese shelling and our VT, our weapon pits will never stand up to it. Most of them will collapse. And even if they survive the Chinese will simply blow them up with satchel charges."

This was the last thing we wanted to hear, but it was true, and we knew it. "It's all very well for 10 Platoon," added Rupert. "They've got three tunnels in which they can take cover. But we've got nothing."

"So what do you suggest?" I asked.

"Start digging a tunnel. Then, if and when we're overrun, everyone retires to the tunnel until the VT has finished."

We all agreed it was a sound idea so later in the day I put it to Earl Gray. I got no support. He said the idea had come far too late to be practical and that our whole plan revolved around fighting the Chinese off from our weapon pits, not making a quick run for a giant funk hole as soon as we saw them coming, which was bound to happen if the men thought they had an easy means of escape. He shrugged off being overrun and having our weapon pits destroyed by satchel charges as an occupational hazard. I returned to 12 Platoon riled by his attitude, as I so often was. I had further words with the section commanders and Rupert and we decided we had a choice: dig or die. So we decided to dig. We would dig a tunnel, no matter what Earl Gray or anyone else said. We'd just get on and do it. I assumed that since most of the platoon were Yorkshire men they would be steeped in mining traditions and therefore have sufficient know-how to make a reasonable job of it.

As it turned out, none of them had ever been down a pit in their lives and they had no more idea of what was required than I did. Bertie Mee became our self-appointed expert on the grounds that he was from the Rhondda and his father and uncle were still working down the Maerdy pit. It was not, perhaps, the greatest qualification, but it was the best we could come up with.

Our main difficulty was the lack of timber with which to prop-up and reinforce our tunnel. So we went for depth instead. Bertie said that if we went deep enough timbering wouldn't matter, that if we went down twenty feet our head-cover would be impregnable. This sounded very reasonable but my confidence in Bertie was severely shaken when he proposed that since the tunnel was going to link our forward trench to the main lateral trench, leading to 10 Platoon and company HQ, we would save time by digging from both ends simultaneously.

"Then there will be six men working around the clock instead of three," he declared. "It will halve the time taken."

"What happens if they don't meet in the middle?" I asked.

"Won't matter, sir. Just means we'll have two tunnels instead of one."

That concluded Bertie's role as our tunnelling expert. As usual, I turned to Rupert. He was far more reassuring. He harked back to Flanders again. It seemed the Krauts came off best so often because they dug in depth. They often went down thirty feet and incorporated rest centres, sleeping quarters, and first aid posts. At that depth they were as safe as houses from Haig's artillery barrages that went on for days and were said to be heard in England. "The Krauts just sat there in perfect safety," explained Rupert, "and when the shelling stopped they went up top, set-up their machine guns, and mowed down Kitchener's army to the tune of 20,000 dead in a day."

So we settled on digging two 20 foot vertical holes at the sides of the front trench and the main lateral trench and then striking through the hill from the former to the latter. We got cracking straight away. I rearranged the platoon routine so that three men were digging in relays night and day, which meant that the amount of sleep we got suffered. Men were lucky if they got more than three hours in every twenty-four.

We produced what was probably the crudest and most amateur tunnel ever dug. At one stage Corporal Underwood came round to have a look. "Bloody hell," he exclaimed. "Do you realize that you're going downhill? You're going down at the rate of about one in six. You'll surface down in the bottom of the valley, just in time for Christmas. Is that flat-footed idiot Harry Wilmott master-minding this lot?"

"Harry's dead."

"Oh dear … Sorry to hear that. What happened?"

"One of the weapon pits collapsed on him."

"One he'd just renovated?"

"Yes."

"Oh, well … hardly surprising. All I can say is that if you are going to shelter in this abortion of a tunnel, you'd better start digging it level. And where are you going to get your timber supports from?"

"We're going for depth," replied Rupert. "The Chinese don't have timber supports in their caves."

"Their caves are dug into the bottom of damn great hills … And another thing. Don't forget a couple of zigzags. One at each end."

"Zigzags?"

"Of course. You don't think the Chinks won't come down after you, do you?"

"No."

"Well if you don't have zigzags, or dog-legs, all they'll have to do is stand at the end of the tunnel and mow you all down."

"Um …"

Despite these basic flaws, we decided to keep digging and progressed rapidly. There was only room for one to work with a pick at the face; the other two shovelled the spoils into sandbags and used them to reinforce the entrance holes and create zigzags. The diggers emerged from the tunnel covered in dirt and dust and their faces streaked by perspiration. It was really hard graft but the men stuck at it. For one thing, they were safe from shelling while they were down there. It was also something they believed in. The further it progressed the more obvious it became that it should have been done ages ago, as in 10 Platoon. Most encouraging of all, when the Chinese sent over their milk rounds the tunnel remained as solid as a rock, not even trickles of earth falling from the roof.

At one stage Rupert and I went to 10 Platoon to take a closer look at their tunnels. They made us shudder. They were so professional it just wasn't true. They were using air-pressure drills and their use of timber was a work of art with thick 4X4 vertical supports cut to order. Their roofs were even finished off with tongue and groove planking. We approached Corporal Underwood with a view to 'borrowing' some of their material but he wouldn't hear of it. He said he was strictly rationed and only got the supplies he needed. "And it's a hell of a job getting it up here," he said. "Everything has to come up by the Korean porters."

Mention of the Korean porters brought Animal Evans and Kim to mind, and they didn't let us down. Soon, gangs of porters were arriving with timber they'd siphoned off from the Engineers' depot. It was never enough, but at least we were able to make a token effort at shoring up our tunnel. We dug the tunnel about five foot high so that one could walk along it without stooping too much and it came as a great relief when we struck (more by luck than judgement) the twenty foot hole we'd dug on the side of the lateral trench. Even Corporal Underwood was impressed by that. "Biggest fluke ever, sir," he told me. "Still, never mind. You did it. Well done."

Then it started raining. At first it was fairly light but it soon became harder and more persistent. It was nowhere near as bad as the spring rain but it was enough to cause trouble. Several weapon pits began to sag or list dangerously and at one stage the three men digging the tunnel suddenly appeared in the CP. All of them were soaked to the skin, dripping water all over the place.

"The tunnel's filling up fast, sir," said Bertie.

"How fast?"

"Too fast for comfort. Up to our knees at both ends. And the dip in the middle is like the deep end of a municipal swimming pool."

"Is it coming down from the roof, or from the bottom?" asked Rupert.

"Damned if I know. We just got out while the going was good. All that water means it'll collapse, like the coal pit did in *The Stars Look Down*."

"Best get Underwood to have a look," suggested Rupert.

Underwood was reluctant to come round because his tunnels were also flooding and he was busy draining them with battery-powered pumps. Eventually he arrived wearing a pair of fishermen's waders and he insisted that a rope be tied around his waist as a life-line before he ventured down. When he got the bottom of the ladder he disappeared up to his knees in muddy water. Five minutes later he reappeared.

"Well you bastards have really made a balls-up this time. I reckon you've struck the source of the Imjin."

"What can we do about it?" I asked.

"Damned if I know ... I suppose you could call in the Royal Marines."

The following morning Underwood came back, full of belligerence. "I've reported your bloody lot to my CO," he told me. "He'll be coming round later to tell you a thing or two."

"Good! Any advice is always welcome."

"Yeah ... Well ... He'll have a bit more than advice, don't you worry."

It took Major Robshaw three days to show up and during that time the sun came out and the ground dried quickly. Robshaw was a very youthful major, a charming fellow rather in the mould of Colonel Gibson, a gentleman devoid of any aggression or assumed superiority. We treated him to a cup of coffee and he soon put us at ease by saying: "Ah! Absolutely disgusting! Just like all coffee in Korea. But yours is the worst yet." Then he leaned forward and admired my picture of Katsumi which I'd pinned on the wall. "Been on your R and R then?" he laughed.

"Not really, sir. I was in Japan for a few months."

"A few months, eh? Lucky you, by the look of it." He drained his cup of disgusting coffee and I took him to our entrance hole. He looked down in amazement and then went down to inspect the tunnel. When he returned, he said: "Not a bad tunnel. A bit patchy, but done in good time. But I am surprised that you blokes are happy to commit suicide ..."

"How do you mean, sir?"

"It's a question of the entrance holes. Essential for you to get in and out, of course, but if the Chinese overrun the hill all they'll have to do is drop a couple of satchel charges down each hole and you're finished. And apart from that, all the shelling is bound to fill up your holes with debris. And twenty feet of debris will be the very devil to dig out. Then, of course, a shell might go straight down, in which case the blast will finish off the lot of you. As things stand now, you're tunnel is a death trap."

"Staying on top will be even more suicidal," I replied.

"Granted! But don't look so gloomy, young fellow. I'm not saying you can't do anything about it. What is needed is quite simple. Two very solid covers. Man-hole covers if you like. But they'll have to be very strong. Strong enough to survive any shells that land nearby.

They'll have to be reinforced which means it will be a two-man job to lift them in-and-out of place."

"Sounds like a job for Animal Evans," I said to Rupert.

"You've got a resident muscle-man?"

"As strong as most, I think."

"Well, we'll soon see. What I'll do is measure up and get a couple of man-hole covers made for you. It'll take a day or two. But believe me, you can't do without them."

It took the Engineers three days to make the covers. They came in two sections. First there was the heavy part built around a thick steel plate, with two rings welded onto the top for lifting out and another ring underneath for dragging it into position once we were inside. On top of the covers were detachable wooden trays. These were packed with soil to make them look like part of the trench floor to fool any marauding Chinese.

Finally, Animal Evans came round from his weapon pit to see if he could manage the brutes. He approached one of them as though he was a weight lifter, hissing air in and out of clenched teeth and tightening his web belt. He grabbed the two rings and managed to lift it, but it was obvious that he'd never be able to carry it any great distance. With two men, one on each ring, it became more manageable. The final problem was removing the covers to enable us to get out. For this, Robshaw supplied a long pole (like a cut-down rugby post) with a square of timber screwed on the top, the technique being for two or three men to grasp the pole and heave the covers up, rather like three men simultaneously tossing the caber. It worked beautifully.

Mail continued to come up once a week. Corporal Turnbull brought it round. We could always tell when he was coming by his heavy footsteps. It was a far cry from the golden days when we gathered around the platoon CP with Bridges standing on top of the trench wall, pondering over each envelope and making comments before passing them on. Now, there was no time for larking about. Turnbull just dumped them in the CP and I had the job of distributing them. Each time I took them round I flipped through them to see who was lucky. In the latest batch I had two. I recognized the hand-writing on both envelopes. One was from Dad and the other from Nacker. I went through the envelopes again, hoping that I might have missed one from Katsumi. When I found nothing, I tore open the one from Nacker, expecting to find one inside from Katsumi, but I was again disappointed. Instinctively I sensed that something was amiss and it made me so nervous that I read Dad's first.

He opened with what was now a routine greeting: "Dear Din," and then related the usual type of news, including the turnover figures of a new tyre and battery depot in Mitcham. He mentioned Miss Beaumont far more than Mum, and he obviously enjoyed responding to my news about having a Japanese girlfriend. I visualized him chortling with delight as he wrote: "Why should I mind if you have a Jap girlfriend? It depends on what she's like. Whether or not she does as she's told! So don't expect me to be upset because she isn't English. You might think of yourself as English, but I'm Indian, even if I behave more like the English than the English do themselves! What's more, I'm an Indian with an English girlfriend (as you must surely realize!) and a Welsh wife, so what difference will a Japanese daughter-in-law make? Mind you, Din, for God's sake don't tell your mother about her just yet. No need to stir up a hornets' nest ..."

I grinned as I tossed his letter to one side and steeled myself to read Nacker's. My nervousness was justified. I received the greatest shock of my life. I was no stranger to personal disasters, as when Gran and Mr. Muckey died, and when Charlie Smith was buried beneath molten lead at the Works in Lomond Grove; but this was in a different category altogether.

To start with, Nacker waffled on about how pleased he was that I was still in one piece and how he and Katsumi were desperately worried about me being on the Hook. It had a totally false ring to it and I was immediately suspicious: he was about to spring something fateful on me. I dreaded that he was going to tell me that he had split up with Akiko and was now going out with Katsumi.

I soon regretted this unworthy suspicion, a totally unwarranted slur and lack of faith in Katsumi. Eventually he told me that Katsumi had been taken ill. Then he took another long paragraph to tell me about her illness. By the time I'd got to the nub of the matter, I'd already guessed. She had the early symptoms of radiation poisoning, the result of having been caught in the Black Rain after Hiroshima.

She had never made a secret of being one of the Exposed. I recalled several occasions when she'd mentioned it quite openly, especially when telling me about Eddie's efforts whilst her nakado; but she had always treated it as of no consequence. She was so young and fit and healthy, and had such unshakable faith in Buddha looking after her, that she had discounted any possibility of being struck down by it. Like an idiot, I'd done the same. It was so easy to brush aside such unpleasantness as something that only happened to others. Now, I felt totally shallow and thoughtless. I should have realized the danger. The number of Japanese dying from it was common knowledge.

Nacker's letter went on to explain that she had humming in her ears and kept vomiting, together with a heavy loss of hair. He'd tried to get her treated at the Base Hospital, but they had refused on the grounds that they had no expertise in that field, so she had been taken to the Red Cross Hospital in Hiroshima.

That sounded reassuring until I read on further and learnt that no one (not even the Americans) had the faintest idea how to cure atomic poisoning. Japanese doctors steered clear of it and the only people taking any responsibility for the victims were the hospitals in Hiroshima, many of which were still in a state of disrepair after war. The doctors simply concentrated on minimizing the victims' suffering. The most crushing part came when he told me that two of her friends, both caught in the Black Rain alongside her, had already died as a result of it, one only two months before.

I read his letter through several times. Then it fell through my fingers to the ground. I lay back onto my bunk and stared at the ceiling. I didn't know what to think. Tears stung my eyes. Without her, life would be meaningless. I had expected plenty of problems, but I never for one moment doubted that we would fight them together and triumph over them. Yet how could we overcome radiation poisoning?

I had no idea how long I lay there. Eventually, Rupert picked up the letter and sat on the side of my bunk. He asked me what had happened. I motioned him to read the letter. As he worked his way down it, heavy shelling started up but I took no notice. I no longer cared about the bloody Hook.

Rupert did his best to be optimistic. He pointed out that despite the ignorance of doctors, it was possible that she would make a natural recovery. He reckoned it was far too early to be alarmist, that there was bound to be hope: there was always hope.

I didn't contradict him, but I knew it wasn't true. Black Rain victims always died. In an attempt to make him believe I'd swallowed his reassurances I sat up, then moved around the bunker and even made some more disgusting coffee. Deep in my heart I knew that to accept Rupert's blind optimism, or even to entertain it for a moment, was fantasy on a par with Katsumi's blind faith in Buddha.

The news of Katsumi's illness affected me in strange ways. Strangest of all, I took to prayer. So far in Korea I hadn't prayed once, not even when facing death, but now I did little else besides pray, ignoring the blatant hypocrisy of it. I didn't go in for the pious type of prayer, on my knees, hands clasped before my face. My prayers were personal and secretive, thoughts which kept repeating themselves over and over again. I prayed that she would recover and not suffer, that someone would suddenly discover a miraculous cure; and as I went around the platoon with these prayers spinning about my mind it made me careless and indifferent to everything else going on. On numerous occasions I left the CP for no good reason and wandered around the trenches, ignoring shells and mortar bombs. Several times, Rupert restrained me. Once he even barred the doorway to me as I tried to go into the trenches whilst the milk round was at its height. On Ronson patrols I twice acted like an idiot. When the Chinese attacked us, instead of standing our ground and repelling them, I suddenly leapt out of the slit trench and ordered my men to charge them. Thank God, on both occasions the Chinese were so surprised they scattered in alarm. My men were equally alarmed. On the second occasion Animal Evans, who would have followed me into hell itself, said: "I don't think you should do that too often, sir."

Many in the platoon were convinced that I was cracking up. On one occasion, when I was seen wandering down the trench, muttering to myself, 'Bugger it! Bugger the whole bloody world and everything in it!', there was speculation that I would soon join Phillip Barrow and disappear in the dark of night, never to be seen or heard of again.

Eventually, during a quiet spell in the CP, Rupert had judicious words with me. We were such close friends that he had no hesitation in telling me to pull myself together; that Katsumi was no more than ill; that I wasn't the only one to suffer bad news; and however distressed I felt, I was still responsible for the lives of the platoon; and I must never duck or minimize that responsibility. If I did, I would be responsible for tragedies just as bad or even worse as my own.

I knew he was right and I did my best to take his advice. From thereon I wrote to her at every opportunity. They were anguished letters full of love and encouragement, and although she was too sick to reply I soon got letters back from Nacker giving me her latest condition. It was always the same: there had been no change. This made Rupert optimistic, but I wasn't fooled. I saw 'no change' as Nacker's euphemism for an inevitable deterioration.

32

Third Battle of the Hook

Then something happened which put my problems in perspective. On May 18th Fred Tremlett took out the first Green Finger patrol. Bright moonlight filtered through the clouds. For two hours everything was quiet. Then they saw a lone Chinaman walking up the hillside towards them. They watched in disbelief. They suspected that it was a trick or a diversion of some kind. Yet the man was unarmed, no signs of a Burp gun. When he got to within twenty yards of them he stopped. He waved cheerfully and called out: "Howdy! Howdy!"

Tremlett and his corporal went forward cautiously, the rest of the patrol ready to cover them. There was an impasse as they confronted the Chinaman. His only word of English was "Howdy!" and when Tremlett's corporal tried his 'Gook-talk' on him, it got him nowhere. Eventually, the corporal grew weary of the Chinaman repeating, 'Howdy!' He stepped forward, grabbed the man's arm and said: "Howdy my arse! You're coming with us, Chinky-boy."*

With that, he went behind the Chinaman, prodded him up the backside with his bayonet, and marched him back to the rest of the patrol. The corporal then assumed command and Tremlett escorted the Chinaman back to 10 Platoon.

Our first prisoner of the campaign!

We could hardly have got a better one. Private Hua Hong of the 2nd Battalion of the 399th Regiment was exceptionally well informed. It turned out that he had criticized Chairman Mao and had been reported to his battalion's political officer, which convinced him he had a far rosier future with the UN than with the Chinese Peoples Volunteers. When he got to brigade headquarters he sang like a canary. He professed to know all about the coming attack. He explained that four highly rated assault regiments, the 396th, the 397th, the 398th and the 399th had been specially trained to capture the Hook. They were confident of a breakthrough and once this had been achieved, Hua Hong said that the enormous build-up of troops opposite the Hook would pour through the gap and launch a

---

* The greeting "Howdy!" came from an American propaganda leaflet frequently dropped behind the Chinese lines. The pamphlet (in Mandarin) had a seductive picture of Mae West and the caption, "Come over and see me sometime. Just say 'Howdy!'"

two-pronged offensive, one turning east to outflank and roll up the UN's front line, and the other to head due south for Seoul. They hoped for such a quick breakthrough that the UN would not have time to establish themselves in the reserve fortifications known as the Kansas line.

It meant that the initial blow falling on the Hook would be devastating with Dog Company outnumbered by approximately 10 to 1. Hua Hong said the Dukes were rated as a weak link. He even had the date of the attack, even though not the exact time.

All this information was duly relayed back to the platoons and it galvanized us into even greater efforts to improve our defences. It was a wise move. On the morning of May 22nd the Chinese milk round hit us as usual, but instead of coming to an abrupt halt it went on throughout the day; and this time there was a significant difference. The Chinese had introduced much higher calibre guns into their armoury. They had a flat trajectory and they were rifling in at us direct; their equivalent to our Centurion 20-pounders. As a consequence they were systematically destroying the weapon pits, their shells in some cases going straight through the embrasures, killing everyone inside.

So many weapons pits were being damaged, or demolished, that extra Engineers were drafted on to the Hook for repairs and reconstruction, and in 12 Platoon I formed an emergency squad which stood by to dig men out of weapon pits which had collapsed on them. The Chinese even targeted the 12 Platoon CP. Rupert and I were confident that our bunker would survive, but when dust and rubble began to fall on us, and several rats either scurried under the entrance blanket or disappearing into their holes in the walls, I turned to Rupert and said: "This is like the blitz at my old man's factory in Camberwell Green.."

"Did you get a direct hit?" asked Rupert.

"No. Thankfully not. But the building next door did. It was flattened. No survivors."

No sooner had I imparted this cheerful news than we received three direct hits in quick succession. The roar of the final explosion was like the knell of doom. The bunker stood no chance. The overhead wooden beams cracked, then snapped and splintered, and the concrete lintel over the doorway sheared in half, at which point the bunker folded up, collapsed like an old-age pensioner's face deprived of dentures. Timbers, sandbags, earth, and even a few remaining rats, fell down on us. I was flung from the ammunition box on which I was sitting and pinned to the ground by broken beams, one across my chest and the other over my legs and groin. I was knocked unconscious and when I came to I was only aware of dust and smoke. I couldn't see anything. I panicked and yelled to Rupert, asking if he was all right, and much to my relief he answered, albeit in a muffled and unconvincing tone. It took us several seconds to establish that we had no broken bones or deep cuts, or stab wounds from jagged timbers. At the same time, we were well and truly trapped, unable to shift any of the timbers on top of us. No matter how hard we pushed, nothing budged. For some time we just lay there, helpless, even though Rupert kept repeating: "They'll soon have us out of here, Saj."

To start with, I didn't care much whether they did or not. After the news of Katsumi, I was indifferent. Death no longer held such terrors. Now, it was more the manner in which I went. I dreaded losing arms or legs, or being sliced in two, like the man I'd seen during our first day on the Hook. I forced my mind on to other things, knowing that on this occasion at least I had escaped that fate. The one thing I decided was that if I survived the Hook I would lose no time in claiming my R and R in order to go back to Kure. That would give me at least a few days with Katsumi.

Eventually, Corporal Holroyd and his rescue squad arrived. He had drafted in Animal Evans to help, knowing that brute strength would be necessary. Having established that we were alive and unharmed, they got to work. It was slow and painstaking and the first thing that happened was that timbers they moved caused others to fall on Rupert. They didn't injure him but they caused him sufficient pain to make him yell out in protest and curse them roundly. I was luckier and they got me out without too much difficulty. Of all the rescues carried out in 12 Platoon, ours was probably the easiest.

Later on, when Rupert and I had recovered, we set about rebuilding the CP. As the nerve-centre of the platoon it got top priority. Underwood gave all the assistance he could. After the visit of Major Robshaw he had become far more co-operative and the swift rebuilding of the CP was mainly down to the skill of his Engineers. Everything was dragged clear until there was nothing but a hole in the ground. A rats' nest, a rusted American carbine, and a crumpled Turkish steel helmet were exposed where the walls had crumbled, so we cleared them all out and squared off the walls, ready for pre-cut timbers which were brought up by the porters. Several hours later we had a brand new, tremendously strong, wooden-framed bunker that it would have stood against just about anything---anything but Chinese satchel charges as we soon discovered.

For three consecutive nights there were vicious patrol clashes all along the frontage of the Hook. Each one was a prolonged small-arms battle with heavy casualties on both sides. The Chinese were probing our defences, trying to establish our strong and weak points. Then, at dawn on the fourth day, May 28[th.], the milk round started early and went on all day. Trenches began to cave in. They became clogged up by powdered earth, reducing them to half their normal depth, depriving us of decent cover, making safe movement within the company impossible.

It was the final softening up.

That afternoon we had a visit from Colonel Bunbury. He came unannounced, alone, with no retinue, not even Earl Gray or Copper Bowden. It was a personal visit. As I accompanied him around the platoon he ignored the shells, giving me no option but to do the same. I crouched the whole time, but he strode along unheeding. He had a few words in each weapon pit, sometimes no more than, "We'll give you all the support we can. Good luck!" How wise he was. The lads didn't need a pep talk. The last thing they wanted was a windbag trying to immortalize himself, with a journalist in tow itching to get a bye-line on a dramatized account of a prepared speech. The whys and wherefores of our presence in Korea had long been settled. The issue was now simple: them or us. For the Dukes: either glory or humiliation.

The shelling stopped just before dusk. We stood-to in fading light, with the dust and smoke still settling. There was no evening milk round. Everything was suddenly peaceful. The hills ahead of us were fading away into a dark blue haze. A silvery, spooky mist spread along the valley, gradually moving up the hills, ideal cover for the Chinese. There was serenity, but we weren't fooled. Hidden away behind the innocent-looking hills confronting us were thousands of Chinese bent on mass slaughter.

All we could do was wait. We had done everything possible. Weapons had been checked and re-checked and were in perfect order; abundant ammunition was to hand; every man knew the value of fighting in pairs, watching each other's backs. All standing patrols had been cancelled, every man withdrawn into his weapon pit. Every weapon was cocked and ready to spit out defiance. Behind us, the Gunners, both British and American, stood by to unleash an unprecedented volume of fire. On our flanks the machine guns of two battalions were ready with enfilade fire that would cover our entire frontage. Out in no man's land the Colonel's two-man patrol was lying up in a hide, ready to relay a wireless message as soon as the Chinese spilt out of their caves and assembly points.

The message came through. Massed ranks of Chinese were on the move. Earl Gray contacted his three platoons.

"Attack imminent! Stand fast the Dukes!"

The shelling became a dual of giants, with us well and truly sandwiched. The Hook shuddered like a blancmange. It was so intense it seemed impossible for it to last more than a few minutes, but it did. Shells pounded down, one after the other like giant hammer blows, the explosions merging into one continuous roar.

I was in the Look Out with Animal Evans and his team of three men. From there, I hoped to see the Chinese approaching along the Ronson and Green Finger ridges, but at first we saw nothing, blinded by all the earth being thrown up. Then came the shrill note of Chinese bugles, a Hades chorus coming from all quarters. As the Chinese swept up the hill and entered the minefields we heard a multitude of fresh explosions. Then things cleared a little and in the beams of searchlights, the moonlight effect of gunnery flares, and the spotlights of the tanks, we saw them. They were fighting their way through great gaps which had been torn in our wire. They were being fired on from all directions. All the supporting arms were in action, none firing more urgently than the three platoons on the Hook. I left Animal Evans and sprinted through the trenches to see what was happening in our front trench. The first weapon pit I ducked into was manned by Corporal Jackman, Bertie Mee, and two others. They were firing flat out, arcing their weapons like firemen using hoses. I leaned forward and peered out of the embrasure. I saw a wall of Chinese advancing. The leaders were smudgy and indistinct, many of them hurling themselves forward onto the wire so that others could trample over them, using them as stepping stones. Others were trying to break through the wire individually, but they were tangled up in it, struggling desperately to free themselves. Behind them, well to the rear, Chinese bugles blared out, urging them to press forward.

The Chinese started to return our fire. It did them no good. As they paused to fire their Burp guns, they attracted a hail of bullets that cut them down. All of them were doomed. Great gaps were being hacked in their ranks. It was human slaughter. Men were being shot time and time again, or else torn to shreds by high explosives and shrapnel. They had no chance of covering the thirty yards separating them from our trenches. Yet they were undeterred. Not one of them turned back or shied away. They simply belched forth, more and more of them coming up from the rear, a seemingly endless supply of cannon-fodder.

A mound of dead began to accumulate along the length of our wire and those at the rear had to clamber over their dead comrades, only to die themselves and tumble forward, making the mound inch its way up the hill. The carnage was beyond belief. For several minutes I couldn't drag my eyes away from it, but eventually I left the weapon pit and ran up and down the trench, yelling: "Keep firing! Keep firing!"

It was a pointless exhortation. Every man was already pouring out as much fire as he could. The barrels of their weapons were glowing red hot. Yet still I kept up my parrot cry of "Keep firing!" until eventually the number of Chinese appearing over the crest of the hill decreased dramatically. Our small-arms fire subsided and men reverted to single shots to pick off the survivors.

Their attack had been repelled. The cessation of small-arms fire was like a reprieve, even though we knew it was no more than a pause--- round one in a long contest. The shelling no longer seemed to matter, an inconvenience we could well endure. I checked for casualties, but there were none. As I made my way back down the trench, making for the CP, I called in at every weapon pit on the way and called out: "Well done, lads! Keep watching for them."

In the CP, Rupert was in a state of rare agitation. He was being hounded by endless demands over the 88-set. Eventually, having replied "Roger! Wilco and out," he yanked the head-set off and turned to me. "Earl Gray! He never stops asking what the situation is ..."

"So what is it?"

"God only knows." Rupert laughed, then added: "I told the silly old sod, 'Nothing to report' and he did his nut."

"Well we've beaten off their first wave ..."

"Maybe. Just! But the Chinese got into the 10 Platoon trenches. They were dealt with. But they won't be next time. Tremlett is pleading for permission to draw everyone back into the tunnels."

"It seems the only answer," I said. "VT and then counter-attack. There are plenty of reserves waiting at the jeep head."

"The last thing the Earl wants is a counter-attack. He keeps saying we've got to hold. No withdrawal to our funk holes until he gives the order for VT."

The second assault came an hour later. It was a repeat of the first. The line of advance was again along Ronson, Green Finger, and Warsaw, with the Chinese following close on the heels of a fresh barrage by their artillery. This time all the mines had been exploded and the barbed wire was no longer an encumbrance. Worse still, this time their numbers were truly breath-taking. They were like the ocean rollers of an incoming tide, remorselessly getting nearer and nearer, piled up as far as one could see, with nothing on earth that could stop them reaching their destination. Our searchlights pin-pointed wave after wave emerging out of the murk. They were charging straight at us, more determined than ever, making their first attack no more than an exploratory probe. I kept urging the lads to maintain their fire and every now and then I would stop to help them, either by firing my Sten through an embrasure or by breaking open new boxes of ammunition, or handing out fresh Bren magazines.

More lines of Chinese were mown down. The ground was thick with their dead, stretching back to the mound of corpses which marked the limit of their first assault. Yet they kept edging nearer. Those coming up in the rear were forcing the others on, making any hesitation or retreat impossible. Our situation was soon perilous. My early optimism melted away. We had no chance of holding them. The nearer they got, the more accurate their Burp guns became, and soon they were lobbing grenades at us. None of them succeeded in going through the embrasures and instead most of them rolled back down the hill and ended up among the throwers before exploding.

The first indication that the Chinese had penetrated the 10 Platoon defences came when Animal Evans's men opened up in the Look Out. It meant the Chinese had broken through 10 Platoon and were swarming towards the peak of the hill. If Animal was unable to hold them off it would only be a matter of time before they came round the rear of us and dropped down into our front trench, demolishing our weapon pits with satchel charges. Our lads wouldn't stand a chance.

I dashed back to the Look Out. Animal was cock-a-hoop. Without looking up he assured me they could keep the Chinese in check; but even as he shouted above the noise of his Browning, there were several ear-splitting explosions in 10 Platoon and clouds of dust, smoke and rubble rose into the air. The Chinese were using satchel charges. Several more explosions came and then a fresh wave of their infantry climbed out of the trenches and headed up the hill, straight towards the Look Out. Their numbers were such that any realistic hope of containing them vanished.

"Bloody hell!" muttered Animal.

I ran off again, this time to the CP. I needed the latest situation from Rupert. It was bad news. In both 10 and 11 Platoons the Chinese were blowing up everything with satchel charges. Tremlett's men had already taken to their tunnels and 11 Platoon had suffered heavy casualties. Both platoon commanders had been pleading over their 88-sets for Earl Gray to call down VT. Then, as I stood over Rupert, he suddenly broke off. He threw his headset to one side. "Standby for VT shortly."

I didn't hang around. It was vital to get the men into our funk hole as quickly as possible. When I arrived at the front trench men were already evacuating their weapon pits. One pit at the far end of the platoon had been blown in by the Chinese coming up from 10 Platoon and rather than wait for a similar fate, others were running along the trench towards me. Even as I stood there, shouting at them to hurry, a great gang of Chinese appeared above me on the trench top, driven down from the peak of the Hook by Animal Evans. They ran along the trench wall, towering over us. Some were still falling under fire from the Look Out, but others jumped down into the trench, straight in amongst our lads fleeing from their weapon pits. They were some yards off so I sprinted forward, straight into a gang of men who had become inextricably mixed up. I was in the middle of free-for-all, hand to hand fighting at its deadliest.

We had the advantage over the Chinese from the start. Very few of

them had bayonets fixed, many relying on knives, whereas our Stens were ideal for close-quarter fighting: small and light, with a sturdy bayonet and a solid wooden butt one could swing round easily to deliver knock-out blows.

I can recall few details of what happened. In hand to hand fighting men rarely do. They develop tunnel-vision and only see what confronts them directly. Everything is instinctive, spontaneous and utterly ruthless. The over-riding skill is to pick out the most vulnerable among the enemy, ones you can surprise, often men already struggling with one of your mates, with no compunction about striking from the rear, just go at them like a maniac and finish them off with a single blow or thrust, hoping to God that your mates are watching your back, ready to do the same for you.

I know I sank my bayonet into at least five Chinese. Looking back, I wonder how I did it, but I did, and without hesitation, animal-like in my eagerness. All the time I was yelling and screaming, just like everyone else. Men were killing by any means available. One of our lads was using a spade, another a pick, and a third his steel helmet, slashing the rim of it into the eyes of those confronting him before finishing them off with a knife. It was Fletcher, mashing them up for all he was worth.

The fight was still raging when Animal Evans and his team arrived from the Look Out. How and why they got there, I never did discover, but they were able to look down from the top of the trench and systematically put single shots into the Chinese. We killed all of them. They killed five of us. The bodies piled in the trench were a gruesome sight but no one hung around to worry about it. I ordered everyone to make for the tunnel. I was damned if I was going to wait for the Earl's final order to go to ground. No sooner had we started to move along the trench than more men came sprinting towards us from 10 Platoon. Behind them was a bunch of Chinese, firing into their backs, killing many of them without trouble. Animal Evans immediately prostrated himself in the bottom of the trench and when the surviving 10 Platoon men had leapt over him he opened fire on the Chinese. He pumped short bursts into them and within seconds he'd accounted for them all. He grabbed up his Bren and sprinted after us.

When I reached our tunnel the cover had already been lifted and men were scrambling down the ladder. I urged them on and as they went down I raced back to the CP. Rupert was no longer on the 88-set. It lay discarded on the floor. He said Earl Gray had just given the final order for VT. It was due to arrive within two minutes. Rupert was delving into the ammunition box for our Verey pistol. He took it out, together with a couple of cartridges. We went back into the open trench and he fired them both. As we made towards the tunnel two more green flares went up, this time from 11 Platoon. Then two from 10 Platoon.

Everyone was heading for their funk holes!

When we got back to ours, the last of the men were disappearing down the ladder. The only one left on top was Animal. He was in his favourite position, lying in the bottom of the trench, his Bren pressed against his shoulder. He looked round, saw me, and shouted: "More Chinks coming down the trench. Get down the tunnel quick. I'll cover you …"

"You'll have to …"

"Get down into the tunnel, for Christ sake! I know what I have to do."

I was about to protest again when the Chinese appeared. Animal opened fire and both Rupert and I joined him in the bottom of the trench, firing our Stens. Rupert suddenly leapt to his feet. "Oh, Christ! I've forgotten the 88-set. I'll get it."

"It doesn't matter. Leave it!"

He took no notice. He started to run off. He'd only gone a couple of yards when a bullet hit him in his left thigh. Judged by his reaction it was no more than a flesh wound. He fell to the ground, his face twisted in pain, but then he rejoined us and resumed firing. The exchange didn't last long. When we'd disposed of the Chinese Animal turned to us: "You two get down the ladder, quick! Before more appear. I'll follow you."

We did as he said. Rupert went first. He moved slowly, limping heavily, but he was able to make the tunnel all right. We started down the ladder. I was at the bottom when Animal's Bren started up again. I went back up the ladder but just as I got to the last three or four rungs the Bren stopped. There was a momentary pause and then the man-hole cover crashed down into place. I got to the top of the ladder and tried to raise it again, but it was far too heavy. I manoeuvred myself further up the ladder and lowered my head so that the top of my shoulders and base of my neck were against the cover. I heaved upwards, but it still wouldn't budge. I called out to Animal but got no answer. Then I heard more small arms fire. This time the Burp guns were predominant. Then everything went quiet again. I made another vain attempt to raise the cover. I was still heaving upwards when I heard fresh shells exploding with a tremendous roar, but this time the earth didn't shudder. The VT had arrived. There was no hope for anyone still on top of the hill. Every living thing would be shredded.

Reluctantly, I joined the others in our funk hole.

It was pitch dark. I couldn't see a thing. Ahead, there was a cacophony of voices, loud and excited, many hysterical. Everyone was huddled together in the middle of the tunnel, in the dip, our deep-end. I had no idea of how many there were. Nor how many of them were wounded, or how badly.

"Where's the bloody hurricane lamp?"

"God knows! It could be anywhere."

"How the fuck do we know ..."

"Well look for it."

"How can we? It's bloody dark."

"Then feel! Everyone feel around."

"Who the fuck organized this funk hole?"

"Shut up! Just feel around."

"Animal? You here, Animal?"

"He's up top."

"Then he didn't make it. He's still up there. Christ, he's had it then ... Jesus, I never thought they'd get old Animal"

"There is no fucking hurricane lamp here. We're wasting our fucking time."

"They got Bertie, too ..."

"Poor old Taffy."

"Bollocks! He's well out of this fucking lot."

"Everyone keep quiet, Shut up! No more talking. Not anyone. Keep quiet and listen. Anyone got a torch?"

"Of course they haven't. They'd be shining it by now if they did, you pillock."

"Belt up, Fletcher! That's more than enough out of you. What about matches, then? Or a lighter? Someone must have something."

"I've got some matches."

"Right! Give them to me." I groped around until I had the matches. I opened the box and felt inside. "There are only three in here!"

"Well that's three more than any other bugger's got."

"What fucking bastard organized this funk hole?"

"I did! Now shut up. I'll strike a light ..."

"Cor strike a light!"

Several men laughed. It was hysteria, not amusement.

"Bloody get on with it then."

I struck the match several times, but nothing happened. "They're damp. They'll never light."

"He probably pissed himself all over them."

"Get stuffed. There's nothing wrong with my matches."

I struck another match and it worked. A tiny flame sparked into life. I caught a momentary glimpse of the men. There were about twenty of them. They were haggard, totally exhausted, gripped by terror, scared witless, with the long, drawn faces of men who had in most cases given up hope. The light wavered, the match curled. I held it aloft until it burnt my fingers and vanished.

"Fat lot of good that did us. Fucking roll on ..."

"Fletcher! Just shut your moaning hole. Any more out of you and you're on a charge."

"Oh no! Oh, my God! Not that! Anything but that, please!"

Men laughed and I flushed with anger. "Everyone turn out their pockets! Anything that will burn. Then hand it to me and I'll make a fire of it... Paper, letters, handkerchiefs, anything."

All sorts of things were handed to me in the darkness. I placed them in a pile on the trench floor. Then I picked out the last match and prayed that it would light. It did, and I had a spill of paper ready. It blazed merrily and we soon had a small fire going. I knew it would only last a minute or so, but that gave me a chance to discover how many wounded we had and whether there was anything we could do for them.

Then, just as the flames faltered, someone yelled: "There's the bloody hurricane lamp! Over there! You're bloody near sitting on it, Fletch ... You stupid bastard!"

I lit the hurricane lamp and put it in the centre of the floor. Eerie shadows flickered but its wavering light calmed everyone. It gave us a chance to check on who exactly was there. As suspected, Bertie Mee and Corporal Jackman were missing, as were all of the young bandsmen apart from Corporal Jennings. Of the original platoon only Rupert, Fletcher, Holroyd and myself remained. We had three wounded men so I had them moved so that they were lying together. One had a stomach wound. It looked as though he'd been bayoneted since there was no exit hole in his back. He looked likely to die at any moment. The second one was from 10 Platoon and he had a very nasty bullet wound to the neck. He was smothered in shell dressings and his mate was comforting him, promising to look after him, assuring him that he wouldn't leave him.

"He's bleeding down in his throat, sir," he told me.

"So what can you do?"

"Blood keeps clotting in his throat, stopping his breathing. So I just stick my finger down and hoick it all out."

"And he goes on bleeding?"

"Yeah. But he'll be okay."

It was about the most hit and miss piece of first aid I'd ever encountered, but since I had nothing better to suggest I passed on to Rupert, our third wounded man. He'd had the sense to lower his trousers and tie a handkerchief around his thigh as a tourniquet. The wound itself was ugly and still bleeding, but there was no damage to his femur. As I examined it he seemed cheerful enough. So far, he hadn't said a word, but now he smiled at me and said: "A Blighty touch."

"A Blighty touch!" mocked Fletcher. "You think you're going to get out of here, then?"

"With a bit of luck," replied Rupert.

"What fucking luck, mate? Our luck's just run out for good. We've fucking had it. The Chinks won't even know we're down here. So we're buried alive. We've got no fresh air. And if they find the tunnel they'll just blow it in, like they did the weapon pits. Trapped like bloody rats."

"The Dukes will save us ..."

"What are you talking about? We are the fucking Dukes. So how the hell can we save ourselves?"

"The others ..."

"They'll be no better off than we are, mate. We've all had it."

Someone started to mutter: "Oh, God! Oh God!" and another kept repeating: "Hail Mary, Mother of God!"

"Now look what you've done, Fletch. You've sparked off the religious nuts. They'll be at it all night."

"I'll mash the bastards up if they do ..."

"Just shut up, Fletcher! When we get out of here you're definitely on a charge."

"Oh yeah! And why's that?"

"Causing alarm and despondency."

Fletcher laughed. "Me? Causing alarm! So now it's all my fucking fault!"

Eventually, more through tiredness than anything else, we lapsed into silence, physically and mentally spent. Above us shells continued to explode. There was no sound of small-arms fire, but I put that down to our depth. Several men fell asleep. One snored atrociously. The man tending his mate's throat wound was the only one to speak. After a long session of his mate wheezing, he said: "Here we go again, my old pal," and with that he'd inserted his finger into the man's throat and retrieved a whole lot of blood and unidentifiable gore. He flicked it on to the ground. The man's wheezing stopped, and he started breathing properly again. "There we are then! Right as rain now."

The man with the stomach wound soon died. I knew he was bound to, and most of us were relieved when he did. It put the poor fellow out of his agony. There were men on either side of him, holding his hands. When it happened, one of them said: "He's gone," and the other muttered, "Good luck, mate" as though he was going out to open the innings for his cricket club.

The dead man's muscles relaxed and his bodily functions took over. The smell was appalling. The two men tending him carried him off and put him at the far end of the tunnel, but the smell persisted.

For the rest of the night we sat and waited. There was nothing else we could do. There was no point in trying to break out until daybreak. Then, God only knew what we would find. If the Chinese were still occupying the hill, they would most likely shoot the first of us to appear and then fling satchel charges down the tunnel. On the other hand, if a counter attack had been successful we had a good chance of being rescued.

Occasionally men showed signs of stress or even panic. They cursed and swore and blamed all kinds of people for their predicament. Tempers were fraying, attitudes becoming childish. One man kept asking the time, to which another responded: "Why don't you belt up. You got a bus to catch, or something?" I went round everyone and had a few words with them, explaining the likely outcome. I was far from honest. I encouraged them to tell me what had happened to them and then tried to convince them that we'd been through the worst and now had only to sit tight, stressing that there would bound to be a major counter-attack.

One of the men from 10 Platoon was a corporal. He had no trouble sleeping, but every time he woke up he tried to assert his authority; to inject the correct spirit into us. He was determined that we should have a sing-song. "Come on, lads! Must keep our spirits up. We're not dead yet! Sing! Like the Navy lads did when they were torpedoed on Atlantic convoys ...."

"Go back to sleep, for Christ's sake ..."

"No, come on lads! We mustn't buckle under. When men were cast adrift in small boats and rafts in the Atlantic they always sang to help them survive ..."

"Get lost, you silly bugger."

It was Fletcher again. Scathingly, he pointed out that we weren't bobbing about in a rowing boat or a raft and that the poor sods who had been, only sang to keep conscious and prevent themselves from freezing to death. The corporal couldn't see the difference. Twice he tried to spark the singing off, first of all with 'Roll out the Barrel' and then 'Run Rabbit'. Everyone ignored him and he never got further than the first two lines, which was all he knew anyhow.

I was lying on the ground next to Rupert. The hurricane lamp was between us. His face was lined and grown old, caked in dust. I could tell he was in pain by the way he rocked from side to side. We didn't say anything until about two or three in the morning and even then we spoke in whispers, as though it was highly confidential. We reminisced about Catterick and tried to fathom out how on earth we had managed to end up like this. Really, we knew exactly how and why, but it seemed so totally surreal, as though there was something we had missed along the line. I made him smile when I speculated on what Gough would think if he knew what had happened to the worst Intake he had ever known. In a more serious moment he questioned me about Animal Evans. I explained how he had sacrificed himself by choosing to stay on top in the interests of us all.

"Yeah ... Well, in your interests, anyhow!"

I studied his face in the flickering light. Despite his pain he was smiling and it suddenly dawned on me what his theory was about Animal; the odd interest he had first shown in our company way back at Miss Daniel Soldiers' Home in Catterick. When I made no reply he changed the subject. "You didn't put your letter from Katsumi on the bonfire."

"No."

"You're more concerned about her than anything else, aren't you?"

"Yeah. Personal things always come first. They mean the most to us. Like your poems. You were going back for them when you were wounded. I know that. You were never going for the 88-set."

He laughed. "True. But they've had it now."

"You'll have to write them again."

"Impossible! They were from the heart. It makes a difference, you know."

"Yes, I suppose so."

"So what are you going to do about Katsumi?"

"Once out of here, I'll apply for leave. All that's owing to me. Not just five days R and R. And I'll go back to Kure. So that I can at least see her again."

"Good idea, Saj. It'll give you a far better idea of her condition."

His words were slurred and he said no more. I thought he'd fallen asleep, but he'd lapsed into unconsciousness through loss of blood. I examined his wound as best I could. It was still bleeding so I tightened up the shell dressing on it. I felt his pulse. I didn't know what to expect, but it was there and regular.

I knew it would start getting light around 0530 hours. Above us, the silence indicated that the battle had either passed on to battalion headquarters and beyond, or else the Chinese had been given such a bloody nose that they'd given up any hope of capturing the Hook. My guess was the latter. If the battle was raging on further south I reckoned it would be going full blast and we would still be able to hear it.

At 0445 hours I made sure everyone was awake and told them that I intended to try to break out, using the pole made for us by the Engineers. If it worked, three of us would venture on to the hill to find out what had happened. I nominated Holroyd and the corporal from 10 Platoon to accompany me. I told them that we would go unarmed. If the Chinese had won the day, it would be pointless to fight any further and we would have to take our chance on whether they shot us out of hand or took us prisoner. If the latter, we would direct them to the tunnel to round up everyone else. If the Dukes were back in control, we wouldn't need any weapons anyhow.

At 0530 hours several of us assembled beneath the escape hatch to remove the cover. In practice, it had always worked perfectly. We got the pole into position and on my word we heaved. Nothing happened: no suggestion of movement. We tried several times, but still without success. Two others joined us to increase our thrust, but there was still no movement. We took the pole down the tunnel to the far exit. Once again, nothing shifted. We were well and truly trapped, buried alive in a stinking tunnel that was to have been our salvation. It was our worst moment. We returned to the centre of the tunnel and gathered around our hurricane lamp. It was beginning to splutter. It would soon be out. Then there would be the added terror of pitch darkness. The corporal from 10 Platoon started to sing:

> "Show me the way to go home,
> I'm tired and I want to go to bed ..."

33

The Human Cost

Corporal Underwood, the Engineer poofter from Surrey, rescued us.

He hadn't been on the Hook during the battle. He'd been asleep in a bunker beyond battalion headquarters, knowing that come dawn he would have one hell of a day ahead of him. He had experienced the second battle of the Hook with the Black Watch, so he knew what to expect.

In the tunnel, the sing-song never caught on. We lapsed into silence. God knows what the others were thinking, but I was back to praying. I'd done a lot of it, lately. I was either praying to God to look after my own skin, or was praying to Buddha, imploring him to save Katsumi. What amazed me was that despite my split loyalties, God was kind enough to answer my prayers by having us rescued.

The first signs of hope came when we heard noises. Several of us dashed to the base of the ladder and strained to hear more. It was impossible to distinguish any words, but it was definitely human voices. Then came the sound of digging. It became progressively more distinct. Now, everyone was clustered around the ladder and men kept yelling out: "We're here! Down here!"

Twenty minutes later the cover moved slightly. Then it jerked upwards and daylight burst in, blinding us for a second or two. Dust and rubble and glorious fresh air also flooded down and when it cleared, and our eyes grew accustomed to the light, we saw the outline of a solitary figure staring down the hole at us.

A torch beam was flashed in our faces. Then a familiar voice said: "I thought so! You stupid buggers! I warned you ... but you wouldn't listen."

I'd never before been so thankful to see someone. All around me the lads were cheering. The 10 Platoon corporal yelled up: "Who won, mate?"

"We did, you silly bugger. Do I look like a Chink?"

We thought that was enormously funny. Right then, everything was funny. God, how we laughed and cheered. I ushered these happy men up the ladder. Everyone wanted to let everyone else go first, such manners! I had to push them up, one by one. As they got on the hill they were full of chatter and banter, with Corporal Underwood continually saying: "Never mind all that. For God's sake shut up and get down to the jeep-head before more shelling starts."

I was the last out, apart from the wounded. Both Rupert and the man with the neck wound needed piggy-backs up the ladder. We left the dead man down there, to be sorted out later.

When I stepped on to the hill and looked around properly I recoiled. I had expected devastation, but not on this scale. The trenches had been flattened and the hill was nothing but a tangled, bloody, junk yard, reminiscent of the East End in the blitz except that instead of domestic debris, bricks and mortar, here there were broken timbers, barbed wire, discarded and mangled-up weapons, sandbags, steel helmets, and above all dead bodies. Oh God, those bodies! They reminded me of newsreel shots of Belsen, only instead of skeletal bodies, these were butchered bodies. It was impossible to visualize anything more hellish. There wasn't a complete body to be seen. Limbs and chunks of flesh were scattered about indiscriminately. If ever there was evidence of Satan's presence on earth, this was it. It was no longer the hill we had known with its labyrinth of trenches. They had been reduced to V-shaped scoops and there wasn't a weapon pit left standing. The only men now on guard against a further Chinese assault were those who had earlier done a counter-attack to rid the hill of any surviving Chinese. They were simply lying behind improvised cover made up of broken timbers and torn sandbags.

Then, to my horror, I saw that one of the nearby corpses was Animal Evans. His body was complete except for a foot. Underwood saw my reaction. "One of your lads," he said. "I recognized him right away. When we found your tunnel we started digging and eventually came across him. He was lying on top of the cover. He must have been caught by the VT as he was about to go down."

"No," I said. "He replaced the cover and stayed up there deliberately. I heard him holding off more Chinese coming down the trench."

"Yeah ... Well he got them all right. We've dug out nine of them." Underwood saw me move towards Animal, a gesture of affection and respect. "Don't worry about him now, sir. Blokes will be coming round later to pick up our dead. There will be dozens of them all buried in this shit. And some still alive, hopefully. Like you lot. For Christ's sake get down to the jeep-head. And get your wounded into the morgue. Once we've dug people out, the Fusiliers are coming up here."

A stretcher appeared from somewhere. We lifted the man with the neck wound on to it and he was carried away. There was no stretcher for Rupert, so Holroyd and I got on either side of him. He wound his arms around our necks and we carried him back to company headquarters. We stopped there momentarily to report to Earl Gray in the company CP. It was still standing, battered but intact. No one was there. I assumed they had been killed during the night, but I later discovered they'd survived intact, but had been ordered by Earl Gray to pull out as soon as the Engineers arrived on the scene. The bastard had buggered off, not even waiting to see his men rescued or to hand-over to his opposite number in the Fusiliers. I'd never had any time for him, but that did surprise me. Whoever had said he was callous and lacked compassion was dead right.

At the jeep-head dozens of ambulance jeeps were scurrying about, engines revving, drivers shouting to each other. Some were arriving, others leaving, the remainder being loaded with the wounded. In the trench leading down to the jeep-head a long procession of stretcher bearers were taking more wounded to the morgue. Most of them were from 11 Platoon. To one side of the jeep-head there were two troop carriers which had been hit by shelling during the night. Several bodies were still littered about with a lone medic going around them, checking that they were dead. Nearer the morgue entrance was the usual pile of discarded stretchers and well to the rear were several trucks, stacked with fresh timbers in readiness for the engineers to start rebuilding the defences.

When we reached the morgue we edged inside, fearful of what we would see. Our fears were validated. Over fifty stretcher cases were littered about. It was a nightmare, a concentration of ugly wounds: split skulls, exposed intestines, broken limbs, severed blood vessels, body parts, and amputated limbs. At the far end of the bunker a man was shouting, "I can't see! I can't see!" Others among the wounded were moaning and above it all were the shouts and orders of the medics, trying desperately to deal with each new emergency that arose. Only the dead lay silent.

Holroyd stayed with Rupert while I went in search of attention. The medics were frantically busy and ignored me. Eventually I came across Doc Mackey. Despite the chaos around him, he was perfectly composed. He was attending to a nasty groin wound but he found time to glance up. "You've made it all right then, Din? We wondered what had happened to you."

"We survived. But I've got a man who needs attention."

Mackey nodded to an adjacent stretcher case lying on the floor. "He's next to go. Put your laddie down there and we'll see to him. How bad is he?"

"Not too bad. Wounded in the leg."

"Right. We'll see to him. But don't hang around. You'll only get in the way. All fit men are reporting back to battalion. Earl Gray came through about half an hour ago."

As soon as the stretcher case was removed I went back to Holroyd. We took a stretcher from the pile outside and put Rupert on it. Then we carried him to the vacant spot. He smiled wanly as we set him down. "See you later," I said. "You'll be okay. In good hands now."

We went outside. It was good to get away from all the gore, out into the open air. The survivors of our tunnel were standing in a forlorn group by the monsoon ditch. I went over to them, intending to tell them to head for battalion headquarters. Before I could say a word, Fletcher piped up. "We've been waiting for you. We're going back up to help dig the others out."

"Who told you to?"

"No one. But we're going. You two coming?"

"Of course," said Holroyd.

When we got back on the Hook the others made for their old positions, whereas Holroyd and I went down to 10 Platoon, to the forward slope overlooking Ronson, Green Finger, and Warsaw. As we looked down into the valley we saw a large collection of Chinese wandering about, retrieving their dead and wounded, as was their custom. They had a hell of a job ahead of them. The number of the dead was numbing, masses still entangled in the shredded barbed wire. As was the case in front of 12 Platoon, a large mound of corpses had formed in the centre of the slope. My estimation of the Chinese dead was three or four thousand, so numerous that it was pointless trying to count them. They went a long way to explaining why everything was now so quiet, with no shelling. It was an admission of defeat by the Chinese, a gesture that made it clear that, for the time being anyhow, they'd had enough. Their breakthrough just hadn't happened and there was, after all, a limit to the punishment they were prepared to take.

The Engineers and Assault Pioneer Platoon were giving priority to digging out the 10 Platoon weapon pits. They were having some success and they had already dragged several men out alive. The 10 Platoon tunnels had been opened up and stretcher bearers were busy tending the wounded and preparing to take them down to the morgue. Holroyd and I went back to 12 Platoon and while he helped to drag away timbers at the weapon pits, I headed for the platoon CP. It was among the least damaged, no doubt due to the extra strength when we'd rebuilt it. It was mostly damaged by fire and everything inside was scorched and black and thick with soot. I knew what I was looking for: not more casualties but two very personal things. My officer's valise containing presents and general memorabilia from Kure, and for Rupert's kit bag in which he kept his poems, the one's he'd intended to retrieve when he was wounded. I was determined to salvage them for him. It was the very least I could do. I knew only too well how much they meant to him.

I found them easily enough. Both had been badly scorched and partially burnt, but they were sufficiently intact for me to carry them

away without losing any of the contents. I went back to Holroyd and the others. They were making good progress. Two men had come out alive. I joined Corporal Jenkins and helped to open up his weapon pit. Among the things lying around was his bugle. It was dented, crumpled and twisted but when he put it to his lips he got notes out of it. He suggested that he should play The Last Post and I agreed. He went to the top of the hill and his first piercing notes startled the Chinese. Bugles were usually their prerogative. Some ran off, but the rest stood firm and watched. The Last Post echoed around the otherwise silent hills, and when his final tribute was done, everyone went back to clearing away the dead.

Around 1030 hours the Royal Fusiliers relieved us. As I handed over our wasted piece of ground to my opposite number we laughed. I said: "All yours now ... Such as it is ..." and he replied, "Thanks!"

We regrouped at battalion headquarters. We were a sorry sight. All companies had suffered badly, Dog Company most of all. Both Tremlett and Barren were dead. So was Copper Bowden. We had a roll call and were then transported to a reserve position. For a change, everything had been prepared for us in advance and the lads were soon sitting around, smoking and drinking and exchanging details of what had happened. I asked around for news of Rupert and was told he'd been taken to the nearest MASH Unit, further down the MSR.

I drew a jeep from MT and set off. I drove wildly, not through fear of more shelling but through exhilaration. At least Rupert and I had survived and I knew he would be ecstatic that I had saved his poems. I found the MASH unit easily enough. Casualties from the Hook occupied three marquee-style tents. I located an orderly and he advised me that the quickest way to find Rupert was to wander around until I spotted him. I went around twice but there was no sign of him. I came across a nurse carrying a clipboard. She told me that in all probability he was in surgery. "Is it important?"

"Yes. I've got his poems and it's important he knows."

She looked at me as though I was very odd, but she promised to try to locate him for me. Just when I thought she forgotten all about me, she reappeared.

"I'm so sorry. Bad news, I'm afraid. Private Sandwitch died a couple of hours ago."

"Died!" I was staggered. I couldn't believe her.

"Yes, I'm afraid so."

"But I've got his poems and he only had a leg wound."

She consulted her clipboard. "That's right. Left thigh flesh wound. It wasn't considered life-threatening, but I'm afraid it was ... It was probably a result of shock ... It can happen like that ... A delayed effect

... I'm terribly sorry. Was he one of your men?"

"Yes. My batman. And my friend."

"I'm so sorry. Perhaps you could identify him for us? Just a matter of confirmation."

"Yes, of course."

I still couldn't grasp that Rupert was dead. I was sure she was wrong, that she would show me the body of someone else and that Rupert would later be found hopping around on a pair of crutches, spreading good cheer among those less fortunate than himself.

We went out to the back, to a long row of body bags. The nurse went along them, reading the labels. Eventually she stopped. "Here he is. Sure you don't mind?"

"No ...."

She unzipped the top half of the body bag and there was Rupert.

He looked incredibly calm, in fact serene. I stared down at him. Then I stooped and touched him and had no option but to believe it. A tingling sensation zapped through me like a charge of electricity. Images flashed through my mind: memories of all the good times and all the dangerous times. Kaleidoscopic images filled my brain like a giant migraine. I didn't know how long they lasted, but eventually I felt the nurse's hand on my shoulder. My reverie was broken. I looked up and said something that must have struck her as incredibly stupid.

"That's him, all right. But it's only the body he used whilst he was here on earth."

It was what Dad had said to me when we had viewed the bodies of Gran and Mr. Muckey. In all honesty, I didn't believe it then, any more than I did now. I was trying to find comfort, groping desperately for a vindicating explanation for something so totally abhorrent and futile.

The nurse took me to see one of the surgeons. He looked worn out, obviously just back from the operating theatre. His clothing was still blood-stained. She had a few words with him. He opened a drawer in and brought out a piece of paper. "He died peacefully. He came in quite lucid, but when he started to deteriorate he wrote a short message." He squinted at the piece of paper. "Are you Saj?"

"Yes. Sajit Contractor."

"For you, then. You'd better keep it. It has no official importance. You can pass it on to his next of kin, if necessary. "

I took the piece of paper and read it. It was a short poem.

"Tell 'em, Saj! Let your ink
Gush and flow bright red.
How it really was: our fears
And how freely we bled.

No poetic fantasies, please.
No symbolic flights of a dove.
Just how we held the Hook with
*Dukes pride and agarpy love." ***

The nurse took me by the hand and led me back to my jeep, pretending not to see my tears. Someone drove me back to the Dukes. I called in at Dog Company headquarters to let them know that Rupert was dead. "Just for your records," I told Corporal Turnbull. In the background Earl Gray was listening. He looked up but said nothing: no regrets, no sympathy. For a mad moment I wanted to poleaxe him with biting sarcasm, to shame him by asking how many weeks' pay he would be deducting from Rupert for having got killed. I didn't, of course. It was a stupid thought; symptomatic of my state of mind.

---

* Later I realized that Rupert had deliberately misspelt 'agarpy' for my benefit. Really, it is 'agape' (Greek, pronounced agarpy). It means ultimate, non-physical love, especially among men. The same as he had been driving at with Animal Evans and me.

34

No Sympathy

For the next two months I took little interest in our military activities, even though I went through all the required motions. I'd got an excellent new sergeant named Simpkins and I let him run things. I just mooched around, putting in enough appearances to avoid criticism. Thoughts of my dead comrades began to recede but my concern for Katsumi never ceased. The more I thought of her, the more I became obsessed by a curious notion that she would survive. It wasn't because Nacker's letters held out any fresh hope. It was just a personal conviction, a feeling that because things had plunged to such an all-time low, they were now bound to improve. My prayers to God for our rescue had been answered, so why not my prayers to Buddha for Katsumi?

I wrote to Nacker letting him know I had survived on the Hook. I told him I saw it as an omen. That if I'd been reprieved, escaped certain death, then why not Katsumi? I told Nacker that I would claim all the leave due to me and return to Kure so that I could be with her again. I was convinced that my presence would boost her morale so dramatically that it would inspire her to recover.

Of course, I was just being damned silly. Mentally, I was in a hell of a mess.

I heard back from Nacker very quickly. This time he was blunt, knowing that he had no other option. He told me my optimism was misplaced, that the Hiroshima hospital had admitted there was no hope. She would die within a week or two.

Right away I lodged my application for leave with Corporal Turnbull. Earl Gray summoned me to the CP. I stood before him at attention. "What's this, Contractor? You've applied for leave!"

"Yes, sir."

"You've got a damn nerve ..."

"A nerve? Why's that, sir?"

"Good God, you've only just come back from months in Kure."

"It's nearly two months ago now, sir. And anyhow, I'm entitled to leave just the same as everyone else."

"Are you indeed! I'll be the judge of that. And I need hardly remind you that whilst you were living in the lap of luxury the rest of us were doing some proper soldiering. Not playing rugby in Tokyo, or wining and dining in the Officers' Club. To say nothing of looking after Japanese house-girls. I suppose there's a Japanese girl behind this application?"

"What I do on leave is entirely my own affair, sir."

"I thought so. Wasn't four months enough for you?"

"My time in Japan was strictly on duty."

"So that's how you see it ... Well I'll tell you straight, Contractor. If you think you can just breeze off again then you've got another think coming. Request denied. Not now. Nor in the near future. If and when the armistice is signed, then by all means. But not before."

"In that case I'll have to take the matter up with the Colonel."

"Take it up with who the hell you like."

First off I went to see Captain Hawthorn. He was in an ebullient mood. He even called me 'Din' and he'd elevated me to the 'old boy' category. His fresh attitude was due to having been recommended for a Military Cross. Apparently, a very deserved one.

He listened to my problem courteously. Then he shook his head sadly and confirmed that it was pointless bothering the Colonel since the decision was Earl Gray's. "Mind you, Din, old boy, you could outflank the Earl rather neatly by applying for compassionate leave." He chuckled at the very thought. "If the Padre agrees, you'll scupper the Earl well and truly. Well worth a try, I'd say. Good luck, Din, old boy!"

I knew that asking for compassionate leave would be a waste of time, and it was. At first the Padre assumed I was seeking an early return to the UK , but when he realized I wanted to go to Kure to visit a girlfriend his attitude immediately hardened. However, I related what had happened. "The point is this, Padre," I said in desperation. "Those who go down with radiation poisoning have very little hope of survival. It's expected to be fatal. With not a lot of time left."

"Did you mention this to Major Gray?"

"No, sir."

"Why not?"

"I didn't consider it any of his concern."

"You knew he'd still say no?"

"Yes, Padre."

"So what precisely is the nature of this friendship? Are you engaged, or anything like that? Or is she pregnant? And have any arrangements been made with the army for her to travel back to England?"

"No, sir. None of those things."

"And what was her job at the headquarters?"

"A house-girl ..."

"Your house-girl?"

"Yes, sir."

"And how old is she?"

"Nineteen, sir,"

It was a deliberate lie, such a blatant lie that I blushed guilty. My affair with Katsumi started when she was fifteen. Shortly before I left Japan, we celebrated her 'seventeenth' birthday and it was then that I discovered that in Japan people were regarded as one year old when they are born. It made Katsumi below the age of our consent when we had first slept together. This, together with the way I had flouted the anti-fraternization regulation, and lived with her in War Department Property, meant that from the army's point of view I was more deserving of a court-martial than compassionate leave.

"So you've had an affair with your Japanese house-girl," continued the Padre, "and because she's been taken ill you think that is grounds for compassionate leave?"

"Yes, sir. We are very much in love."

He looked at me in despair. It was not what he expected from an officer. "Mr. Contractor, I have no desire to be offensive, but you must approach this with far more maturity. This isn't an English girl. She's a complete stranger to your family .... A Japanese girl with whom you shouldn't have been fraternizing. You may have enjoyed a physical relationship, but that's all. And it can't possibly be grounds for compassionate leave. If I granted compassionate leave on the grounds of sleeping with house-girls, there would be no limit to it ...."

"But she's dying ..."

"That's tragic, of course. But it doesn't make any difference."

He stood up and smiled. "Believe me, I've seen enough of the world to know that however strong your feelings are now, you will get over it. You've had a very hard time up on the Hook, I know that. And your abhorrence at yet another death, especially a young civilian, does you credit. But it will pass, just as the death of your men will. Our Christian faith is our salvation. Initial horror and sorrow are perfectly natural, but in the final analysis we must always bear in mind what Jesus said. 'Let the dead bury the dead.' The love of God will see us through it all."

We parted without bitterness. His argument was irrefutable. Only someone who had met Katsumi could understand my passion for her, my desperation to see her just one more time.

Now, my only chance of seeing her again would be in August when I returned to Kure in order to catch the trooper home.

35

Home Again

My reunion with Katsumi never came about. Early in July I had a letter from Nacker telling me to abandon all plans to visit her. She was determined I should not set eyes on her again. She wanted me to remember her as she was, at her incomparable best, not as someone toothless, hairless, covered in cheloids and weeping sores, more like a weird little alien from outer-space than a beautiful young girl. She knew her time was up and she was reconciled to it. She wanted it to come quickly and as privately as possible.

A few days later Nacker wrote again. She was dead. He said that Akiko and he had been with her and they could only be thankful that her suffering was over. At her request, her body had been handed over to the American Atomic Bomb Commission.

About the same time the Dukes moved back into the line in the middle of the Commonwealth Division. Rumours increased that the Peace Talks in Panmunjom were about to be concluded and, sure enough, on July 27th, an armistice was signed with a free exchange of prisoners-of-war.

There was a lot of celebrating. Troops on both sides were allowed to meet in no man's land and there was a general exchange of souvenirs, with the communists taking full advantage of distributing propaganda material. I kept well clear of any celebrations. Indeed, the whole thing would have been a non-event to me had it not been for a surprise visit from Kim.

It was some weeks since I had seen him. He had never been allowed on to the Hook, but we had met several times in or around the morgue; and he had, of course, been instrumental in getting us supplies of timber for our tunnel. Since then, and with the death of Animal Evans and others, we had drifted apart. When he suddenly turned up at my CP I was surprised to see that he was no longer wearing his cut down uniform or his beret. He smiled, because he always smiled, but he was ill at ease.

He told me that he had come to say goodbye, to thank me and 12 Platoon for having befriended him. Now, he said, he was going back home, to reclaim his family smallholding in North Korea. He said he had enough money to start again from scratch, to grow rice in his paddies and ginseng on his south-facing slopes.

"I'm going back to a normal life, sir. Where everyone will leave me alone."

I didn't try to reason with him. I knew exactly how he felt. I wished him all the luck in the world. We shook hands very formally, as befitted both of us. I wanted to hug him, as though he was my young brother, but I didn't. It is something I've always bitterly regretted. I heard him go off down the trench. I waited a minute or two and then went round to the OP. I watched him go down the minefield path, across our half of the valley and then join a group of fraternizing troops. After a minute or two he waded across the Samichon and a Chinese soldier led him away. I watched him until he disappeared behind the Chinese hills.

I've never seen or heard of him since.

When my movement order arrived for my journey back to the UK it turned out that the Devonshire would sail direct from Pusan. We would not be calling in at Kure after all. I was glad. It meant a clean break. I would forever cherish my memories of Kure but now was not the time to rekindle them.

More than anything, I wanted time alone. I needed to sort myself out. I had been granted my first-hand experience of war. I now knew what it was like: exactly what it entailed. I knew what it was to kill, to see the mangled remains of countless friends; and I'd had the love of my life snatched away from me. For all the comradeship, the laughs, the moments of excitement, the courage and devotion to duty, the inherent evilness of war overrode everything. It even sucked in the young and the innocent, mere kids like Kim and Katsumi who deserved nothing but peace and happiness.

No truer words were ever written than Rupert's lines:

> *"In the end war always wins,*
> *Notice the cross-bones of death, sir,*
> *And the skull above it that grins."*

I was in no doubt as to what I had to do. I had to cry out against the futility of it all. I didn't expect it to work; indeed I knew it wouldn't work, the human race being as it is; but I had to try just the same. I had to get everything down in writing without delay, whilst it was still burning red-hot in my mind. I had to write the great anti-war novel.

How I would do that was another matter. I hadn't the faintest idea how to write a novel. The technique of crafting a story, presenting believable characters, handling descriptive passages, and creating fluent dialogue, were a complete mystery to me. All I had was a premise, a desire to unleash on the world what Korea had been like; and this was so deeply embedded within me that I just plunged in regardless. It was a reflex action, guided by instinct, nothing else.

I got some foolscap sheets of paper from the Devonshire's Purser, installed myself in a corner of the trooper's small library, and did nothing but write; day after day, from early morning until late at night, breaking only for meals. When we got into the Indian Ocean the heat drove me to a shady nook on the promenade deck. At the same time I took a break from my own writing and started to sort out Rupert's poems. Several had been destroyed completely, and others had been burnt or singed so badly that only parts were readable, but I managed to make sense of them.

I saw at last what his full-length poems were like. I was enormously impressed. I had expected them to mimic established war poems, to be full of symbolism, strained metaphors, and abounding in self-pity, doom and damnation, what W.B.Yeats once described as, 'all blood, dirt, and sucked sugar stick'. I should have known better. His poems were strikingly direct and reflected things exactly as they had happened.

My high opinion of them was vindicated in a curious way. Not by so-called intellectual critics, but by young men who had experienced the very events described. Men who were in a real position to judge, for there's a lot more to poetry than flowery and beautiful language; it is just as much a matter of the emotions that linger in the human heart.

As I sat at a small desk on the promenade deck, I was accustomed to others wandering about taking exercise or playing deck games, and I was aware that I struck a curious figure. On one occasion a noisy party of subalterns came around looking for some light relief. On seeing me, they decided on some harmless fun at my expense. They were led by a Duke named Bransby Oliver. He snatched one of Rupert's poems out of my hand and then, amid much laughter, he held it aloft and declared: "Well I'll be damned! Old Din is writing poetry."

He read it aloud. Within two lines they ceased to mock. Bransby Oliver's derisory tone grew solemn. The others listened in rapt attention. The poem was 'The Sniper'. It was not one of Rupert's best, but it was typical of his attitude towards war.

The Sniper

Now sits a man within my sights.
He's smiling and relaxed, at leisure;
Sublimely unaware that his frail life
Lies entirely within my pleasure.

He basks in the sun and waffles on,
No doubt regaling his friends and cronies
With the rights and wrongs of army life
And denouncing all officers as phonies.

What crazy duty demands that I should kill
This man who cannot remotely matter?
If I shoot the poor sod, what comfort in that?
To see his skull implode, then shatter?

So it's safety catch on and rifle to rest,
My softness acknowledged by a profanity.
Yet inwardly I rejoice, with peace of mind,
Thankful to have retained my humanity.

When Bransby stopped reading, nothing was said. They were young veterans; every one of them had taken life and seen it taken. The poem spoke for them. Bransby handed it back to me and they walked off, not a word exchanged among them.

We headed up the English Channel, towards Southampton. We were due to arrive around midday. A big reception awaited us on account of the returning ex-POWs on board. As we edged up the Solent, all manner of vessels fought the choppy waters and came out to greet us: tugs, pleasure steamers, dockyard run-arounds, hundreds of individual pleasure yachts and cruisers, and small craft which had put to sea for the first time in years. Even people in rowing boats.

In Southampton the decks of visiting ocean liners were crowded by passengers eager to catch sight of us. As we tied up alongside them, the liners let out great blasts on their sirens, and on the quay itself the huge crowd awaiting us cheered wildly. It was an unforgettable experience.

On board, we lined the port decks and threw down streamers and did our best to pick out relatives and friends, and every time there was a success those below let out joyous cries and waved back all the harder.

The massed bands of the Brigade of Guards was in pride of place, roped off in a red-carpeted square. Amongst them was Dad. He was almost alongside the band, as though he was an honorary appendage. How he'd wheedled his way into such a prime spot, I'll never know. I waved to him and laughed at the way his camel hair overcoat was flapping open, just as it always did, and how his Tyrolean hat with its coloured feathers was tilted back on his head. Then, to my amazement, I saw that twenty or thirty yards away, not daring to encroach upon the band's domain, was Mum. Miss Beaumont was there too. Then I saw James and--- wonder of wonders!--- even old Brother Nothing! What a turn out!

Suddenly, as though operated by a switch, the ships' sirens stopped and the massed bands struck up the National Anthem. Everything else went silent. Being a military occasion, there was no singing. Everyone showed due respect: officers saluted; the other ranks stood rigidly to attention; men doffed their hats; and women dabbed their eyes. When the band finished the National Anthem, there was a pause, not a murmur anywhere, everyone expecting them to play something else, like Rule Britannia or Land of Hope of Glory. However, they didn't and stillness enveloped everything.

Dad seized his opportunity. He went right up to the edge of the quay, cupped his hands around his mouth, and bellowed, as only he could bellow:

"DIN!   DIN!   DIN!
WHERE   THE   BLOODY   HELL   YER   BIN?"

The End

EPILOGUE

On the voyage home, news came that Private Fletcher, who was serving an extra 28 days in Korea in lieu of time spent in Colchester Detention Barracks, had been drowned whilst swimming in the Imjin.

Major Gray was awarded the DSO. When he retired he was still a major. Animal Evans was Mentioned in Despatches. Corporal Holroyd got a Military Medal. I was awarded the Military Cross.

I sent Rupert's poems to every poetry publisher listed in the reference books but they all returned them. I eventually self-published them under the title, *The War Poems of a Young Soldier*. The book is still in print.

Nacker Gilbert brought Akiko-san back to the UK as the first Japanese war bride. He later became one of Britain's top surgeons. We remained firm friends until he died in 2003.

In the 1990s I featured in a TV documentary about National Service and was able to visit the graves of my former comrades. When I saw how proud the people of Korea were of the nation they had built-up I realized our efforts had not been in vain.

My novel about my experiences in Korea (*The Dead, the Dying and the Damned*) was published in 1956. It was an immediate best-seller and is now estimated to have sold over 3 million copies. (See pages 347, 348.)

The Duke of Wellington's Regiment no longer exists. Our generals and politicians have done what no enemy ever could do--- wipe them out. So a family regiment, drawn from The West Riding of Yorkshire, which distinguished itself in such places such as Dettingen, Ally Ghur, Dehli, Corunna, Peninsula, Waterloo, Alma, Inkerman, Sebastopol, Kimberley, Mons, Marne, Ypres, Somme, Suvla Bay, Afghanistan, Dunkirk, Anzio, Sittang Bridge, and among the Chindits, is now no more. Their lonesome stand on the Hook, which played such a vital part in bringing the Korean War to an end, became their final Battle Honour. I am proud to have served with them in what was, and will now forever remain, their finest hour.

Appendix One

The one/two-sided fighting patrol

The success of this patrol had lasting consequences. The technique used (shell craters as cover, striking first with grenades, and using two Bren Groups 'floating' at the rear) was later adopted by other units. It helped to regain the initiative in no man's land and brought a decline in British casualties.

Years later Major A. J. Barker, (advised by Dom Alberic Stacpoole, known as John Stacpoole when a subaltern in the Dukes) published a book entitled *Fortune Favours the Brave*. It was highly critical of the patrol and cast doubts on the competence and fighting spirit of those who took part in it.

The reason for this is impossible to tell since Barker and Stacpoole have since died, but evidence, in the form of a letter from Stacpoole to Hollands, suggests that it was Stacpoole's riposte to Hollands's best-selling anti-war novel (*The Dead, the Dying and the Damned*) in which there was no reference to The Duke of Wellington's Regiment and their heroic role in the Korean War, it being strictly a work of fiction. As a consequence, a claim of libel was made against Pen and Sword Ltd of Barnsley, the publishers of *Fortune Favours the Brave*. Pen and Sword Ltd. admitted liability and made a financial settlement out of court, with a written apology and an assurance that future editions of *Fortune Favours the Brave* would be amended to give a true (but concise) account of what happened, as per the Gazetted Citation for 2nd Lt. D.J.Hollands's Military Cross. (To clarify matters this is printed in full in Appendix Two.)

Appendix Two

London Gazette, February 1954

"2/Lieut HOLLANDS has taken part in a number of very daring patrol actions. On more than one occasion he has ventured, with one man as escort, behind enemy lines, returning with vital information.

"He has also commanded several fighting patrols. Once, he found his patrol surrounded by an enemy ambush party which outnumbered him by about three to one. With great coolness and presence of mind 2/Lieut HOLLANDS immediately manoeuvred his patrol into an advantageous position and acted with such speed that he was able to open fire before the enemy. A four minute small arms and grenade battle followed during which the enemy were pinned to the ground, after suffering casualties. Realizing that he was outnumbered, 2/Lieut HOLLANDS gave orders for a withdrawal and so skillfully was this carried out that the patrol were able to return to their own lines without casualties.

"Throughout this action, and all other actions in which he has been involved, 2/Lieut HOLLANDS displayed the highest qualities of bravery, persistence and leadership."

Original recommendations: Lt Col. F. R. P. Bunbury
                                                    Major E. J. P. T. Emmet

Response:
Brigadier D.(Joe) Kendrew, 29th Brigade: "Strongly recommended."
Major-Gen M. West, Div. Commander: "Recommended."
Lt-Gen H. Wells, Commander-in-Chief: "Recommended."
The award was granted: "In the field."

Appendix III

The poems of Private Robert Sandwitch:

The details of how the poems of Private Rupert Sandwitch were rescued from the battlefield are explained in the main text. Some of the poems were badly burnt, even though they were still in Rupert's kitbag. Some had been destroyed completely and others were unreadable.

However, after piecing bits together it was possible to get them in chronological order.

As already mentioned, they were eventually published under the title, **The War Poems of a Young Soldier**. The poems that follow are a selection from those he wrote. Anyone wishing to have a copy of **The War Poems of a Young Soldier,** which includes all Rupert's poems, should contact the following Email address:

hollands12010@hotmail.com
Price £7.50 including postage.

THE POEMS OF RUPERT SANDWITCH

Rupert Sandwitch often referred to Tommy Atkins, so it is not surprising that he wrote a poem about him. Tommy Atkins was a 'Duke' who died of multiple wounds in the war of the First Coalition, 1794-95. Old Nosey (The Duke of Wellington) never forgot Atkins's last words and it led to Tommy Atkins being used to typify all British troops.

Tommy Atkins

Out of the eternal snows of the Hindu Kush
And the blistering heat of the Mysore bush,
Was spawned the spirit of the old Thirty-Third
And a humble soldier, famed for his final word.

Atkins was a veteran serving in his twentieth year
And in that time he'd got no higher than grenadier,
An illiterate giant but the regiment's best man at arms
A Tyke who inspired others to fight without qualms.

It was in a Flanders field that he eventually fell,
With the Thirty-Third's rout bordering on hell.
Twice he'd been shot, and sabre-slashed galore,
Lethal wounds numbering close on a score.

Yet when he was found and removed to the rear
He alone was quiet, resigned, devoid of all fear.
Round about him comrades moaned and cried out,
Men racked by pain, panic, and harrowing doubt.

Then up rode Old Nosey, splashing through mud,
And seeing Atkins lying there, soaked in blood,
Asked how he kept calm while others went berserk.
'Nowt to it, sir,' said Atkins. 'All in a day's work.'

OLD NOSEY

Rupert Sandwitch joined the Royal Corps of Signals at Catterick straight out of school, aged eighteen. We underwent basic training together but were parted when I was transferred to the potential leaders wing. Throughout his basic training, Rupert was forever in trouble. It got so bad that he and several others were transferred to the Yorkshire Infantry Brigade at Strensall. There, they did basic training all over again.

They got into further trouble when they deliberately threw an assault course competition, which resulted in them being posted to The Duke of Wellington's Regiment which was about to leave for Korea. It was then that I was reunited with them, having in the meantime been commissioned. Together, we formed the nucleus of 12 Platoon, Dog Company. He wrote this poem about his basic training whilst on the troopship Devonshire, en route to Korea.

Basic Training
at Catterick

Bugles blared, echoing from a remote Asian shore,
And news broke of nations stampeding back to war.
I took note, but even with National Service beckoning
Fears of involvement never entered my reckoning.

My call-up papers came and to the army I departed.
Basic training at Catterick, but I'm not downhearted.
Square bashing and bullshit the order of the day,
But I'm young and eager and at least there's pay.

Shining dull brasses with NCOs bawling
Sleeping in lectures with officers drawling.
Arms drill! Fire drill! Dawn inspections!
A sadistic MO, blunt-needled injections.

Left turn! Right turn! At the double!
CO's orders for too much stubble.
Pressing trousers and Blancoing gaiters.
Food's inedible, with black-eyed 'taters.

Sweaty bodies and blistered feet.
Excused boots: now there's a treat!
But no luck for me, although my blister's a beauty,
The MO, the bastard, prescribes 'medicine and duty'.

"Bloody this!" and "Bloody that!"
"Shut your gob!" "No bloody chat!"
"Salute it!" "Paint it!" "Stand by your bed!"
Pointless bullshit we soon come to dread.

Winter comes and Catterick instantly freezes.
With no shelter from north-eastern breezes.
So each night to the garrison cinema we retreat.
Not for the flicks, but warmth at a tanner a seat.

Tedious routines make the months drag out.
Naafi buns sustain us and we're all on snout.
Map reading, field craft, endless weapon training;
An assault course contest thrown without straining.

They treat us as though guilty of treason,
Punishing us beyond all rhyme or reason.
Jankers all round and we're inspected hourly.
'No leave for you lot,' our officer says sourly.

But we cock them a snook and laugh in their faces,
Confident we'll soon be serving in sunny places.
But we're too cocky by far and come to rue our boasting:
They have the last laugh: you should see our posting!

When hen Rupert Sandwitch and the others were transferred to an infantry regiment, they found themselves at the regimental depot of the 1ˢᵗ Battalion The Duke of Wellington's Regiment in Halifax. They were there for only a short time, but they soon got to know the town well.

The Dukes

Footsloggers we are now, my boys!
Doomed to crawl on our bellies.
Proudly we march under new colours,
Part of the Duke of Welly's.

> *Dukes, Dukes, we are now, my boys,*
> *Bloody and heroic is our story.*
> *Tommy Atkins was one of us, my boys,*
> *So ours to enhance his glory.*

To the Ridings we're sent, without dissent,
To a fine county inspired by traditions.
Yorkshire men all, sturdy and tall,
Born and bred into fighting conditions.

> *Dukes, Dukes, we are now my boys,*
> *Bloody and heroic is our story*
> *Tommy Atkins was one of us, my boys*
> *So ours to enhance his glory.*

Halifax is our base. God, what a place!
With barracks like an old prison.
It's a town of flat caps, bombed-out gaps,
And tarts who are hardly a vision.
> *Dukes, Dukes… etc*

In alleys they lurk, half-hidden in murk,
Every one poised like a painted vulture.
Enticed by their gall the lads screw them all,
And become addicted to Halifax culture.
> *Dukes, Dukes… etc*

Then the inevitable comes and the War Office (the bums!)
Hit us with an embarkation order,
So days on the moors and the comfort of whores,
Give way to a Commie marauder.
Dukes, Dukes… etc

For Korea we're bound, where nothing is found
But death and harrowing mutilations,
And where civil strife rules, we're the poor fools
Who will fight as the United Nations.
Dukes, Dukes… etc

At Soton we debus with a minimum of fuss,
Voices raised in songs raucous and bawdy.
Bunting is flying and relatives are crying,
With the old trooper resplendent and gaudy.
Dukes, Dukes… etc

A parting at sea is a new one on me
And fresh thoughts of death are distressing,
But why give a damn, fool that I am,
Hasn't the Padre just given us his blessing?

Dukes, Dukes, we are now, my boys.
Bloody and heroic is our story.
Tommy Atkins was one of us, my boys,
So ours to enhance his glory.

Rupert had never been abroad before and it was one of the few things he was looking forward to. I had little contact with Rupert and the others whilst on the troopship. Fraternization between officers and Other Ranks was not encouraged. Officers had luxury cabins whilst below decks the Other Ranks did their best to sleep in hammocks. However, the following poem makes it pretty clear that Rupert found it a fascinating experience.

The Voyage Out East

For those who lack the will to wander
And whose spirit is sadly inert,
The sight of the sea and points yonder,
May well their outlook convert.
> *Away we go, me muckers,*
> *The whole wide world to see.*
> *Many a sight we'll gawp at,*
> *But not for a tourist fee.*

For many of the lads it was just such a case.
First Gibraltar, lonesome and mighty,
Then into the Med, dolphins leaping with grace,
And in Cyprus the call of Aphrodite.
> *Away we go, me muckers,*
> *The whole wide world to see.*
> *Many a sight we'll gawp at,*
> *But not for a tourist fee.*

Port Said was exposed as the bowels of the earth,
With a repugnant smell straight from hell,
While the flotilla of bumboats jostling at our berth
Dipped and rocked in time with our swell.
> *Away we go my muckers,*
> *The whole wide world to see.*
> *Many a sight we'll gawp at,*
> *But not for a tourist fee.*

So eastwards we steamed from port to port:
Imperial forts with a tortuous past
Where many a Tommy invaded and fought
And jolly Jack Tar bled at the mast.

Away we go me muckers,
The whole wide world to see.
Many a sight we'll gawp at
But not for a tourist fee.

Colombo, Singapore, and finally Hong Kong,
Each one sporting the old bamboo.
Girls lithesome and slinky in sari and sarong,
Gloriously sexy, but strictly taboo.
Away we go me muckers,
The whole wide world to see.
Many a sight we'll gawp at,
But not for a tourist fee.

Finally we docked between Pusan's rotting piers
And beheld a country so obviously at war;
But bravado prevailed and we set off amid cheers,
For satanic hills steeped in blood and gore.
Away we went, me muckers,
Half the wide world we saw.
Many a sight impressed us,
But none prepared us for war.

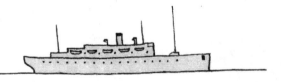

'*The General's Tool*' *was written after our first pay parade in Korea. Throughout our time in Korea, Rupert was continually being put on company orders and docked a week's pay by Major Earl Gray. His crime was that he continually spouted poetry at inappropriate moments. What Earl Gray objected to most was that he pinned them on the platoon notice board for everyone to read. He got into further trouble when the command of 12 Platoon passed on to my replacement, Mr Denning. He forbid him to put anything on the board. On this first pay parade it dawned on Rupert how grotesque it was that we were being paid peanuts for fighting a war. National Service privates got a pound a week, less barrack room damages!*

The General's Tool

We Tommies are paid but a pittance
And we're never required to think,
Especially up at the sharp end:
Up there, blind obedience or sink.
But it's a pretty safe bet (with the idiots we get!)
That our orders up front will be suicidal.
Yet still we must obey, without any say,
Or be charged with being plain bloody idle.

Oh Tommy, you're only a laggard!
Oh Tommy, you're such a poor young fool.
Don't ever think for yourself, me lad,
You're nowt but a general's tool.

We Tommies have fought in the jungles,
Against guerrillas and swamps and all.
We've also fought in the mountains,
From the Alps to the heights of Nepal.
In deserts we've always been victorious,
With Kitchener and dear old Monty supreme,
And we fought the mad Mahdi without question
Though when we saw 'em we didn't 'alf scream.

Oh Tommy, you're only a laggard!
Oh Tommy, you're such a poor young fool.
Don't ever think for yourself, me lad.
You're nowt but a general's tool.

We Tommies have also known invasions,
And stormed across fortified beaches,
To say nothing of scaling sheer cliffs
Where we clung on to nowt like leeches.
But whatever the tricks we resort to,
And regardless of the press's ballyhoo,
When we hold out a paw, we get a quid (no more)
And then march off to our next Waterloo.

Oh Tommy, you're only a laggard!
Oh Tommy, you're such a poor young fool.
Don't ever think for yourself, me lad,
You're nowt but a general's tool.

The Samichon River position (Yong Dong) was regarded as a soft area in which new units could acclimatize themselves. In our case this turned out to be a fallacy. Rupert describes his first glimpse of no man's land and he refers to the vexed question of patrolling and the domination of no man's land. In his second poem he describes our first major confrontation with the Chinese. This followed a disastrous patrol in which we got lost and were caught in no man's land in broad daylight.

No Man's Land

No man's land! A paddy jungle where men lurk
Like rabid canine strays,
Taking advantage of murky darkness in order
To weave their evil ways.

I wait for dawn, anxious to appraise this
Eerie, inscrutable, divide:
A killing-ground where shifting shadows drift
And human hunters hide.

But as the light of day edges over the hills
I sense only morning calm,
With a soft mist wafting along the valley,
A veil of beauty and charm.

Bald hills protrude through the damp haze,
Resembling scattered isles,
Each one of them scarred by twisting trenches
Snaking coastward for miles.

Soon, we too will be tracking and stalking
Over this venomous land
For Earl Gray has decreed nightly patrols
To secure the upper hand.

Ambush

Behold, the enemy! Each one squat and thick-set,
An eerie and harrowing sight,
Padding softly, alert and eager, unsuspecting of
An ambush masked by night.

My nerves are taut, my mind agog, dreading
The havoc that lies ahead.
Oh that my life should come to this! A killer,
Poised to shoot men dead!

As ordered, we hold our initial fire, waiting
For the whites of their eyes.
Then comes the command for rapid bursts
To ensure every bastard dies.

Bullets belch forth and we shout and scream,
Exacerbating utter confusion,
And with spitting Stens and thudding Brens
There is but one conclusion.

Then I see a Burp gun levelled in my direction
So I pepper him head to chest.
Dramatically he staggers, teeters, twists and turns,
And bleeds towards eternal rest.

Some survive and to a man stampede into the
Minefield rather than succumb,
And as they rampage through darkness we hear
Them blown to kingdom come.

When all is still I relapse into shock:
A reaction that is rife.
Bodies, bodies, littered everywhere,
But not a spark of life.

Oh dear God! Did we really do that?
Oh yes … Oh yes …

A Blighty Touch!

The shells cascade down, sudden and unexpected.
Men caught in the open, exposed and unprotected.
One is hit and as his mates rush to render first aid,
And up goes the familiar cry, the one always made.
  'You're reet, lad. A Blighty touch!'

A mendacious cry to hide the wound's gravity,
A deliberate lie however horrendous the cavity.
A lie always welcomed and implicitly believed
The truth simply too appalling to be perceived.
  Luck at last, a Blighty touch!

No pain, no feelings: nerves temporally shattered.
A smile serene, as though nothing else mattered,
Convinced by their promises that he is safe and sound,
He glows with joy happy to be homeward-bound.
  Thank God for a Blighty touch!

When frantic shouts for stretcher-bearers ring out
They bring comfort and reassurance, never doubt.
Then drowsiness clouds his visions of hospitalization:
Fading images of nurses, clean sheets, and relaxation.
  All the joys of a Blighty touch!

Pain surges as they jerk and jolt him down the hill,
And odd spasms are succeeded by a macabre chill.
Then, as they near the morgue at the end of the trench,
Darkness descends: life ousted by an ominous stench.
  The MO gives him a cursory glance
  Then back to men still in with a chance.
  So much for a Blighty touch!

We were still opposite the Boot when Earl Gray decreed that each platoon was to provide a sniper. The selected man was to establish a "hide" in no man's land and watch for enemy activity through a brand new, highly developed, telescopic sight. We didn't have any marksmen within the platoon, so knowing that Rupert thrived on solitude--- and it being advisable for him to be kept in a low profile--- I appointed him platoon sniper, on top of his usual wireless responsibilities. For weeks he went off on his lonesome vigil but never achieved any results, unless one counts the following poem.

The Sniper

Now sits a man within my sights.
He's smiling and relaxed, at leisure;
Sublimely unaware that his frail life
Lies entirely within my pleasure.

He basks in the sun and waffles on,
No doubt regaling his friends and cronies
With the rights and wrongs of army life,
And denouncing all officers as phonies.

What crazy duty demands that I should kill
This man who cannot remotely matter?
If I shoot the poor sod, what comfort in that?
To see his skull implode, then shatter?

So it's safety catch on and rifle to rest,
My softness acknowledged by a profanity.
Yet inwardly I rejoice, with peace of mind,
Thankful to have retained my humanity.

*'Motivation' highlights a problem we all faced-- the need for privacy. If men weren't being disturbed by a mate or Chinese shelling, they could always rely on Beau Brummell to stick his oar in. Rupert craved privacy in order to compose his poems and read them out loud, and to this end he was often reduced to muttering to himself whilst using one of the latrines. The comment he makes in **'Motivation'** about "free of stench" refers to the fact that the hills in the front line had been fought over several times and human remains were never far beneath the surface, giving a distinctive odour of varying intensity.*

Motivation

Seeking privacy, I wandered along the lateral trench
And chanced upon a spot pleasantly free of stench.
An ideal haven, away from the madding crowd,
To meditate a mo, before composing out loud:

"I often wonder what inspires our Tommy most?
What crosses his mind when he hears Last Post?
What are his emotions when he fights for others?
Certainly not the fear of joining dead brothers."

Thus, as I cogitated, searching for divine inspiration,
Old Brummell hove-to, wrecking my concentration.

"Laddie! Stop buggering about with that pen and paper.
Get back to your bunker. And I will deal with you later!
I know why the buggers are so vicious and bold:
It's 'cause I've taught 'em to do as they're told!"

I scurried down the trench, put to flight.
Come to think of it, he's probably right.

Then came our 'Blue-on-Blue' incident with the tank. In all, around a dozen 20-pounder shells were pumped into our position, with a number of casualties. The most frustrating thing was that we could not convince Major Earl Gray that it was one of our own tanks firing on us. In the end Sergeant Brummell took things into his own hands and organized the evacuation of those in danger. This heroic action, which went completely unacknowledged by battalion headquarters, led Rupert to modify his opinion of Beau Brummel.

Blue-on-Blue

The glow of dawn bursts forth like a reprieve:
Darkness dissolves, leaving no cloak to deceive.
A time to unwind, to eat, sleep, relax, and rest,
Maybe just mooch around, free of any behest.

But we know better than to ignore possible surprise,
And stand ready for any disasters which may arise,
Our vigilance is based on a dawn we'll forever rue
When we suffered the tragedy of a blue-on-blue.

High on a flanking position, diagonally to our rear,
Came a new Centurion, its briefing none too clear;
And at break of day, when they spied us on our hill,
They mistook us for the enemy and went for a kill.

Twenty-pounders were soon streaking in our direction,
Methodically flattening the bunkers in our rear section.
Timbers were torn asunder, strewn across the slope,
Leaving several occupants with precious little hope.

Then, rising above the cacophony of bursting shells,
Came despairing cries and a chorus of piteous yells.
Old Brummell, acting instinctively and without delay,
Grabbed a nearby stretcher and plunged into the fray.

He and a volunteer waited for the next muzzle-flash
And as the shell landed, set off on a suicidal dash.
Bullets from a machine gun chased them all the way,
Earth spouting, with the screams of many a ricochet.

By sheer good luck they survived and on their return
Dumped their load and sped back with no concern.
They defied the odds and ran the gauntlet thrice,
But within sight of safety paid a sickening price.

Eventually an enquiry was called to apportion blame,
But 'Accident' was decreed, with no guilt or shame:
A predictable whitewash which we'll forever deplore
And an odious snub for the bravest act we ever saw.

During the blue-on-blue incident I was caught by the blast of a 20-pounder on our last 'home run'. I bled like a pig (as one does with head wounds) but in the end my injuries amounted to nothing more than split ear drums and total, but temporary, deafness. A helicopter ambulance evacuated me to an American MASH unit and eventually I was sent back to the British Commonwealth Hospital in Kure, Japan. Once recovered, I was given a soft posting in the local headquarters. I wrote to Rupert several times, telling him what a great time I was having, especially my discovery of sex with a lovely Japanese girl. At the time, I had no idea that 12 Platoon were going through a very rough time on Hill 355. They had also fallen out in a big way with their new platoon commander who forbade Rupert to put verses on the platoon notice board. His only poem of this period was the one he sent to me in Kure. It's message turned out to be very prophetic.

<u>Beware!</u>

We Tommies at the front suffer, sir,
We Tommies in our trenches die,
And all in the name of freedom, sir,
Though few of us understand why.
Yet officers like you abound, sir.
Fornicating and skiving at the rear.
Forever wine women and song, sir,
With nowt but wedding bells to fear.
But your cushy job is an illusion, sir.
In the end war always wins.
Notice the cross-bones of death, sir,
And the skull above it that grins.

A few weeks later Rupert's prophecy came true. I was posted back to Korea and after a short time in other duties resumed command of 12 Platoon. We were very soon back on the Hook, knowing that a major attack was imminent. The horrors of the Hook are difficult to exaggerate. More men died on it than any other hill in Korea. We got off to a bad start, losing a man in our first few minutes on the hill. In these two poems Rupert describes our first impression of the Hook and his reaction to the loss of a friend.

<u>Taking Up the Challenge</u>

Now dawns the day we'll never forget,
Dawns the day we will forever regret,
When came our turn to bear the brunt
And defend the Hook on the UN front.
    The sharpest end of freedom.

Ahead of us dust spirals high in the air,
Ahead of us a hill blown totally bare,
Where shot and shell rage all night:
Continuous mayhem, a pitiless fight.
    The struggle for freedom.

Marching undaunted, refusing to be shaken,
Marching to a hill that must never be taken.
No option but to fight, to see the battle through.
No retreat, no relief: no escaping a bloody do.
    We'll fight like tigers for freedom.

Halfway up, evidence of battle littered around,
Halfway up, recent dead piled high in a mound.
Silence engulfs us and our complexions pale:
The odour of death, so debilitating to inhale.
    Men killed in the cause of freedom.

We plod along in silence, ever upwards;
Plod to the summit, facing northwards,
Relieving exhausted and depleted Jocks,
Men who've stood firm, steady as rocks.
    Men who've given their all for freedom.

We take over bunkers, deep and musty.
Take over Brownings, worn but trusty.
Weapons that swing and arc at will,
All rates on rapid for maximum kill.
The art of defending freedom.

We recoil at a hill in such a cadaverous state.
Recoil at rats, strutting with an arrogant gait.
Mammoth rats, human flesh so nourishing;
Detested rats, numbers forever flourishing.
The horror of defending freedom.

Foul views of Chinese dead decorating our wire,
And foul bunkers with inter-locking fields of fire.
Bunkers weakened by persistent shelling
How long they'll last, there is no telling.
The risk of defending freedom

Tension increases as every man is assigned a task,
A tension exacerbated by the risks they unmask,
Every man jack among us dreading that this will be
The last place on sweet earth that he will ever see.
The end of our freedom?

He looked over the trench and stared ahead;
Looked in curiosity and exposed his head,
Absorbing the details of each Chinese hill,
All dusty and misshapen, suspiciously still.
Too innocent to threaten freedom?

No warning! No sound! One clean strike!
No second chance. Just one dead Tyke.
He paid the price for being reckless
Now he lies there, damn near headless.
Dead in the cause of freedom!

A Lost Friend

Today I lost a good friend,
A loss time will never mend.
He was only nineteen,
Tall, hungry, and lean,
But a bullet went straight through his brain.

Today I lost a good friend.
A lad who would never offend.
So blushing and shy
He had no right to die,
But a bullet still went straight through his brain.

Today I lost a good friend
Who once went on a bend.
And tanked up on beer
He boasted of no fear,
But a damn bullet still went straight through his brain.

Today I lost a good friend
With a love-life to commend.
Promised in marriage, never tempted to stray,
His life ruled by dreams of their happy day.
Then that fucking bullet went straight through his brain.

There was no such thing as a quiet time on the Hook. Shelling pounded the hill continuously and patrolling duties kept men active all night and every night. Men tried to get as much sleep as possible during the day, but this was further curtailed when the decision was made to dig a tunnel in 12 Platoon. This was exhausting work and made sleep all the more precious. We had already had one bad experience of men falling to sleep on duty with one of our Katcoms, and there is no doubt that other men came close to cracking under the strain. Rupert was among them, although he kept it a good secret.

Nodding Off

As stars hang high and the moon drifts
Regally over a peaceful night,
I scan the scarred hills that spread like
Fingers, exploring left and right.

I marvel at such unfamiliar stillness,
The eerie calm of a hiatus,
And I relax, sensing that for a change
Bedlam won't overtake us.

Soon, flickering flares cast ebbing shadows
Over the mouldering terrain,
And sepia tints blur the fading hills flanking
The Samichon's placid plain.

Then out of the gloom vague figures appear,
Our lines their destination:
Ghosts sliding through belts of barbed wire,
Without care or hesitation.

And now I see them sharp and clear, their auras
Too solid to be an aberration,
Their torn and blood-soaked uniforms revealing
Various theatres of operation.

The Old Contemptibles, the Desert Rats,
14th Army, and Red Coats too,
Straight from the raw mayhem of Mons,
Tobruk, Imphal, and Waterloo.

They come to see us tread a battlefield
Such as our forefathers trod,
Knowing many will share their fate and
Rot beneath the foreign sod.

They see us as fresh cannon-fodder who,
Having fought with luck galore,
And endured the passing of many a mate,
Now quake before death's door.

Then my phantoms fade; the spell is broken.
My head jerks back; jaded eyes flash open.
I break into a sweat of panic and contrition,
Ashamed at having imperilled our position.

One thing we all loathed about the Hook was that whenever one looked out of the embrasures in the weapon pits, one was confronted by the sight of dead Chinese left dangling on our barbed wire. Their numbers increased with every attack. It was far too dangerous to remove them and although men often tried to blast them clear with grenades, it seldom worked.

We just had to put up with it, often confronted by the revolting sight of the rats feeding off them. That did at least give the men good target practice.

Hanging On The Old Barbed Wire

Oh how I wish you festering stiffs
Would miraculously go away.
God rot your gaseous guts and make
Your flesh wither and decay.
May rain and shine lambaste you
Into early deterioration,
And a hell-bound wind whisk you
Into eternal damnation.

But there you repose, you poor rotting sods,
Mocking us the livelong day,
Your faces peeling down to skulls, tongues
Lolling limply as if to say:
'Come hither friends. Here it all ends.
Come share our merciful fate.
Death alone brings peace and harmony;
No more lies or political hate.'

So there you dangle, having forfeited
Your lives in the call of duty.
By communist lights, noble gestures,
To commissars, acts of beauty.
But we Tommies see it in a different light:
A vision of how we may expire.
Fetid meat and bloated feet,
Hanging on the old barbed wire.

After we'd been on the Hook three weeks, air reconnaissance reported Chinese forces assembling in vast numbers. Stretching back to divisional HQ, Brass Hats became increasingly anxious about the outcome of the coming battle. Fresh orders were issued daily on how to hold the hill. Here, Rupert records how this did little to boost our morale.

The Agony of Waiting

Orders spew forth and are duly ignored:
The same old gubbins.
The Brass Hats after glory, the price paid
By poor old Muggins.

Shelling keeps the Brass rooted to the rear,
A truancy hardly inspiring
For it is at their behest we are urged to be
Ever vigilant and untiring.

Yet how much longer can we hold on with our
Casualties mounting?
Pride demands that we feign indifference, but
Everyone is counting.

And as the stretcher-bearers shuttle past
In a never-ending procession
The gnawing hunger for a Blighty touch
Balloons into an obsession.

Stand-to! Oh, how we loathe it as the sun
Takes its time to sink,
Leaving us poised, weapons cocked, with
Nowt to do but think.

We stare across the barren, disfigured hills
Imagining divers fates,
Mostly the void of eternal darkness that
Death alone activates.

So we revert to fond images of home
And domestic banalities:
Parents, girlfriends, drinking mates,
And childhood trivialities.

Then, as the sun slips behind the hills, night
Descends like a curtain:
Now is the moment! Now one thing will
Test us out for certain.

With the echoing boom of thunder
The milk-round arrives.
Such vicious shelling it's a miracle
That anyone survives.

It's always the same, as they pound us
Night after night,
With great orange fireballs sparking
Darkness alight.

Down they crunch, each belabouring
Us like a hammer.
No let up, no respite, no mercy:
Constant clamour.

Earth churning and spewing, often
Exhuming the dead,
The darkness buzzing and hissing
With white-hot lead.

Then the milk-round fizzles and silence
Descends: all is still.
We strain for the sound of bugles that
Herald the final kill.

Waiting! Waiting! The tense hours leave
Our tangled nerves twitching
With dank palms and weapons raised, our
Coiled trigger-fingers itching.

Another hour and our eyes ache from
Scanning the wire,
Then another hour of shifting shapes,
Tempting us to fire.

And as these eerie shadows move,
Inching up the slopes,
A mist swirls and twists, forever
Diminishing our hopes.

Deep into the night we are still standing-to
And the enemy has yet to come.
Another Rubicon evaded, so we celebrate
With generous tots of rum.

The night passes in an alcoholic haze as
Peace rules the terrain.
Then on to another day, the same bloody
Waiting all over again.

Eventually we captured a prisoner. He said the attack would come on the night of May 28th/29th: two days before we were to be relieved. He also claimed that if the attack was successful it would herald a full-scale offensive aimed at recapturing Seoul. This is how Rupert visualized things. He pinned this poem on the notice board. It was so mournful I would normally have removed it, but Fletcher got to it first and added a line which gave everyone such a good laugh that I left it well alone.

May 28th 1953

Now dawns a day of awesome fear,
A day of death for which we are fated,
With orders repeated, crisp and clear:
To the last man, or enemy annihilated.
The great unknown descends tonight,
Bringing days of torment to their end.
Our destiny settled in a climactic fight
On which the lives of so many depend.

It's the ultimate test a man can face,
That culminates with God disposing:
Miraculously spared by His grace
Or else scattered wide, decomposing.

God help us all,
God save us all,
Especially those deserving.

"That's cooked my bloody goose then, you bastard." Fletch.

The battle duly came. Rupert and I became involved in some hand-to-hand fighting with the Chinese, and then he decided to make a dash back to the platoon command post before sheltering in our tunnel in order to retrieve his poems. He never did make it on account of taking a bullet wound in his leg. We sheltered in our tunnel for the rest of the night and then Corporal Holroyd and I carried him down to the CAP. He was evacuated to a MASH and despite the mild nature of his wound, he died there. The last thing he did was write a short note for me (another poem, of course) It is the one I've already incorporated in the main text.

Tell 'Em, Saj!

Tell 'em Saj! Let your ink
Gush and flow bright red.
How it really was: our fears,
And how freely we bled.

No poetic fantasies, please:
No symbolic flights of a dove,
Just how we held the Hook with
Dukes pride and agarpy love.*

* Rupert misspelt 'agarpy', no doubt for my benefit. Really, it is agape (pronounced 'agarpy') but Rupert knew I would not be familiar with it. As I eventually discovered, it is Greek, meaning ultimate, non-physical, love.

Dead Dukes

they are now, my boys,

So that concludes their story.

Tommy Atkins

lives for ever, my boys,

So did they

enhance his glory?

ACCLAIM FOR THE POEMS OF

RUPERT SANDWITCH

"I read these poems in awe. They are unique and harrowing ... Brilliant!"

Sir Christopher Ondaatje

"Rarely has a collection of poems so captured the horror, tragedy, humour, and pathos of war."

'The Morning Calm'

The author is clearly passionate about what he wants to say; outspoken about the trial and awfulness of war; and reflective on the life of soldiers in and out of battle ... A very loyal Duke."

'The Iron Duke'

"I found myself reading these poems, putting them down, and then being drawn back to them, either to read another poem or re-read one I had just finished. The book will hold a special place in my library."

Michael Kirk (brother of 1ˢᵗ Bn I DWR Subaltern)

"I've read the book from cover to cover three times, endeavouring to find a favourite poem. Quite pointless. I like them all. They are great. The water colours were an inspired inclusion.

David Gascoyne, (1ˢᵗ Bn DWR, Subaltern)

"As with Owen, Sassoon, and Graves, these poems will be read for as long as wars continue. I marvel at the heart-felt outpourings of a 19 year-old National Serviceman ."

Ed Gaskell (Publisher)

"These poems are more telling and revealing of National Service than anything else I have ever read."

Rev A J Bowyers (Ex-Army Chaplain, Korea)

"These poems will live forever."

Major Alan Fradgley, RE MBE

"No war has ever been so brilliantly chronicled by a single poet … These poems capture the essence and horror of Korea and are incredibly perceptive of human nature."

Paul Willey (Ex-BBC Editor)

"This collection of poems will stick in the mind for years."

Trevor Hunt (Author of Ibiza Shorts)

"When you contrast the smiling young faces on the cover to the stark hell of the poems inside, you get the true spirit of Tommy Atkins."

Guy Bellamy (Secret Lemonade Drinker)

PRAISE FOR THE NOVELS OF JOHN HOLLANDS.

The Dead, the Dying and the Damned.

"A brilliantly angry first novel. The character studies are masterly … Unless some genius (like Hollands) writes a book in which people behave like real human beings … Some people will ask for its suppression. But I would say this: it is only when people as courageous as Hollands dare to write the truth about war, that the miracle will come when it will be no more."

Nancy Spain, Daily Express

"Stands with *All Quiet on the Western Front* as the best war novel of all time."

Paul Wigby, Associated Press

"Admirably done! Sincere, conscientious and factual."
Marie Scott-Thomas, Daily Telegraph

"A truly brilliant piece of writing."

Evening News

"The Korean battles are magnificent and the whole book is a tremendous achievement for a young man still only twenty."

News Chronicle

"It is in the of the school of *The Naked and the Dead*, but much better written.

Reynold News

"A remarkable first novel. Bound to become a best-seller."
Yorkshire Evening Post

"A genuinely moving book. There is no mistaking the strength of emotion, pity, indignation and resentment that has driven him to seek an outlet in words."

Peter Quinnell, Daily Mail

"As fiction, it is grippingly impressive. As a document, it is frightening."
Birmingham Gazette

"Should be read by all politicians."

South Wales Echo

"Impressive and rewarding."

New York Herald Tribune

"The best novel of the Korean war."

New York Times

"The battle scenes are perfect!"

The New Yorker

"An exceptionally fine war novel."

Columbus Despatch

"It rests between such classics as *From Here to Eternity* and *The Naked and the Dead.*"

American Literary Guidepost

"The best novel to be written about the Korean war."

Chicago Sun-Times

"Magnificent!"

Chicago Tribune

"Hollands allows his characters no privacy, but probes each man's thoughts to the roots. He has created a very real group of people who gain the complete sympathy of the reader ... A novel which ranks with Remarque's *All Quiet on the Western Front* and Gibbs's *Now it Can Be Told.*"

Robert Barr, Boston Globe

"I have read *The Dead the Dying and the Damned* many times. The many well-drawn characters, the humorous descriptions of army life, and the masterly battles scenes make it one of the best war novels ever written. It is, without doubt, the definitive novel of the Korean war and, as such, should be readily available to all."

Cyril Coombes, Hawker's War

The Gospel According to Uncle Jimmy

"Of its type, the funniest book I've ever read."

Dr. Desmond Flower, Cassell's

"An hilarious book. As satire, it leaves *Catch-22* standing."

Neil McCallum, Actor

"The best book of its type I have had the pleasure of reading."

Aldelaide Librarian

"I was so impressed by *Uncle Jimmy* that I sold up everything, bought a Land Rover, and followed his journey out to Australia."

Peter Brooke-Smith, teacher

The Exposed

"I found The Exposed moving and extremely convincing. George was a wonderful character, brilliantly real and fresh, and the Japanese heroine (Katsumi) tremendously likable and convincing. The evocation of the era and the eye for details of that time were most impressive."

Maeve Haran, Having it All

"A wonderful story, superbly told, just crying out to be made into a film."

Guy Bellamy, Secret Lemonade Drinker

"One of the most moving, wonderful, happy-and-sad books I have ever read. A work of genius."

Trevor Hunt, Ibiza Shorts

"Marvellous characters. It's a superb piece of work."

John Pawsey, Lit Agent

"The development of the love affair between George and Katsumi is delicately and beautifully handled. As a love story it works superbly, with all the right ingredients.

Bernard Boucher, Opalesque

"Quite brilliant! Plot, setting, characterization, all superb and most perceptive of human nature.

Peter Brooke-Smith, teacher

"A fascinating read. The love story is touchingly told: very funny and ultimately very moving. At times it takes one to the depths of despair but, in the end, its profoundly inspiring message is dramatically and effectively revealed... A very fine piece of work."

John Hogston, Author

"Katsumi is, of course, wonderful... The whole thing is first class."

David Bolt, Authors' Handbook

"John Hollands has written the most superb novel. His easy style and well-drawn characters will make it a sure-fire winner. The wit and charm of the novel, together with the special treatment of the story, makes you want to read it in one sitting. (I managed it in two!)"

Ken Fisher, English Bookshop

"Three things I found really impressive. First of all, the character of Katsumi, which was obviously exceptional and utterly enchanting. And because she was so convincing the final part of the book introduces a spiritual dimension which is also convincing. And the third thing was that the story never lost touch with the ordinary, mundane, world it was set in. The novel is essentially down-to-earth in its presentation--- an honest, square-on view with no spin, just acceptance of things and characters as they were. It is a real achievement. The whole book makes the last paragraph more than just a pious hope."

Jeremy Firth, Eng Lit., Oundle

"The best book I've read for a very long time. I am sure this book will be read over and over again.

Brian Warden, Cornish Libraries

"A beautifully written and intelligent novel with fascinating characters. Funny and hugely insightful. It is a clever portrayal of a very strange occurrence in history, with a wonderful love story between two different characters.

Amazon critic. Five star rating

"An excellent novel based on the aftermath of the Hiroshima bomb, as seen through the eyes of a British National Service officer during the Korean war."

Amazon critic. Five star rating

"Beautiful novel, crying out to be made into a film,. Finely drawn characters you really get to know and care about. Wish the publishers would reprint his earlier novels. There are few better writers today.

Amazon critic. Five star rating

"An excellent novel. It combines humour, drama and romance, all revolving around an unsuitably commissioned officer, his idea of how the army should be organized, and his love affair with a beautiful Japanese girl who witnessed the atom bomb.

Amazon critic. Five star rating

N.B. On Amazon, John Hollands is one of the very few authors with nothing but five star ratings.

The Never Marry Series

"A sheer delight!"

Jack Sockell, Cricket Lovers' Society

"You'll absolutely adore it."

Glynis Roberts, Evening Standard

"A classic in cricket literature."

Express and Echo

Gran and Mr. Muckey

"Amusing, enthralling, poignant. I just loved it. I'm just about to start the second volume… Can't wait …"

Amazon critic. Five star rating

"This book is a gem. I found myself drawn into the lives of the Contractor family and laughing out loud at Sajit and his account of life in Edgware and beyond. I'll have to read it again and again to relive some of my favourite chapters.

Amazon critic. Five star rating

"I enjoyed Gran and Mr. Muckey immensely. The characters are hugely entertaining and the scene where Sajit is in the headmaster's study is masterly."

Robin Lloyd-Jones, Lord of the Dance

"Gran and Mr. Muckey kept me roaring with laughter and had me quoting pieces to all and sundry."

David Quine, St Kilda Re-visited

"Quite apart from being very funny, Gran and Mr. Muckey is a fascinating chronicle of our times, reflecting attitudes which have long since changed. The constructive approach of Hillhead Prep School towards the Common Entrance exam is priceless."

John Hogston, Hawker's War

Glossary

CP	Command Post
OP	Observation Post
FOO	Forward Observation Officer (Gunner)
Sten	Hand-held automatic machine gun
Bren	Heavier light machine gun (two men)
Blue-on-Blue	Friendly-fire casualty
RSM	Regimental Sergeant-Major.
CSM	Company Sergeant-Major
2 i/c	Second-in-command
VT	Air burst shells
Section Commander	Corporal (3 Sections to a platoon)
Bunds	Embankments around paddy fields
Recce	Reconnaissance
Burp guns	Chinese hand-held machine guns
RAP	Regimental Aid Post
CAP	Company Aid Post
C-rations	American convenience rations in tins
JRBD	Japanese Reserve Base Depot
Point men	Two leaders of a patrol
MASH units	Mobile Army Surgical Hospital
TCV	Troop carrying vehicle
Jankers	Form of punishment
Relegated	Put back a course at OCS
OCS	Officer Cadet School
RTU	Returned to original unit
MSR	Main Supply Route

HOOK TRENCH LAYOUT

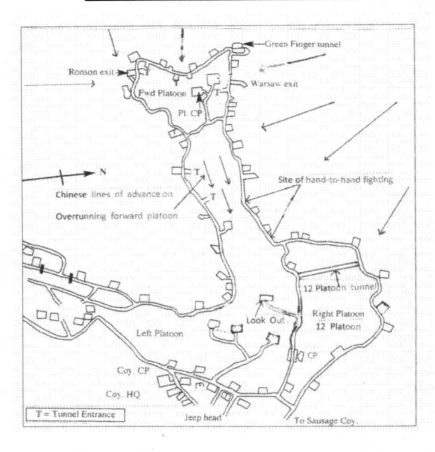